crops & man

History celebrates the battlefields whereon we meet our death, but scorns to speak of the plowed fields whereby we thrive; it knows the names of the King's bastards, but cannot tell us the origin of wheat. That is the way of human folly.

Jean Henri Fabre

FOUNDATIONS FOR MODERN CROP SCIENCE SERIES

Crops and Man
          J. R. Harlan

Propagation of Crops
          J. C. DeLouche

Crop Breeding
          D. R. Wood

Physiological Bases for Crop Growth and Development
          M. B. Tesar

Ecological Bases for Crop Growth and Development
          W. L. Colville

Crop Protection
          W. B. Ennis, Jr.

Crop Quality, Storage, and Utilization
          C. S. Hoveland

crops & man

Jack R. Harlan

Professor of Plant Genetics
Crop Evolution Laboratory
Agronomy Department
University of Illinois
Urbana-Champaign

American Society of Agronomy
Crop Science Society of America
Madison, Wisconsin
1975

Standard Book Number: 0-89118-032-X

Library of Congress Catalog Card Number: 74-21919

Printed in the United States of America.
Reprinted with minor corrections, 1976

Matthias Stelly, Coordinating Editor
Domenic Fuccillo, Managing Editor
Laura H. Paskin, Assistant Editor

Sketches and makeup by Patricia Wolter Jeffson

FOREWORD

The Teaching Improvement Committee of the Crop Science Society of America identified the urgent need for developing contemporary reading materials aimed at upper level undergraduate college students. The accelerated pace of research, augmented by sophisticated instrumentation and techniques, and new opinions, imparts to crop science a rapidly changing character as new discoveries replace and/or add to former concepts. New findings force us to re-evaluate and often reconstruct the foundations on which crop science rests. A current presentation of the dynamic state of modern crop science is, therefore, a formidable challenge worthy of the best talents of eminent research and teaching personnel in the field. This task necessitates assembling the most capable representatives of the various disciplines within crop science and bringing them together in teams of writers to prepare a series of publications based on contemporary research. The Crop Science Society of America and the American Society of Agronomy have undertaken this large assignment by selecting more than 100 specialists who will contribute to making the Foundations of Modern Crop Science books a reality.

The authors and editors of this series believe that the new approach taken in organizing subject matter and relating it to current discoveries and new principles will stimulate the interest of students. A single book cannot fulfill the different and changing requirements that must be met in various programs and curricula within our junior and senior colleges. Conversely, the needs of the students and the prerogatives of teachers can be satisfied by well-written, well-illustrated, and relatively inexpensive books planned to encompass those areas that are vital and central to understanding the content, state, and direction of modern crop science. The Foundations for Modern Crop Science books represent the translation of this central theme into volumes that form an integrated series but can be used alone or in any combination desired in support of specific courses.

The most important thing about any book is its authorship. Each book and/or chapter in this series on Foundations for Modern Crop Science is written by a recognized specialist in his discipline. The Crop Science Society of America and the American Society of Agronomy join the Foundations for Modern Crop Science Book Writing Project Committee in extending special acknowledgment and gratitude to the many writers of these books. The series is a tribute to the devotion of many important contributors who, recognizing the need, approached this major project with enthusiasm.

A. W. Burger, chairman
J. W. Dudley
A. A. Hanson
L. H. Smith
M. Stelly

TABLE OF CONTENTS

PREFACE

It has been nearly a half century since the great Russian agronomist, N. I. Vavilov, started writing and formulating theories about the origin of cultivated plants. It will soon be nearly a hundred years since Alphonse de Candolle wrote his first book on the subject. The time has come for a third round of summary on what is known about crop origins. Vavilov had an opportunity to correct some of the errors that de Candolle had made and to add details of information that had recently become available. It will be my opportunity to correct some of the errors of Vavilov and to add additional information. I shall, of course, produce errors of my own and confess to ignorance of many crops. But each round has approached the truth a little more closely than the former, and bit by bit we are coming closer to a fuller understanding. The next round may well be the best and possibly the last for the evidence is disappearing. Gene centers or centers of diversity are disappearing before our eyes. The ancient traces of plant migrations through the ages are being obliterated by massive importations of new seeds and new materials. Ancient land-race populations are being abandoned in favor of modern, high-yielding varieties, and some old crops are being completely eliminated. It is already almost impossible to assemble meaningful information on the origin and evolution of certain crops as the evidence dims and fades away with each passing year.

The origin and evolution of a few cultivated plants have come into sharp focus in recent years. New studies have been launched on near relatives, their distribution, their ecological behavior, and their genetic interaction with the cultivated races. These patterns have been studied in depth, and the pictures emerging have been relatively clear. Sometimes they have been supported and amplified by direct archaeobotanical evidence. For example, carbonized seeds or identifiable plant impressions have been found in sites reasonably well dated by carbon-14, and sequences of dated sites with plant remains often reveal details of evolutionary history.

Some of the mysteries remain. We still do not know the origin of sesame, there are doubts about the pigeon pea, and the bottle gourd poses some interesting problems. How a genome of Old World cotton came to be incorporated into American cotton has not yet been resolved. How did the American sweet potato become widely distributed in the eastern Pacific by the time of Captain Cook's voyages in the 1770's? Pre-Columbian distribution of the coconut remains rather obscure and the reasons for numerous vicarious domestications generate more speculations than answers.

Recent cytogenetic research has called into question the significance of chromosome pairing and the nature of polyploidy. For several decades wheat has been singled out as a classical case of alloploidy. It has become increasingly clear, however, that while wheat is a polyploid it is not classical in the textbook sense. The genomes are not as clear-cut as we thought, pairing is demonstrably under genetic control, and there is increasing evidence that the B genome has not been properly identified. Indeed, the B genome in wheat may not exist outside of wheat.

New and intensive research on the origin of maize has essentially destroyed the well-known tripartite theory of Paul C. Mangelsdorf and Robert G. Reeves. There is no reason to postulate a wild maize that later became extinct. Teosinte *is* wild maize, but whether teosinte, as we know it, is the direct progenitor of maize has not yet been fully established. Comparative studies of the evolution of cereals have been most helpful in elucidating some of these problems, yet others remain obscure.

The general picture that is emerging from recent studies is far more complex and diffuse than we used to imagine. Neither man nor his crops have obeyed set rules for a sequence of events or stages of development. Some weeds became crops, and some crops produced weeds. Sometimes man has deliberately set out to derive cultivars from wild populations, and sometimes crops have insinuated themselves almost unwanted into the domestic fold. Several crops originated in Vavilovian centers, but many originated elsewhere. Agriculture sometimes emerged in a center of innovation and dispersed out of it, and sometimes it evolved over vast areas with no evidence of a center at all. The real world has not followed any neat and simplistic theoretical models.

In addition to the research activities of geneticists and agronomists, the subject of agricultural origins and dispersals has become popular among some geographers, anthropologists, and archaeologists. There is an increasing self-awareness and humanistic introspection among scholars. Anthropologists find they cannot understand the cultures they study without some knowledge of agricultural practice, and in searching out cultural origins, they are led to origins of agriculture. Studies of human adaptation lead to study of plant adaptation. The currently fashionable ecological approaches to man and his environment inevitably involve the agricultural ecosystem. By the nature of his investigations, the archaeologist is led more and more into studies of human ecology. People in developing countries everywhere are trying to recover their own heritage, through searching into the past. There is a general third world reaction to the colonial era of western domination and a search for independent sources of culture. Agriculture was not a European invention and people in several parts of the world can take some satisfaction in the innovations of their prehistoric ancestors.

This small volume is designed to serve the widening audience of people interested in crop evolution. It cannot be an exhaustive treatment, but is intended as a summary statement of theories, concepts, and of evidence established from recent studies. It is a skeleton which can be enlarged upon and amplified at any point of interest to students of cultivated plants.

Jack R. Harlan
Urbana, Illinois

Chapter 1

PROLOGUE: THE GOLDEN AGE

CROP EVOLUTION

In this book, we shall be dealing with evolution. We shall try to describe the evolution of crop plants from their wild progenitors to fully domesticated races and the emergence of agricultural economies from preagricultural ones. We shall deal with the activities of man that have shaped the evolution of crops and with the influences of crops in shaping the evolution of human societies. Crops are artifacts made and molded by man as much as a flint arrowhead, a stone ax-head, or a clay pot. On the other hand, man has become so utterly dependent on the plants he grows for food that, in a sense, the plants have "domesticated" him. A fully domesticated plant cannot survive without the aid of man, but only a minute fraction of the human population could survive without cultivated plants. Crops and man are mutually dependent and we shall attempt to describe how this intimate symbiosis evolved.

When gods alike and mortals rose to birth,
A golden race th'immortals form'd on
earth
Of many-languaged men: they lived of
old
When Saturn reign'd in heaven, an age of
gold.
Like gods they lived, with calm untroubled
mind;
Free from the toils and anguish of our
kind:
Nor e'er decrepid age mishaped their
frame,
The hand's, the foot's proportions still
the same.
Strangers to ill, their lives in feasts flow'd
by:
Wealthy in fruits; dear to the blest on
high:
Dying they sank in sleep, nor seem'd to
die.
Theirs was each good; the life-sustaining
soil
Yielded its copious fruits, unbribed by
toil;
They with abundant goods midst quiet
lands
All willing shared the gatherings of their
hands.
When earth's dark womb had closed
this race around,
High Jove as daemons raised them
from the ground.

Hesiod, eighth century B. C.
(Translated by Charles A. Elton,
1815)

The word "evolution" means an opening out, an unfolding, a realization of potential as in the opening of a flower or the germination of a seed. It implies a gradual process rather than sudden or cataclysmic events, with each living thing being derived genetically

3

from preceding living things. Evolution as a process means change with time and the changes may be relatively slow or rapid, the time relatively long or short. Thus, the differences brought about by evolution over time may be small or great. As we shall see, some cultivated plants differ very little, if at all, from their wild forms while others differ enormously from their progenitors. The same can be said for the evolution of agricultural economies and the sociological changes that have occurred in the process of developing fully agricultural and industrial societies from hunting-gathering systems.

In order to develop a degree of understanding of what has happened and what agricultural systems mean to mankind, we need some sort of picture of what life was like before agriculture. We need to establish a base line from which we can visualize the domestication of plants and the emergence of agriculture. What kinds of plants did man eat before today's crops were available? What did he know about plants, and what might have caused him to begin the process of domestication? The descriptions given here will necessarily be brief and sketchy, but will give an idea of the condition of man before he began to grow plants on purpose for food.

We also need to know something about man as hunter in order to understand ourselves. Lee and DeVore (1968b) have put it succinctly:

> Cultural Man has been on earth for some 2,000,000 years; for over 99% of this period he has lived as a hunter-gatherer. Only in the last 10,000 years has man begun to domesticate plants and animals, to use metals and to harness energy sources other than the human body. . . . Of the estimated 80,000,000,000 men who have ever lived out a life span on earth, over 90% have lived as hunters and gatherers; about 6% have lived by agriculture and the remaining few percent have lived in industrial societies. To date, the hunting way of life has been the most successful and persistent adaptation man has ever achieved.

As a matter of general education and self-understanding it is important that we know something about this basic human adaptation. There are two general approaches to the problem: 1) we can study surviving nonagricultural societies and examine the ethnographic observations made within the last few centuries, or 2) we can attempt to interpret preagricultural life from the artifacts, refuse, and other clues left by ancient man and recovered by archaeological techniques. In this chapter we shall deal primarily with the first approach but the archaeological record shall be touched upon in later sections.

THE HUNTER STEREOTYPE

Traditionally, agricultural people have looked down on hunting people who are described as "savage," "backward," "primitive," "ignorant," "indolent," "lazy," "wild," and lacking in intelligence. Europeans applied the term "civilized tribes" to some eastern North American Indians who lived in towns and cultivated plants, but these Indians themselves referred to the hunting tribes of the plains as "wild Indians." The prejudice is rather universal.

The stereotype includes the idea that hunting-gathering people were always on the verge of starvation and that the pursuit of food took so much of their time and energy that there was not enough of either one left over to build more "advanced" cultures. Hunters were too nomadic to cultivate plants and too ignorant or unintelligent to understand the life cycles of plants. The idea of sowing or planting had never occurred to them and they lacked the intelligence to conceive of it. Hunters were concerned with animals and had no interest in plants. In the stereotype that developed, it was generally agreed that the life of the hunter-gatherer was "nasty, brutish, and short," and that any study of such people would only reveal that they lived like animals, were of low intelligence, and were intellectually insensitive and incapable of "improvement."

Occasionally, an unusually perceptive student of mankind tried to point out that hunting man might be as intelligent as anyone else, that he had a sensitive spiritual and religious outlook, that he was capable of high art, that his mythologies were worthy of serious consideration, and that he was in fact as one of us and belonged to the same species with all its weaknesses and potentialities. Such opinions were seldom taken very seriously until recently. It is finally becoming apparent that no part of the stereotype is correct and that the widely held presuppositions are almost all false and untenable. Our ancestors were not as stupid or as brutish as we wanted to believe.

WHAT CAN WE LEARN FROM SURVIVING HUNTING PEOPLES?

According to our present understanding, all the people on earth lived by hunting, fishing, and gathering about 10,000 to 12,000 years ago. We do not know the world population at that time, but the estimate of 10 million given by Lee and DeVore (1968a) is probably near the right order of magnitude. At the beginning of the first century A. D., farmers had occupied perhaps half the land suitable for agriculture. By the time of Columbus (about 1500 A.D.) the area inhabited by hunting people had shrunk dramatically and these areas represented regions too dry, too cold, or too wet for easy exploitation by cultivation. When the world population reached 350 million, hunters and gatherers still occupied most of western North America, the whole of Australia, and large sections of South America and Africa. By the beginning of the 20th century (1900 A.D.) when modern ethnographers had begun their observations, the world population had jumped to about 1.6 billion and the hunters and gatherers decreased to less than 0.001%. The present population is racing toward 4 billion, with the hunter-gatherer population heading toward extinction.

The study of hunting tribes that have survived long enough to have been observed by modern ethnographers is full of difficulties and pitfalls. Many tribes had become profoundly modified through contact with and pressures applied by agriculturalists. Some were reduced to the status of slaves or servants, others were restricted on reservations or their normal ranges were constricted by pressures of stronger groups. The social and economic structures of many tribes were in an advanced stage of disintegration at the time of ethnographic description.

The geographic distribution of surviving hunters results in a serious bias. By and large, hunters have survived where agriculture is unrewarding. We find them in the Kalahari Desert and adjacent dry savanna in southern Africa, in small pockets of tropical rain forest, in the frozen wastes of the Arctic, or in western North America, but there are no examples left in the more productive agricultural lands of the world.

At the time of European contact, the eastern forests and woodlands of North America were largely populated by Indian agriculturalists; the people living in the plains and westward mostly maintained hunting-gathering economies. There were enclaves of farmers, such as the Mandan on the Missouri River in North Dakota, and a highly sophisticated agriculture had developed in the Southwest where people practiced irrigation on a large scale and often lived in towns. Some farming was practiced along the Colorado River watershed and into southern California, but most of the California Indians and other tribes of western North America lived by hunting, fishing, and gathering. A substantial body of information has been assembled about them, but we must remember that they did have contact with farming people and some of their cultural elements could have been borrowed.

Data for hunter-gatherers over much of South America are suspect because many anthropologists feel that these tribes are mostly, if not all, dropouts from farming (Lévi-Strauss, 1950; Lathrap, 1968). The Bushman of southern Africa has been studied in some detail, but we know historically that he has long had contact with the livestock-herding Hottentot and farming Bantu tribes. The Congo pygmies often spend part of each year with agricultural people. The Ainu of Japan have taken up some farming in the last century or so. Many of the hunter-gatherers of India are so constricted by agriculturalists that they have virtually become members of a nonfarming caste.

The Andaman Islanders succeeded in preserving a greater degree of isolation, partly by killing off strangers who landed or were shipwrecked on their shores. Still, we know they have borrowed some customs from outsiders. Both pottery and pigs seem to have been introduced about 1500 A.D. (Coon, 1971). It is even possible that they were agriculturalists when they arrived and abandoned the practice when they found it unnecessary.

Perhaps our most reliable data come from Australia. At the time of European contact there was an entire continent populated by an estimated 300,000 people without a single domesticated plant and no genuine agriculture. Although it is true that for some centuries before European contact Malayan traders had been visiting northern Australia on a fairly regular basis, there is little evidence that this resulted in significant changes in use of food resources and it did not induce the Aborigines to take up the cultivation of plants. The Torres Strait is also rather narrow and some contact with agricultural Melanesians might have occurred. That this would influence the whole of Australia very much would seem doubtful.

I shall, therefore, rely more on ethnographic data from Australia than elsewhere, but will remind the reader that *any* reconstruction of a way of life of some thousands of years ago, based on a small, biased sample of living people, is full of hazards and sources of error. The earlier accounts may have more value than some of the later ones because the effects of European contact were rapid and profound.

FOOD RESOURCES OF HUNTER-GATHERERS

As soon as we look at the ethnographic evidence, two features are apparent immediately that do damage to the stereotype of hunting man: 1) a lot of "hunters" do not depend much on hunting, and 2) gathering plant foods does not necessarily take a lot of time or effort.

Lee (1968) classified 58 tribes according to percentage dependence on hunting, fishing, or gathering. The data were taken from the *Ethnographic Atlas* (Murdock, 1967), but adjusted somewhat by transferring the pursuit of large sea mammals from fishing to hunting and shell-fishing from fishing to gathering. The food obtained by gathering is predominantly of plant origin. The class does include small animal foods such as mice, rats, lizards, eggs, insect grubs, snails, and tortoise and shell-fishing is important to a few gathering tribes. In several cases where detailed analyses were made, however, plant foods contributed 60 to 80% of the intake of gathering people.

Estimates of percentage dependence on each class were given for each tribe, but I shall present here only a summary classification by primary dependence, i.e., the activity supplying the greater share of the food. I have also divided the tribes geographically in a very general way.

	Primary dependence on:			
	Gathering	Hunting	Fishing	Total
Tribes at 44° latitude or higher	1	9	15	25
Tribes between 44° N and 44° S	28	2	3	33
Total	29	11	18	58

There is nothing special about the 44th latitude except that it divides this sample rather neatly. There are not many gathering tribes at high latitudes because plant resources are not so abundant there. Tribes like the Copper Eskimo live 100% on meat and fish; they have no choice. In middle latitudes where there is a choice, food is primarily of plant origin for most tribes. The pattern has not changed much

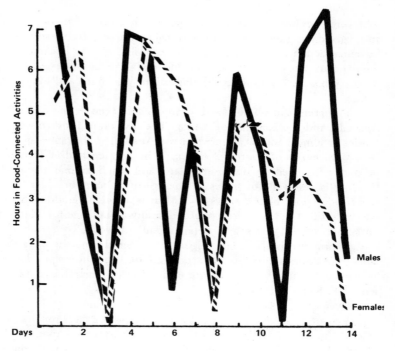

Figure 1
Food-gathering activities of the Australian aborigines
(adapted from Sahlins, 1968).

since the introduction of agriculture; more than 95% of plant foods produced today are grown at latitudes below 44°.

Despite the geographic and ecological bias of the sample it seems reasonable to conclude that in the millennia before agriculture most people were gatherers rather than hunters and that the bulk of their food was of plant origin. In terms of the whole 2-million-year span of human evolution, however, such broad spectrum gathering may have evolved at a relatively late time out of more restricted hunting systems. Several thousand years before the first traces of agricultural activities, man developed techniques that permitted him to exploit a wider range of his environment. He learned about canoes, rafts, and boats of various types and could therefore exploit aquatic resources better than before. As he became more mobile, the rivers and lakes

that were once barriers became arteries of transport. Man also learned
about grinding, pulverizing, and cooking vegetable material and thereby expanded his food resources enormously. As he became more
omnivorous with a wider choice of foods, he could expand and
diversify his ecological range of adaptation (Washburn and Lancaster,
1968).

Gatherers can obtain food in abundance even in the deserts of
Australia and the Kalahari of Africa. The rhythm of food-getting activities is almost identical between the Australian aborigine and the
!Kung Bushmen of southern Africa. The women and children are
primarily involved in obtaining plant and small animal materials.
Hunting is reserved for males at the age of puberty or older but is
more of a sport than a necessity. Meat is a welcome addition to a
rather dull diet but is seldom required in any abundance for adequate
nutrition. Both males and females tend to work for 2 days and
every third day is a holiday (Figure 1). Even during the days they
work, the hours are so short that only about 3 to 4 hours per day are
employed to supply food for the entire group (Australian data presented by Sahlins, 1968).

Over a 3-week study period, Lee (1968) found that the !Kung
Bushmen of the Dobe area spent 2.3, 1.9, and 3.2 days for the first,
second, and third week, respectively, in subsistence activities. He
wrote, "In all, the adults of the Dobe camp worked about 2½ days a
week. Since the average working day was about 6 hours long, the fact
emerges that !Kung Bushmen of Dobe, despite their harsh environment, devote from 12 to 19 hours a week to getting food." From the
relative yields obtained in both studies, it is apparent that hunting is
a high-risk, low-return activity, whereas gathering is a low-risk, high-
return enterprise.

Among the Bushmen, neither the children nor the aged are
pressed into service. Children can help if they wish, but are not expected to contribute regularly to the work force until they are married. The aged are respected for their knowledge, experience, and
legendary lore and are cared for even when blind or lame and unable
to contribute to the food-gathering activities. Neither nonproductive
children nor the aged are considered a burden.

What does one do with all this leisure time in an illiterate and
nontechnological society? Apparently one sleeps a lot, but there are
diversions: music, dances, ritual, and ceremony, storytelling, rites of
passage, creative arts, making useful and decorative articles, and

Table 1
Diet of the !Kung Bushmen (adapted from Lee, 1968).

	Protein, g/day	Calories/person per day	Percent caloric contribution of meat and vegetables
Meat	34.5	690	33
Mongongo nuts	56.7	1,260	67
Other vegetable foods	1.9	190	
Total	93.1	2,140	100

similar activities. Life appears easy, but generally dull. Perhaps as a consequence there is a great deal of coming and going; the camp population is fluid and camps may be moved on the slightest pretext or for no reason at all.

Understandably, there is a tendency to concentrate on the foods most easily obtained at a given time, and these are likely to change from season to season and, to some extent, from year to year. Groups of people in many gathering societies tend to be very fluid for that reason. When food is at maximum abundance, there is a tendency to gather in large bands. This is the season for rejoicing, celebrating, observing ancient tribal rituals, arranging marriages, and having naming ceremonies and coming of age ceremonies, and so on. The tribe is more fully represented at this time. During the most difficult season of the year, the people may break up into microbands to better exploit the gathering range and to avoid exhausting the food supply near the larger camps.

Many Australian aborigines maintain part of the yearly cycle even after becoming dependent on European agricultural-industrial systems. For most of the year they find jobs as ranch hands, laborers, mechanics, etc., but they may quit whatever they are doing, take off their store-bought clothes, and take a 3-month "walkabout" during their traditionally festive season. Gathering is still easier than working at that time of year.

Heavy dependence on only one or a few plants may occur during some seasons or even year-long. To the !Kung Bushman of the Dobe area of southern Africa, the mongongo nut (*Ricinodendron rautanenii* Schinz) is basically the staff of life. These nuts are available year-round and are remarkably nutritious (Table 1). The average daily per-capita consumption of 300 nuts weighs "only about 7.5 ounces [212.6 g] but contains the caloric equivalent of 2.5 pounds

Table 2
Analysis of wild and cultivated wheats (adapted from
Harlan, 1967).

	Ether extract	Crude fiber	Crude protein	NFE*
		%		
Wild einkorn	2.64	2.33	22.83	60.04
Modern wheat	1.62	2.78	14.50	68.70

*Nitrogen-free extract or carbohydrates other than fiber.

[1,134 g] of cooked rice and the protein equivalent of 14 ounces
[396.9 g] of lean beef" (Lee, 1968).

The Australian aborigines in the dry heartland of the continent
depended heavily on seeds and pods of *Acacia*, grass seeds, and seeds
of other plants, while those in the more tropical north had a wider
selection but exploited yams (*Dioscorea*) very heavily. Many of the
California Indians were dependent upon acorns for their primary
food source and some tribes of the Southwest gathered mesquite
(*Prosopis*) beans and pods as a staple.

The West Coast tribes of North America seemed to have been in
an especially productive zone. There is no way of knowing with any
degree of accuracy the number of Indians in the region at the time of
European contact, but all estimates agree that the population density
was high for hunting-gathering people. Baumhoff (1963) presents
some estimates that suggest a population density of 0.4 to 2.0/km²
over most of California, but local areas exceeded 4.4/km². This is
greater than that of the agricultural Pueblan Indians of the Rio Grande
(about 2.8/km²). Baumhoff concluded that 250,000 people were
living primarily on acorn-fish or acorn-game diets in California. Nutritionally the diets should have been excellent.

I once made a little study of the amount of grain that could be
harvested from wild wheat (einkorn) (*Triticum boeoticum*) in Turkey
(Harlan, 1967). I found no difficulty in collecting over 2 kg of head
material or the equivalent of 1 kg of clean grain per hour. More surprising was the very high nutritive value of the wild wheat compared
to modern bread wheat (*T. aestivum*) (Table 2). Both George Beadle,
a geneticist, and I have collected wild maize (teosinte) (*Zea mexicana*)
in Mexico and kept records of the amounts gathered in a period of
time. We approached the problem somewhat differently and used
different harvesting methods. He was able to get more than I, partly
because he persuaded Mexicans to do the harvesting and they prob-

ably knew how to do it better than I did. Even so, I calculated that a standard 3.5-hour gatherer's working day would yield slightly more than an 11-day supply at 150 g/day.

Chevalier (1932) described in some detail grass seed harvests in Africa which employ a swinging basket woven of palm leaf. Harvesting is done early in the morning when dew is on the grass. The easiest to harvest is a species of *Panicum* (either *P. laetum* or *P. turgidum*). According to Chevalier, an adult harvester could gather 10 kg in a morning with no difficulty. There is no evidence that he actually weighed the material, but such a yield is not inconsistent with other experience in grass seed harvests.

In 1841 Sir George Grey warned us that the standard stereotype did not fit the facts: "One mistake, very commonly made with regard to the natives of Australia, is to imagine that they have small means of subsistence, or are at times greatly pressed for want of food. . . ."

As far as we can tell from surviving gathering peoples, populations are maintained well below the carrying capacity of the range. Droughts, locusts, fires, or other natural disasters have little effect on food supply. At the time that Richard Lee was studying the Bushmen, there had been a serious drought prolonged over several years. Nearby farmers had lost their crops repeatedly and in desperation came into the desert range of the Bushmen and asked them how to live. The Bushmen taught the farmers what plants could be eaten and a substantial number of ex-farmers survived because of this. The countryside continued to produce enough food for both populations.

The very fact that hunters and gatherers have survived only in areas where agriculture has been unable to penetrate reminds us that these systems are stable, reliable, permanent, and basic. The hunting-gathering system is so secure that Marshall Sahlins (1968) described it as "the original affluent society." One can be affluent, he says, either by having a great deal or by wanting very little. Hunting-gathering people, in general, want very little. They are almost constantly on the move and do not want to be burdened by many possessions. While life as a hunter-gatherer may not be all that pleasant by modern standards, it does resemble, in a way, the golden age of Hesiod. For those of us who have given up our leisure time to earn our bread by the sweat of our brows, there is, at long last, a faint promise that the industrial age may permit us to regain the leisure time that we lost when we took up agriculture thousands of years ago.

WHAT DO GATHERERS EAT?

In his *List of Foods Used in Africa,* Jardin (1967) has compiled an
extensive and complex list of species. I have attempted to remove
cultivated plants and introductions and reduce the synonymy as
much as possible. There still remain more than 1,400 species that
could be grouped into classes as follows:

Grass seeds	ca. 60 spp.
Legumes	ca. 50 spp.
Roots and tubers	ca. 90 spp.
Oil seeds	ca. 60 spp.
Fruits and nuts	> 550 spp.
Vegetables and spices	> 600 spp.
Total	>1410 spp.

Most of Jardin's reports concerned agricultural tribes and only a small
fraction of the list represented foods of gatherers. This suggests that
1) many more species have been gathered from the wild than have
ever been domesticated, 2) even after agriculture is fully developed,
gathering wild plant foods is still a worthwhile effort, and 3) wild
plant resources are of the same general kinds as domesticated plant
resources.

    Yanovsky, in his *Food Plants of the North American Indians*
(1936), lists 1,112 species of 444 genera belonging to 120 families.
About 10% of these are crops or imported weeds; the rest are native
American plants. The bulk of the plants listed was gathered by nonagricultural tribes. Plants gathered in Central and South America
have not been conveniently compiled, but the number of species is
very large. A partial listing is given by Lévi-Strauss in the *Handbook
of South American Indians* (1950).

    Our most reliable information might again come from Australian
areas where agriculture was not practiced and where none of the
plants was domesticated. Lists compiled by Maiden (1889) and Irvine
(1957) are of help here, although neither list is complete; there are
problems of identification and synonymy, and many of the ethnographic records contain native names because the observers were not
botanists and could not identify the plants. Even so, Australians

were recorded as having gathered and used over 400 species belonging
to 250 or more genera.

Some observations are grouped below according to general kinds
of plant food resources.

Grass seeds (potential cereals)

Seeds of wild grasses have long been an important source of food
and are still harvested on a large scale in some regions. A. C. Gregory
(1886) commented:

> On Cooper's Creek (Australia), the natives reap a *Panicum* grass.
> Fields of 1,000 acres [405 ha] are there met with growing this cereal.
> The natives cut it down by means of stone knives, cutting down the
> stalk half way, beat out the seed, leaving the straw which is often
> met with in large heaps; they winnow by tossing seed and husk in the
> air, the wind carrying away the husks. The grinding into meal is done
> by means of two stones—a large irregular slab and a small cannon-
> ball-like one; the seed is laid on the former and ground, sometimes
> dry and at others with water into a meal. . . .

Stickney (1896) described methods of the wild-rice (*Zizania
aquatica*) harvest by the Ojibwa of Wisconsin late in the 19th century.
Two women, working together in a canoe, took a large ball of cedar
bark twine and tied up sheaves just below the panicles when the seed
was in the milk stage. Later, they went back when the seed was ripe
and beat the sheaves over the canoe. Each woman knew her own
bundles and the right of ownership was scrupulously respected.
Sometimes sheaves were not previously prepared and the woman in
the back would pole slowly forward while the other reached out with
a curved stick and bent a bunch of stalks over the canoe and hit them
with a straight stick held in the other hand. "About a gill is detached
at each blow." When the canoe became heavily laden in the front,
the women exchanged implements as they kept their places and the
canoe was poled back in the opposite direction. When the canoe was
fully loaded and low in the water it was beached and the wild rice removed. The wild rice was dried in the sun or on a platform over a
fire. Dehulling was done by men who placed seed in a skin bag and
treaded it in a pit dug in the soil. Dehulled seed was stored in bark
boxes or large skin bags; sometimes so much seed was stored that it
lasted until the next harvest.

Wild races of common Asian rice (*Oryza sativa*) were once harvested on a considerable scale in northern Australia:

> The wild rice of the Carpenteria swamps (*Oryza sativa* Linn.), however, needs to be carefully cleaned from its spiny chaff, which may be done by rubbing in wooden troughs. This must be the most important grass-food in Australia, being little inferior to cultivated grain. The plant grows 6 feet [1.8 m] high, and produces a good crop even in the latitude of Brisbane. The "paddy" is black with long awns. It is interesting, in Australia, to find one of the original sources of a cereal which has been cultivated in Asia for thousands of years.
>
> *Bancroft, 1884*

The wild races are still harvested in India despite the cultivation of domesticated forms for at least four millennia:

> In the Central Provinces the Gonds and Dhimars harvest this rice by tying the plants together into clumps and thus preventing the grains from falling. These grains have also got a certain demand in the market as they are often used by devout Hindus in these parts on fast days besides being sold to the poorer classes.
>
> *Roy, 1921*

Burkill (1935) makes a similar observation:

> The poor do not ignore it [wild rice], but tying the awns together before maturity save the grain for themselves, or they collect the fallen grain, which is made an easier process by the length of the awns.

Ping-Ti Ho (1969) has documented the harvesting of wild rice over much of southern and central China during a span of an entire millennium. One report, dated 874 A.D., from Ts'ang-chou, Hopei Province, to the emperor may be paraphrased: "Wild rice ripened in an area of more than 200,000 mu [13,333 ha], much to the benefit of the poor of local and neighboring counties" (Ho, 1969). It is to be noted that rice had been a major crop in China for over 4,000 years at the date of this report, but that the gathering of seeds of wild rice was still worth the effect.

Other species of rice, *O. barthii* and *O. longistaminata*, are regularly harvested in Africa, sometimes in sufficient abundance to appear in the markets (Oka and Chang, 1964; personal observation).

Claude Lévi-Strauss (1950) reports the harvesting of *O. subulata* (*Rhynchoryza subulata*) in Uruguay, Rio Grande do Sul, and the marshes of the upper Paraguay and Guaporé Rivers in South America. He also reports the technique of binding before harvest:

> The Tupí-Cawahíb of the upper Madeira River gather the seeds of an unidentified wild grass that grows in the forest, and in order to facilitate the harvest they tie together several stems before they are ripe, so that the seeds of several plants fall on the same spot and pile up in small heaps.

Panicum has been a favorite of grass seed gatherers the world over. In North America, *P. capillare*, *P. obtusum*, and *P. urvilleanum* have been listed as harvested in the wild (Yanovsky, 1936) and *P. sonorum* has been domesticated in Mexico (Gentry, 1942). Seven species are listed for Africa (Jardin, 1967), with the most important being *P. laetum* and *P. turgidum*. Four species are recorded for Australia, with *P. decompositum* occurring in thousand-hectare fields. Two species, *P. miliaceum* and *P. miliare*, were domesticated in Eurasia and India, respectively. It appears that food gatherers are attracted to similar plants.

At least five wild species of *Sporobolus* were harvested in North America, three in Africa, and three in Australia. Species of *Eragrostis* were gathered in North America, Australia, and Africa. For Africa six wild species are listed and one was domesticated as a cereal, *E. tef* (Ethiopia). *Eleusine* and *Dactyloctenium* were harvested in Australia, India, and Africa with one species (*E. coracana*) domesticated. Species of *Digitaria* were harvested in Australia, India, Africa, and Europe. *D. exilis* and *D. iburua* were domesticated in Africa, *D. cruciata* in India, and common crabgrass (*D. sanguinalis*) was cultivated as a cereal in central Europe until the 19th century without actually being domesticated (Körnicke, 1885). The differences between cultivation and domestication will be discussed in Chapter 3.

Mannagrass (*Glyceria fluitans*) was harvested in substantial quantities from the marshes of central and eastern Europe as late as 1925 (Szafer, 1966). The seed was even exported from the port of Danzig to countries around the Baltic. Yanovsky (1936) reports that the same species was harvested by Indians in Utah, Nevada, and Oregon. Wild oats (*Avena barbata* and *A. fatua*) were harvested by the Pomo tribe in California after these weedy plants had been introduced from the Mediterranean (Gifford, 1967).

In all, Jardin (1967) lists about 60 species of wild grasses that have been harvested for their seeds in Africa within recent decades. Yanovsky (1936) lists approximately 38 for North America, and Irvine (1957) and others mention about 25 for Australia. The exact number cannot be given because of problems with synonyms and identification. Relatively little is known about wild grass harvesting in Europe and Asia although *Oryza, Panicum, Digitaria,* and *Glyceria* have been mentioned.

Legumes (potential pulses)

Gathering peoples are evidently attracted to Leguminosae of various kinds. Whole pods may be used, as well as seeds only, pods only, or even the tissues inside the pods surrounding the seeds. Some legumes have edible tubers, and others have leaves or young shoots suitable for pot-herbs. Not infrequently the material harvested is poisonous and must be detoxified before use. Poisonous materials can be used for stunning fish, stupifying emus, or making arrow poisons.

As with the Gramineae, certain genera appear frequently on plant lists and several distinct species of a given genus may be used in different parts of the world. Genera with very wide distributions may be very widely used. For example, many species of *Acacia* are exploited in Australia, several are used in Africa and Asia, and only a few are used in the Americas. However, more species of *Prosopis* (mesquite) are used in the Americas than in Africa, Asia, and Australia. Different species of *Canavalia* are harvested in Central and South America and in Southeast Asia and Australia. Various species of *Parkia* are collected in Africa, Asia, and Australia. *Vigna* and *Dolichos* are widely exploited in Africa, Asia, and Australia while several species of *Phaseolus* are harvested in the Americas. *Tephrosia* spp. have been used for fish poisons on five continents.

Root and tuber plants

Roots, tubers, rhizomes, and bulbs have been widely harvested for untold millennia. The choice depends more on what is abundant and available than anything else. The genus *Dioscorea* is very large and includes about 250 species distributed throughout the warmer parts of the world. Many produce tubers that are edible or rendered edible after detoxification. About 30 species are harvested in the wild in

Africa (Jardin, 1967) and several have been domesticated. Wild yam harvests are important in India, Southeast Asia, the South Pacific, Australia, and tropical America.

Tubers and rhizomes of the Araceae are widely harvested in the tropics and a few are found in the more temperate zones. Bulbs of the Liliaceae are popular where they occur. Yanovsky (1936) lists about 90 species belonging to the lily family (*Liliaceae*) that supplied food for North American Indians. No less than 17 species of wild onion (*Allium*) were listed, and even the death camus *Zygadenus* was eaten after suitable detoxification. Tuberous legumes, Solanaceae, *Ipomoea, Nymphaea,* and *Eleocharis* were widely harvested, and *Cyperus rotundus* has supplied food in North America, Africa, Asia, Australia, and Europe.

Oil plants

Most gatherers had periodic access to animal fats, but sources of vegetable oil were also sought. In the wetter tropics the fruits of various palms (*Palmaceae*) were especially attractive. The African oil palm (*Elaeis guineensis*) is still exploited in the wild as is its counterpart in South America (*E. melanococca*). Other palms also supply oil in quantity including, of course, the coconut (*Cocos nucifera*). Seeds of Compositae, Cruciferae, and Cucurbitaceae are harvested on every continent, partly for their oil content. Many nuts and some fruits are high in oil and are still harvested in the wild. Some familiar ones are *Aleurites* (candlenut or tung-oil tree), *Persea* (avocado), *Theobroma* (cocoa), *Pistacea* (pistachio), *Olea* (olive), *Butyrospermum* (shea butter tree or karité). Several species of *Sesamum* and *Linum* are harvested for their oily seeds.

Fruits and nuts

Long lists of fruits and nuts can be compiled, but it is not necessary to go into much detail here. We need only point out that the same patterns prevail as for grass seeds, legumes, and oil plants in that different species of the same genera are exploited almost everywhere they occur. In temperate zones, for example, species of walnut (*Juglans*), hickory (*Carya*), hazelnut (*Corylus*), chestnut (*Castanea*), beech (*Betula*), oak (*Quercus*), hawthorn (*Crataegus*), hackberry (*Celtis*), plum-cherry (*Prunus*), bramblefruits (*Rubus*), grape (*Vitis*),

elderberry (*Sambucus*), pine-nuts (*Pinus*), and others were popular
with gatherers in Europe, Asia, North America, Africa, and Australia.
In the tropics, some of the popular genera were (and are) *Ficus,
Citrus, Musa, Eugenia, Pandanus, Spondias, Adansonia, Artocarpus,
Annona,* and *Carica.* If a plant appeals to one gathering tribe, a similar
plant is probably used by another tribe, even on another continent.

Vegetables and spices

Because the same general pattern is operative, it might be worthwhile
to call attention to repetitive patterns in two families whose produce
appeals to gatherers.

Solanaceae

The genus *Solanum* is found on every continent and includes
several hundred species. About 15 species are gathered for food in
Africa, 9 are listed for North America, and several are found in South
America, India, and Australia. Some must be detoxified before being
eaten. The fruits are the parts eaten in most cases, but leaves may be
used as pot-herbs and a number of species in the Americas have edible
tubers. *Physalis* is another genus widely exploited with at least 10
species gathered in North America alone plus others in South America, Africa, Europe, Asia, and Australia. Species of wild *Capsicum,
Cyphomandra,* and *Lycopersicon* were gathered in the Americas. The
genus *Nicotiana* was a favorite of gathering tribes in the Americas and
Australia. Several distinct species were involved and they were
utilized almost wherever they occurred. In the Americas, the tobac-
cos were both chewed and smoked, while it was a masticatory only in
Australia. Lime of some sort was often mixed with the quid. *Datura*
was used as a drug, medicine, or halucinogen in both eastern and
western hemispheres.

Cucurbitaceae

Plants of this family were often attractive to gathering peoples
and in some cases were very important because of their abundance. In
Australia, Maiden (1889) observed that *Cucumis trigonus* Roxb. was

sometimes "growing in such abundance that the whole country seemed strewed with the fruit." In southern Africa the landscape may be almost cluttered with wild watermelon (*Colocynthus citrullus*) where it may serve as the only source of water for man and animals alike over extended periods of the dry season (Story, 1958). Tropical *Cucumis* and *Mamordica* species are still gathered in the wild in Africa and Asia. The genus *Cucurbita* is confined to the Americas and was extensively exploited by the Indians; several species were domesticated. The white-flowered bottle gourd (*Lagenaria siceraria*) has been widely exploited, primarily for the hard shells of the fruits which make excellent containers. Its use has been recorded in the Americas, Africa, Asia, and Australia, but its distribution as a wild plant is not well known. The fruits of the Australian races are said to be purgative or even poisonous according to Maiden (1889) but are eaten by the aborigines after being processed. The fruits of some domesticated races may be eaten when young without special precautions. *Luffa* is also widely used in Asia and Africa, but is a fish poison in Australia (Palmer, 1883).

Finally, we might return to the plants gathered by the Australian aborigines as, perhaps, representing a most authentic selection by surviving nonagricultural peoples. A short list of genera that include one or more species harvested in the wild by native Australians is given in Table 3. I have attempted to indicate where species of each genus are harvested in the wild in addition to Australia. It seems evident from these data and the foregoing discussion that gatherers exploit about the same range of plants wherever they find them.

It is not surprising, therefore, to find independent domestications of different species of the same genus, and if the genus is widespread, the different domesticates may have originated in different continents. Examples of such vicarious domestications occur in the following genera, among others: Mesoamerica and South America— *Amaranthus, Annona, Canavalia, Capsicum, Carica, Chenopodium, Cucurbita, Gossypium, Opuntia, Pachyrrhizus, Phaseolus, Physalis;* Africa and Asia—*Amorphophallus, Cucumis, Digitaria, Dioscorea, Dolichos, Hibiscus, Oryza, Piper, Solanum, Vigna;* Old and New Worlds[1]—*Amaranthus, Canavalia, Dioscorea, Gossypium, Ipomoea, Lepidium, Lupinus, Panicum, Prunus, Setaria, Solanum, Spondias.*

---

[1] In this book, Old World refers to the eastern hemisphere, and New World to the western hemisphere.

Table 3
A short list of genera that include one or more species
harvested for food by native Australians. Abbreviations in
parentheses indicate species harvested in the wild in addition
to Australia; Am = America, Af = Africa, As = Asia, E =
Europe, O = Oceania, ♀ = modern domestication.

Acacia (Af, Am, As),*	*Loranthus*
Adansonia (Af, As),*	*Lucuma* (Am),*
Aleurites (As, O),*	*Luffa* (As),*
Alocasia (As, O),*	*Macadamia* (♀)
Amaranthus (Am, As, Af),*	*Marsilia*
Amorphophallus (Af, As, O),*	*Mucuna* (As),*
Araucaria (Am, O, ♀)	*Musa* (As, O),*
Boerhaavia (Am, As)	*Nasturtium* (As),*
Bowenia	*Nelumbium* (Af, As),*
Calamus	*Nymphaea* (Am, Af, As),*
Canavalia (Am, As),*	*Ocimum* (Af, As),*
Capparis (As),*	*Oryza* (Am, Af, As, O),*
Chenopodium (Am, Af, As),*	*Oxalis* (Am, Af, As),*
Citrus (As, O),*	*Pandanus* (As, O),*
Cucumis (As, Af),*	*Panicum* (Am, Af, As, E),*
Cyperus (Am, Af, As)	*Physalis* (Am, Af, As, E),*
Dactyloctenium (Af)	*Piper* (Am, Af, As, O),*
Digitaria (Af, As, E),*	*Podocarpus* (Af, As, O),*
Dioscorea (Am, Af, As),*	*Polygonum* (Am, Af, As, E, O)
Dolichos (Af, As, O),*	*Portulaca* (Am, Af, As, E),*
Eleocharis (Am, Af, As),*	*Rubus* (Am, Af, As, E),*
Eleagnus (As, E),*	*Rumex* (Am, Af, As, E)
Eleusine (Af, As),*	*Sambucus* (Am, Af, As, E),*
Eragrostis (Am, Af),*	*Sesbania* (Am, Af, As),*
Eriochloa (Af, As)	*Solanum* (Am, Af, As, E, O),*
Eucalyptus (♀)	*Sorghum* (Af, As),*
Eugenia (As, O),*	*Spondias* (Am, Af, As, O),*
Ficus (Am, Af, As, O),*	*Sporobolus* (Am, Af)
Gastrodia	*Tacca* (As, O),*
Geranium (Am, As, E),*	*Terminalia* (As, O),*
Grewia	*Trigonella* (As),*
Haemadorum	*Typha* (Am, Af, As, E, O),*
Hibiscus (Am, Af, As, O),*	*Vigna* (Af, As, O),*
Ipomoea (Am, Af, As, O),*	*Vitex* (Am, Af, As, O),*
Lagenaria (Am, Af, As, O),*	*Vitis* (Am, As, E),*
Lepidium (Am, Af, As, E),*	*Zamia* (O)
Linum (As, E),*	*Zizyphus* (Af, As),*

* One or more domesticated species somewhere in the world, but not in Australia.

UNDERSTANDING LIFE CYCLES OF PLANTS

What do nonagricultural people know of the life cycles of plants?
Do they know that flowers lead to seeds and that seeds can be sown
to produce more plants? Is this something that must be learned or

discovered in order to commence the domestication of plants or is this a part of the general botanical knowledge of gathering peoples?

A look at the ethnographic evidence shows first that some gatherers do plant seeds. Seven of 19 groups studied by Steward in Nevada sowed seeds of wild plants (Downs, 1964). No tillage was practiced; the seedbed was generally prepared by simply burning the vegetation the previous fall and seeding in the spring. The seeds sown were of entirely wild plants; the most frequently mentioned were species of *Chenopodium, Oryzopsis, Mentzelia,* and *Sophia* (Steward, 1941).

The Paiute tribe of Owens Valley, Nevada, practiced irrigation but did not plant or cultivate. The irrigation was designed to increase production of wild plants such as *Nicotiana attenuata, Salvia columbariae, Chenopodium fremonti, C. album, Helianthus bolanderi, Oryzopsis hymenoides,* and *Eleocharis.* The earthen dams were simple, but the rather extensive canals required considerable labor. One block covered about 5 km² (2 mi²) and another close to 13 km² (5 mi²) (Steward, 1934). However, as previously pointed out, the Great Basin Indians could have been influenced by neighboring agriculturalists and their botanical knowledge may not be typical of gatherers in preagricultural times. Let us look elsewhere.

To the Andamanese, the goddess Puluga symbolizes the southwest monsoon that brings violent winds and rains from April to October:

> Puluga owned all the wild yams and cicada grubs that the people ate, and all the beeswax that they used in hafting, calking, and cordage. Women who dug yams had to replace the tops to fool Puluga. . . .
> *Coon, 1971*

Indeed, if Puluga caught the people misusing her property she would get very angry and send bad weather. Here we find the practice of planting reinforced by a religious belief. The practice is useful to the people, but does not of itself prove understanding.

An early observation of Sir George Grey (1841) concerning Australian aborigines is more revealing:

> The natives have, however, a law that no plant bearing seeds is to be dug up after it has flowered; they then call them (for example) the mother of *Bohn,* the mother of *Mud-ja* [*Haemadorum* spp.] , etc.; and so strict are they in their observance of this rule that I have never seen a native violate it, unless requested by an European, and even then they betray a great dislike to do so.

The practice is confirmed by Gregory (1886):

> The natives on the West Coast of Australia are in the habit amongst other things of digging up yams as a portion of their means of subsistence; the yams are called "ajuca" in the north and "wirang" in the south. In digging up these yams they invariably re-insert the head of the yams so as to be sure of a future crop, but beyond this they do absolutely nothing which may be regarded as a tentative in the direction of cultivating plants for their use.

There seems to be little doubt that the life cycles of plants were well understood by native Australians. The aborigine was equipped with all the knowledge necessary to practice agriculture, but did not do so. The situation is summed up succinctly by Flannery (1968): "We know of no human group on earth so primitive that they are ignorant of the connection between plants and the seeds from which they grow. . . ."

GENERAL BOTANICAL KNOWLEDGE

We should not be surprised if gathering peoples know a lot about plants. They are the real "professional botanists;" for them, life depends on an adequate knowledge of plants. We have seen that gatherers are familiar with hundreds of species and their uses for food. We have noted that many are poisonous and must be detoxified before they can be eaten.

Since "ignorance" is part of the stereotype developed by agricultural people about gatherers, I would like to call attention to an episode described with some apparent pleasure by Sir George Grey (1841). Some of the crew of Captain Cook's expedition of the 1770's observed the aborigines eating seeds of *Zamia* (a cycad). The crew tried some of their own harvest and became very ill. They concluded that the aborigines must have very strong constitutions to be able to live on such food. Later, on shipboard, they fed *Zamia* seeds to some pigs, and a few died. Their admiration for the physical stamina of the natives increased substantially. The aborigines, of course, had removed the poison before eating their seeds, and were, no doubt, amused at the "ignorance" of their European visitors.

Detoxification is required for a considerable number of plants used by the North American Indians, the Australian aborigines, and gatherers in tropical zones. Some plants are deadly poisonous without treatment, others only unpleasant. Several acorn species are sweet and need no treatment, others contain various amounts of tannins. Among California Indians, some of the bitterest oaks were the most popular; when properly leached, the original tannin content did not cause any harm. Tribes on the edge of the "acorn belt" were often more selective since they did not depend much on acorns and did not want to go to the trouble of leaching. Leguminous seeds, Solanaceous fruits, *Dioscorea* spp., and Aroid tubers are still among the more common poisonous foods consumed by gatherers.

Detoxification is usually by heat, leaching, or both. The plant material is frequently reduced by grinding or pounding in a mortar to facilitate treatment. Boiling water may be poured through the meal, the material may be boiled in several changes of water, or sometimes prolonged soaking in cold water is enough. Some foods are roasted, pounded, and then leached. Sieves, strainers, cloth sacks, wooden troughs, or sand-beds may be produced for the purpose. Pottery is not necessary; water may be boiled in baskets, hides, wooden boxes, or pits in the ground by dropping fire-heated rocks into the water.

Gatherers not only know how to make poisonous foods safe, but they also know a great deal about drugs, narcotics, medicines, fish poisons, arrow poisons, gums, resins, glues, dyes and paints, bark cloth, woods for spears, arrows, bows, shields, fire sticks, and canoes. They have also used their botanical knowledge in spinning and weaving, basket-making, and constructing household utensils, fish traps and weirs, masks, figurines, and ceremonial objects.

The Australian aborigine was fond of chewing a wild tobacco (mostly *Nicotiana suaveolens*). Wood of *Acacia salicina* was burned to provide ash to mix with the quid. Why this particular species out of dozens of *Acacia*? Johnston and Cleland (1933) analyzed the ash and found it extraordinarily high in calcium sulphate, "sulphuric anhydride 30.09% and lime 40.70%." The alkaloids are more soluble in alkaline solutions. Perhaps any source of lime would do, but the practice reminds one of the custom in India of burning heartwood of *Acacia catechu* to obtain "cutch" which is mixed with other ingredients and used when betel nuts are chewed.

Another masticatory of the aborigines was *Duboisia hopwoodii*. This is of a different order of drug potency and contains hyoscyamine, norhyoscyamine with scopolamine in the younger leaves (Johnston and Cleland, 1933). Both narcotics were confounded under the general name *pituri* and were important articles of trade over great distances, "shields, boomerangs, spears and other articles being sent in return for them."

Nearly a century ago, Father Trilles, a French missionary to Gabon, West Africa, observed pygmies making arrow poison. The process was long, complex, and dangerous for the poisons were extremely potent. Ingredients of 10 different plants were used; 8 were poisonous and 2 were gums to be impregnated with poison and stuck to the arrowheads. Two animal poisons were also included: beetle larvae and venom of a horned viper. The procedure is described in *The Hunting Peoples* by Coon (1971) who added this comment:

> A tourist driving along a forest-lined road, seeing an elderly, diminutive black man clad in a bark-cloth breechclout, would have no reason to suspect that this child of nature knew the properties of many medicinal plants, some still undescribed in Western science, and how to combine them for their greatest effect. With the forest and marsh his pharmacy, his laboratory a secret nook in the shade of tall trees, and a minimum of equipment, the Pygmy poison-maker performs a delicate, dangerous, and highly skilled sequence of operations as exacting as some modern professions.

The more one studies the wealth of plant lore of gathering peoples the more one is impressed by the extent and coverage of their botanical knowledge. Man knows what he needs to know or learns what he must or else he dies. The security and stability of gathering economies are from necessity, rooted in an extensive body of information about plants.

MANIPULATION OF VEGETATION

Many tribes of nonagricultural people are known to deliberately alter vegetation. The most common method is by burning. Hunters may set fires to drive game, to increase the grass cover, or to attract herds of grazing animals that prefer the new shoots that come up after a fire. Gatherers appear to be well informed about the ecological effects of fires and frequently burn in order to increase certain species that they harvest. In the Great Basin 15 of 19 groups studied by Steward regularly burned to increase growth of wild plants (Downs, 1964).

In Australia land ownership was respected during the burning season. It was considered a serious offense to burn another's foraging range. The time and place of a burn were carefully chosen and serious attempts were made to keep the fires within prescribed bounds (Warner, 1958). Fires were primarily designed to encourage certain desired food plants, but the burns were also exploited as an adjunct of the hunt. Lines of hunters were deployed to intercept animals fleeing the fires.

The extent of such activities as the deliberate protection of plants in flower and producing seed or tubers and deliberate planting is often not realized. The following observation of Sir George Grey (1841) is of particular interest:

> In the Province of Victoria, as already stated, I have seen tracts of land several square miles in extent, so thickly studded with holes, where the natives have been digging up yams (*Dioscorea*) that it was difficult to walk across it. Again, in the sandy desert country which surrounds for many miles, the town of Perth, in Western Australia, the different species of *Haemadorum* are very plentiful.

There would seem to be little difference between such huge "natural" yam patches and cultivated fields especially where the tops of the yams are replaced at harvest time.

In the Sahara, stands of wild range plants are protected from grazing until after seed are harvested. The practice is observed by the Tuareg (Nicolaisen, 1963) and other nomadic or seminomadic pastoral tribes and we cannot ascribe it to those peoples who depend fully on gathering at the present time. Considering the prehistoric record of agricultural evolution in the Sahara, there is a strong possibility that protection of the local flora for the purpose of wild seed harvesting may date back to preagricultural times.

FOOD PLANTS IN RITUAL AND CEREMONY

Some California tribes, heavily dependent on acorns for food, conducted an annual ceremony, usually in April, for the purpose of increasing the crop. The participants went out at night, visited specified trees, and implored them to yield abundantly. The trees were supposed to respond (Loeb, 1934).

First-fruit ceremonies are practiced by the African Bushmen. When the fruit of a certain species begins to ripen at the onset of the big rainy season (usually February), a day is appointed and the women go out and ceremonially gather fruit from previously designated trees. The men stay in camp and all the camp fires are extinguished. When the fruits are brought to camp, a composite sample is carefully selected and presented to a head man, who kindles a special fire and ceremonially appeases the fire for a plentiful harvest. He then eats the fruit. After the ceremony both men and women can partake freely of the fruits, but it is an offense to eat them before the ceremony (Marshall, 1960).

Among various Bushmen tribes at least simple first-fruit ceremonies are performed for a dozen or more different plants. Each of the major veld foods has its own *choa* ceremony (Thomas, 1959). The !Kung observe a first-fruit ceremony dealing with tubers. The rite is performed by the head man on a selected day. One of the prayers translates: "Father, I come to you, I pray to you, please give me food and all things that I may live" (Schapera, 1951). The tubers must not be touched until the ceremony is performed.

Spencer (1928) describes, in some detail, yam ceremonies on Melville Island, Australia. These are celebrated as rainy season initiation rates. One particular yam, called *Kolamma* or *Kulemma,* has small rootlets, like whiskers, all over it. It is supposed to make whiskers grow on boys and so is involved in growing-up rites. Girls may be initiated at the same time, but no female can touch the yams or the ceremonial fire until the rites are completed. One of the lines chanted is: "Yams, you are our fathers!" The natives assert that after the ceremony all kinds of yams will grow plentifully.

It might be mentioned here that the New Yam Ceremonies are the most important in the ceremonial calendar of yam-eating tribes of West Africa. It is important not to dig some species of *Dioscorea* too early in the season and this sound agricultural practice is reinforced by religious ritual. A similar protective ritual is observed by the non-agricultural Andamanese (Coursey, 1972).

The Warramunga tribe of Australia has a yam totem; the Kaitisha tribe has a grass seed totem and celebrates a grass seed dance and ceremony. Rain dances are performed by both Bushmen and Australian natives to increase food resources. These are but a few of the many examples that could be given to show how plants that are important sources of food or well-being are venerated and intimately woven into the religious and ritual life of gathering peoples.

CONCEPTS OF OWNERSHIP

This topic is perhaps slightly peripheral, but some economic determinists make a big point of the effects of private ownership. Karl Marx, for one, would trace much of the social evils of the world to the institution of private property and some have suggested that the institution arose with agriculture. In agricultural societies, power resides among those who control the land. We shall only point out here that the concept of ownership is widespread and deeply ingrained in gathering societies.

In many areas tribal territories are clearly defined, and even foraging microbands or families may be allotted specified regions, groves, or stands of useful plants. They very rarely harvest on land reserved for other bands. Springs and water holes may be owned by specified groups and the outsider must ask permission even to drink. This is true in both South Africa and Australia.

If a pygmy finds a bee tree, he can mark it, and he alone is entitled to harvest the honey. To steal from a marked tree is a serious offense. Among Bushmen the same holds true for ostrich nests as well as bee trees and stealing either one can be punished by death. Some of the hollow trees of Bushmen ranges fill with water and provide an important source of water in a semidesert land. The trees may be individually owned and inheritance may pass from father to son (Marshall, 1960).

Tree marking is also observed in Australia:

> A native discovering a *Zamia* fruit unripe will put his mark upon it and no other native will touch this; the original finder of the fruit may rest perfectly certain that when it becomes ripe he has only to go and fetch it for himself.
>
> *Gregory, 1886*

Property rights are demonstrated by the custom of breaking off the top of the "grass tree" (*Xanthorrea*), which will then rear large edible grubs. The one who breaks off the top owns the grubs that will be produced later (Grey, 1841).

At least one aboriginal family is reported to have owned a rock

quarry. The head of the family removed slabs of rock, broke them
into appropriate pieces, and shaped them crudely as blanks from
which ax heads could be made. The blanks were traded primarily for
spears, and both blanks and spears entered into the long-distance
trading routes established by the aborigines long before European
contact (Coon, 1971).

A number of tribes of the Pacific Northwest kept slaves. These
were captured in raids on neighboring tribes, purchased, received as
gifts in potlatch celebrations, or sometimes generated by voluntary
servitude to settle debts. During the extravagant potlatches of the
19th century, slaves were sometimes killed as a show of wealth.
These rather sedentary tribes had a surplus of goods and commodities
which were either distributed or simply destroyed. Such a luxu-
riant economy does not fit the sterotype of the starving savage
(Suttles, 1968).

Also in the same region, houses, not necessarily made of skin or
bark, were often individually owned, and some tribes built solid plank
houses that were intended to be permanent structures. The Modoc
(California-Oregon border) maintained a scheduled round of nomadic
movements in order to exploit various resources at different times of
the year. In winter camp they lived in plank houses that were dis-
mantled and carefully stacked each spring when they moved to summer quarters. The houses were reassembled on their return in late fall
or early winter (Ray, 1963).

It would appear that private ownership of resources was well
understood by nonagricultural people and probably by preagricultural
people as well. The concept of ownership was and still is widespread
and deeply ingrained in many gathering societies.

POPULATION CONTROL AND THE AGED

As previously indicated, the evidence seems to show that populations
of hunter-gatherers are maintained well below the carrying capacity
of the range. This is, in part, what keeps the system so stable and
durable. When crops fail, farmers die of starvation, but famine is not
recorded among gatherers except when there has been a drastic disturbance by outside agents:

In every well-documented instance, cases of hardship may be traced
to the intervention of modern intruders. Starvation came to the
Caribou Eskimo only after a few Cree Indians, armed with automatic
rifles, had slaughtered a whole migration of caribou in order to cut
out their tongues to sell to white canners.

Coon, 1971

What methods are used to keep the population stable? There
seems to be little consistency in methodology; the only generality
seems to be that some method or combination of methods is employed by each group. Infanticide is common, but far from universal. Since males are usually preferred to females, the practice may
result in markedly displaced sex ratios in the population. Invalidicide
is widespread, although some tribes treat the sick and injured with
consideration and do not withhold customary medicines. Delayed
marriage, late weaning, and wide spacing of children are among the
most common methods of population control, and recent computer
studies have shown that these alone can adequately stabilize a population (Skolnick and Cannings, 1972). Geronticide (killing of the aged)
is also practiced in some tribes. In addition, warfare, raids, feuds,
and similar activities often affect population size.

In general, there seems to be no model that has very wide application. Lee (1968) specifically investigated the situation of the aged
among the Bushmen: "In a total population of 466, no fewer than
46 individuals (17 men and 29 women) were determined to be over
60 years of age, a proportion that compares favorably to the percentage of elderly in industrialized populations."

It is evident, then, that the "nasty, brutish, and short" stereotype of hunting-gathering life styles was a product of an egocentric
sense of superiority and that all features of it are demolished by serious anthropological studies.

CONCLUSIONS

The ethnographic evidence indicates that people who do not farm do
about everything that farmers do, but they do not work as hard.
Gatherers clear or alter vegetation with fire, sow seeds, plant tubers,
protect plants, own tracts of land, houses, slaves, or individual trees,

celebrate first-fruit ceremonies, pray for rain, and petition for increased yield and abundant harvest. They spin fibers, weave cloth, and make string, cord, baskets, canoes, shields, spears, bows and arrows, and a variety of household utensils. They paint pictures, carve masks and ritual objects, recite poetry, play musical instruments, sing, chant, perform dances, and memorize legends. They harvest grass seeds, thresh, winnow, and grind them into flour. They do the same with seeds of legumes, chenopods, cucurbits, crucifers, composites, and palms. They dig roots and rubers. They detoxify poisonous plants for food and extract poisons to stun fish or kill game. They are familiar with a variety of drug and medicinal plants. They understand the life cycles of plants, know the seasons of the year, and when and where the natural plant food resources can be harvested in greatest abundance with the least effort.

There is evidence that the diet of gathering peoples was better than that of cultivators, that starvation was rare, that their health status was generally superior, and that there was a lower incidence of chronic disease (Lee and DeVore, 1968a).

The question must be raised: Why farm? Why give up the 20 hour work week and the fun of hunting in order to toil in the sun? Why work harder for food less nutritious and a supply more capricious? Why invite famine, plague, pestilence and crowded living conditions? Why abandon the Golden Age and take up the burden?

Chapter 2

VIEWS ON AGRICULTURAL ORIGINS

Men ought not presently to believe all they hear, but neither should they be as incredulous as I have sometimes been.

Friar Domingo Navarrete, 1676
(Cummins, 1962)

AGRICULTURE AS DIVINE GIFT

In the classical mythologies of all civilizations, agriculture is fundamentally of divine origin. It arrived in different ways from different deities and under various circumstances, but the underlying theme is recognizable. In the Mediterranean region, the source was a goddess: Isis in Egypt, Demeter in Greece, and Ceres in Rome. In China, it was the ox-headed god Shen-nung; in Mexico, Quetzalcoatl disguised as a plumed serpent or other animal. In Peru, perhaps Viracocha, perhaps the Inca sent by his Father, the Sun, was responsible. The appearance of agriculture in mythology was almost always associated with other features of civilization: settled life, household arts, formal religion, and government by laws. Part of the essence of the classical world view with regard to agriculture can be grasped from the following selections.

According to Diodorus Siculus (as reported in Booth, 1814) agriculture originated in Egypt in this way: five gods were born to Jupiter[1] and Juno, among them Osiris and Isis. Osiris married his sister Isis and,

> performed many things for the common benefit and advantage of mankind. For he was the first that forbade men eating one another; and at the same time, Isis found out the way of making bread of wheat and barley, which before grew here and there in the fields, amongst other common herbs and grass, and the use of it unknown: and Osiris teaching the way and manner of tillage, and well management of the fruits of the earth, this change of food became grateful;

---

[1] Jupiter is a Latin parallel to the Greek *Zeus Pater* (Father Zeus), in turn related to *dyau pitar* (Father Sky) in the Rig Veda of Sanskrit literature. Our word "diety" can also be traced to the ancient Indo-European base for sky-god, *deya*, "to shine."

both because it was naturally sweet and delicious, and men were thereby restrained from the mutual butcheries one of another; for an evidence of this first finding out the use of these fruits, they alledge an antient custom among them: for even at this day, in the time of harvest, the inhabitants offer the first fruits of the ears of grain, howling and wailing about the handfuls they offer, and invoking this goddess Isis: and this they do in return of due honor to her for that invention at the first. In some cities also, when they celebrate the feast of Isis, in a pompous procession, they carry about vessels of wheat and barley, in memory of the first invention, by the care and industry of this goddess. They say, likewise, that Isis made many laws for the good of human society, whereby men were restrained from lawless force and violence one upon another, out of fear of punishment. And therefore Ceres[2] was called by the ancient Greeks, Theomophorus, that is, lawgiver, being the princess that first constituted laws for the better government of her people.

Booth, 1814

In Hesiod, we read:

Demeter, divine one of goddesses, mingling in love with the hero Iasion in a thrice-plowed fallow field[3] in the fat land of Crete, bore Ploutos, a goodly son who goeth everywhere upon earth and upon the broad ridges of the sea. Whatsoever man he meeteth and into whose hands he cometh doth he make rich, and to him doth he vouchsafe abundant happiness.

Fox, 1916

It was Demeter who taught Tritolemous

to yoke oxen and to till the soil and gave him the first grains to sow. In the rich plains about Eleusis he reaped the first harvest of grain ever grown, and there, too, he built the earliest threshing floor. . . . In a car given him by Demeter and drawn by winged dragons he flew from land to land scattering seed for the use of men. . . .

Fox, 1916

Demeter also gave birth to a daughter, Kore (later called Persephone),

---

[2] To the Romans the cereals (*cerealea*) were the gifts of Ceres, the Latin version of the Egyptian Isis.

[3] According to Hesiod's *Works* (Fox, 1916) a fallow field is plowed first in late spring, again in midsummer and a third time just before fall planting. The custom of ritual sexual intercourse in the plowed field at planting time has survived here and there until very recently and may still be practiced in some places. The object is to increase the fertility of the field by sympathetic magic.

who was abducted by Hades. In her widespread searching for her stolen daughter, she also taught the arts of agriculture. Eventually, Demeter worked out a deal with Hades who kept Persephone for 4 months of the year and let her return to Demeter for the remaining 8. The arrangement is said to symbolize the dormant season and the growing season of Mediterranean lands.

Varro, a Roman agricultural writer of the first century B.C. wrote, as reported in Storr-Best (1912):

> First in order, then, I call upon Jupiter and Tellus, who by means of the sky and land maintain the various fruits of farming, and this is the reason why—as they are said to be the universal parents—Jupiter is addressed as "Father Jove", and Tellus as "Mother Earth". Next the Sun and Moon, whose seasons are observed for the sowing and garnering of the crops. Thirdly, Ceres and Liber, as the fruits they send are specially necessary for subsistence: for it is through them that food and drink come from the farm.

In Mesopotamia, an anonymous hymn, recorded in cuneiform, also points to agriculture as a divine gift:

> Father Enlil, tender of the plants in the garden art thou, tender of the grain fields art thou.
> O Enlil, they splendour doth enlighten the fish of the sea;
> The birds of heaven, the fish in the sea thou dost satisfy.
> Father Enlil with song magestically we come, the presents of the ground are offered to thee as gifts of sacrifice.
> O Lord of Sumer, figs to thy dwelling place we bring; to give life to the ground thou dost exist.
> Father Enlil, accept the sacred offering, the many offerings.
>
> *Hawkridge, 1945*

And another symbolic expression of Semitic mythology: "O my lord, the ploughshare thou hast caused to impregnate the earth; the harrow thou hast caused to impregnate the earth" (Langdon, 1931).

The traditions of the Hebrews also developed in the Near East, and while the origin of agriculture was peripheral to the main message of the epic poem of Genesis, it should not be forgotten. Here, agriculture is received as a curse rather than a gift.

> 2:8 And the Lord God planted a garden eastward in Eden; and there he put the man he had formed. . . .
> 2:9 And out of the ground made the Lord God to grow every tree that is pleasant to the sight, and good for food; the tree of life also

in the midst of the garden, and the tree of knowledge of good and
evil. . . .

2:16 And the Lord God commanded man, saying, "you may freely
eat of every tree of the garden; (17) but of the tree of the knowledge
of good and evil you shall not eat, for in the day that you eat of it
you shall die.". . .

3:11 And he said, "Who told thee that thou wast naked? Hast thou
eaten of the tree, whereof I commanded thee thou shouldest not
eat?". . .

3:16 Unto the woman he said, "I will greatly multiply thy sorrow
and thy conception: in sorrow thou shalt bring forth children; and
thy desire shall be to thy husband, and he shall rule over thee."

3:17 And unto Adam he said, "Because thou hast hearkened unto
the voice of thy wife, and hast eaten of the tree, of which I commanded thee, saying, Thou shalt not eat of it: cursed is the ground
for thy sake; in sorrow shalt thou eat of it all the days of thy life.

3:18 Thorns also and thistles shall it bring forth to thee; and thou
shalt eat the herb of the field: (19) In the sweat of thy face shalt
thou eat bread, till thou return unto the ground; for out of it wast
thou taken: for dust thou art, and unto dust shalt thou return.". . .

3:22 And the Lord God said, "Behold the man is become as one of
us, to know good and evil: and now lest he put forth his hand, and
take also of the tree of life, and eat, and live for ever."

3:23 Therefore, the Lord God sent him forth from the garden of
Eden, to till the ground from whence he was taken.

King James Version

In Chinese mythology, P'an Ku separated the heavens and the
earth, created the sun, moon, and stars, and produced the plants and
animals. There followed 12 (or 13) celestial sovereigns, all brothers,
who ruled 18,000 years each, then 11 terrestrial sovereigns, all
brothers, who also ruled 18,000 years each. After that came 9 human
rulers, all brothers, who governed a total of 45,600 years. Among
these was Shen-nung, who taught the people agriculture and developed medicine. In another version, 16 rulers came after the 9 and
these were then followed by the "Three Sovereigns," one of whom
was Shen-nung. There are many variations of this particular theme
(Christie, 1968; Latourette, 1941; Fitzgerald, 1938), including the
following description of Shen-nung by the ancient Chinese historian
Se-ma-Tsien (first century B.C.). Shen-nung, he said, had the body of
a man and the head of an ox, and his element was fire. He taught
the people to use the hoe and the plow and initiated the sacrifice at
the end of the year. He also found drug plants that cured and made
a five-stringed lute (reported in Chavannes, 1895–1905).

Christie (1968) comments that:

> the ox-headed Shen-nung, is said to have invented the plough and to have taught man basic agriculture, but it seems likely that he was first and foremost god of the burning wind, of the technique of clearing scrub jungle by fire in order to set seeds in the area, rich in potash which remains after the fire has passed.

In later Chinese history, Shen-nung is considered to have been an emperor, and a fictitious date (usually about 2800 B.C.) was assigned to his reign. He is said to have instituted the custom of ritually sowing five kinds of grains at the time of spring planting. The custom was preserved as late as the 20th century and the emperor himself participated in the ceremony. Actually, there is no evidence that there ever was a ruler by that name and the date is far earlier than any real date recorded in Chinese history.

The ancient legends have been amplified over the centuries and a veneer of embellishment has been added to the classical myths. The date given to Shen-nung is nonsense, but the myth of the divine origin of agriculture is typical.

The mythologies of the American Indians are enormously varied and complex, but a few selected pieces illustrate the general pattern. In the Aztec creation literature, Quetzalcoatl was described as:

> "God of the air, a divinity who, during his residence on earth, instructed the natives in the use of metals, in agriculture, and in the arts of government. . . ." Under him, the earth teemed with fruits and flowers, without the pains of culture. An ear of Indian corn was as much as a single man could carry. The cotton, as it grew, took, of its own accord, the rich dyes of human art. The air was filled with intoxicating perfumes and the sweet melody of birds. In short, these were the halcyon days, which find a place in the mythic systems of so many nations in the Old World. It was the *golden age* of Anahuac.
>
> *Prescott, 1936* (italics his).

Interestingly enough, both the Aztec and the Maya thought that maize (*Zea mays* L.) was on earth before mortal men. In the Aztecan story, Quetzalcoatl disguised himself as a black ant, stole the cereal from Tonacatepel, and took it to Tamoanchán for the benefit of man. In the Mayan creation myth, the flesh of man was actually formed out of maize meal and snake's blood (Recinos, 1947). It is little wonder

that the maize plant is venerated to this day in Mexico and Guatemala. The Mayan epic also contains oblique references to a garden of
of Eden or golden age in which nature yielded abundantly of its own
accord.

> In this manner they were filled with pleasure because they had dis-
> covered a lovely land full of delights, abundant in yellow ears and
> white ears (of maize) and also abundant in (two kinds of) cacao and
> innumerable fruits of mamey, chirimoya, jocote, nance, white
> zopote, and honey.[4] The foods of Paxil y Cayalá were abundant
> and delicious.
>
> *Popol Vuh pt. III, as reported in Recinos, 1947;* my translation.

From the Royal Commentaries of the Inca Garcilaso de la Vega
(as reported in the 1961 edition), we read:

> Know then that, at one time, all the land you see about you was
> nothing but mountains and desolate cliffs. The people lived like wild
> beasts, with neither order nor religion, neither villages nor houses,
> neither fields nor clothing, for they had no knowledge of either wool
> or cotton. Brought together haphazardly in groups of two or three,
> they lived in grottoes and caves and, like wild game, fed upon grass
> and roots, wild fruits, and even human flesh. They covered their
> nakedness with the bark and leaves of trees, or with the skins of
> animals. Some even went unclothed. And as for women, they
> possessed none who were recognized as their very own.
>   Seeing the condition they were in, our father the Sun was ashamed
> for them, and he decided to send one of his sons and one of his
> daughters from heaven to earth, in order that they might teach men
> to adore him and acknowledge him as their god; to obey his laws
> and precepts as every reasonable creature must do; to build houses
> and assemble together in villages; to till the soil, sow the seed, raise
> animals, and enjoy the fruits of their labors like human beings.

The Inca king and queen arrived from heaven and were given a
sign by which they would know where to establish a capital city.
The place was located (Cuzco) and they set out to teach the savages
"how to live, how to clothe and feed themselves like men, instead of
like animals." The epic continues:

> While peopling the city, our Inca taught the male Indians the tasks
> that were to be theirs, such as selecting seeds and tilling the soil. He

---

[4]These fruits were thought to be: *Lucuma mammosa, Annona cherimolia,
Spondias purpurea, Byrsonima crassifolia,* and *Casimiroa edulis,* respectively.

taught them how to make hoes, how to irrigate their fields by means of canals that connected natural streams, and even to make these same shoes that we wear today. The queen, meanwhile, was teaching the women how to spin and weave wool and cotton, how to make clothing as well as other domestic tasks.

In short, our sovereigns, the Inca king, who was master of men, and Queen Coya, who was mistress of the women taught their subjects everything that had to do with human living.

Garcilaso de la Vega, as reported in the 1961 edition

There is no need to comment on all the various mythologies of agricultural peoples, but lest one be tempted to make too much of the similarities and underlying themes, I must point out that the Australian aborigines, who did not practice agriculture, also had their mythologies and creation stories in which gods taught the people how to gather foods. An elderly aborigine woman recited this part of the creation legend (as reported by Berndt and Berndt, 1970):

Ngalgulerg [a mythical woman] gave us women the digging stick and the basket we hang from our foreheads, and Gulubar Kangaroo gave men the spear-thrower. But that Snake that we call Gagag [Mother's mother] —taught us how to dig for food and how to eat it, good foods and bitter foods.

DOMESTICATION FOR RELIGIOUS REASONS

About the turn of the century, Eduard Hahn (1896, 1909) proposed a theory that some animals might have been first domesticated out of religious concern rather than for economic reasons. He chose the urus (*Bos taurus*), a form of wild cattle, as his model, but the idea was extended to other animals and tentatively to plants (Anderson, 1954). The idea has not dominated anthropological thinking but continues to be revived from time to time and appears in current anthropological and geographical literature (Isaac, 1970). The possibilities are intriguing and the theory should be considered on its merits.

Hahn argued that it would have been impossible to predict the usefulness of domestic cattle before they were actually domesticated. Wild cattle are large and fierce beasts and no one could have foreseen their utility for labor or milk until they were tamed. What motivated man to take the initial steps? They were domesticated, argued Hahn, for ritual sacrifice in connection with lunar goddess cults, for the great curving horns of the urus were crescent shaped. We know that people from western Europe to India have long held special religious feelings about cattle.

Even during the Ice Age, cattle were featured in the cave art of southwestern France and northeastern Spain. The great hall of the bulls at Lascaux is eloquent testimony to the concern for wild cattle. The archaeological site of Çatal Hüyük in Turkey, dating back into the seventh millennium B.C., reveals a series of altars, one above the other, each featuring cattle heads. The animals are also depicted in painted murals on the temple walls. Much later, we find elegantly painted bull-vaulting scenes on the walls of temples at Knossos, Crete. Cattle were sacred to the Egyptians, were sacrificed by the Romans, and are still considered holy by the Hindus of India.

Indeed, to this day, we find a "bull belt" extending from Spain and Portugal to eastern India in which people have a special religious feeling about cattle. At the western end of this region, animals are publicly and ceremoniously slaughtered before thousands at the bull-fight rituals, usually on Sundays. At the eastern end of the belt, naked Sadhus lead riots in favor of antislaughter laws that would protect cattle, and in the southern portion, deep into the Sahara and beyond, cattle-herding tribes have special, mystical attachments between man and beast.

Or, consider the mithan. This is another form of *Bos* (the taxonomy varies according to taxonomist) thought to have been domesticated from the wild gaur of India. Mithan are kept by hill tribes from Upper Burma westward across Assam, the Naga Hills, and into Bhutan. They are not herded, but allowed to range in the woods and meadows. They are, however, individually owned and fairly tame. They are not used for transportation, draft, or milk, but are raised for prestige, wealth, and sacrifice only. Mithan are used to purchase land and pay bride prices, fines, and ransoms. They are sacrificed at certain special religious observances, and sometimes, as a show of wealth. A rich man may sacrifice a number of animals in front of a rival's house to display wealth or humiliate an enemy. The animals are left where they are killed and others come and take away the remains to eat. Mithan are eaten, but only after ritual sacrifice. Skulls and horns are used to decorate temples, houses, and graves.

In parts of Asia, chickens are raised, but neither the flesh nor the eggs are eaten. The birds are used for sacrifice, divination by examining the entrails, or cock fighting. Chickens are thought to have been domesticated from the jungle fowl of southern and southeastern Asia. The art of divination from sacrificed birds seems to have spread with chicken raising at least into the Mediterranean area and was practiced by the ancient Greeks. The practice of rearing for sacrifice but not eating flesh or eggs has also been found in parts of the Americas and has led Sauer (1952), Carter (1971), and others to postulate early trans-Pacific contacts between the hemispheres.

Sheep, goats, pigs, and pigeons were sacrificed in the ancient world of classical times and it has been suggested that these also may have been domesticated to have a supply of sacrificial animals. From the above examples of legends and myths and from other clues, it seems at least plausible that animals may have been used in ritual killings as a substitute for humans. Human sacrifice and ritual killing may have been a very ancient custom.

We know that there are a number of plants, wild and cultivated, that are used for ritual, ceremonial, and magical purposes. Some are drug plants, some produce dyes, and some have colorful leaves or flowers. I know of one plant of the West African forests which has a metallic, iridescent glint to the leaves and is used to mark the sites of secret (Poro) society meetings in the jungle. Anderson (1954) nominated the amaranths as candidates for ritual domestication. The blood-red inflorescences were used in religious ceremonies of ancient South America and I have seen them displayed over doorways in India and Pakistan. The pigment from another species is used in Hindu rituals.

A few tribes of the Pacific Northwest are fishers, hunters, and gatherers but did grow a single crop, tobacco. Tobacco is not the easiest crop to grow and shows that the techniques of cultivation were adequately understood by these people who grew no food plants. This, of course, does not mean that drug and ritual plants were domesticated before food plants were, but it would not be wise, in dealing with human affairs, to ignore the motivations of religious concern.

DOMESTICATION BY CROWDING

Some decades ago, V. Gordon Childe proposed what came to be known as the "propinquity theory." Childe was a social-minded historian and prehistorian who was impressed by the evidence that the climates of North Africa and parts of the Near East had become increasingly desiccated over a period of several millennia B.C. He visualized the rangelands drying up, forcing herd animals and man as well to withdraw to the banks of the few perennial rivers and to the oases where water could be found year-round. This brought man and beasts into more intimate contact than had previously been the case and eventually induced man to domesticate some animal species (Childe, 1952).

In those days, many people still thought that man went through a set, three-phase development. He was first a hunter, then a herder, then a cultivator. The idea goes back to Greco-Roman times and still persists in some quarters. Having become a herder it was not difficult to pass to the next phase. The disturbance of the soil and vegetation by livestock at camp sites, together with manuring, would encourage weedy plants to grow. It was just such weeds that were said to be first taken into the domestic fold, and it was a short step from gathering them from the sheepfold to sowing them on purpose.

Childe (1925) also elaborated on what he called the "Neolithic revolution," i.e. the shift from hunting and gathering to food production. He saw this as a radical and fundamental transformation of human adaptation and the most important development since the discovery of fire. The concept of an agricultural revolution has had more success than the oasis theory of domestication. The latter, however, was instrumental in stimulating a considerable amount of archaeological research because it was, to some degree, testable. Most of the testing was stimulated by the work of Robert J. Braidwood who set out to obtain archaeological evidence for the evolution of food production in the Near East (Braidwood, 1972). A number of archaeologists have followed his example and there is a rather respectable body of evidence on the subject.

The evidence does not bear out the propinquity theory very well, but in a later chapter we shall have to come to grips with the fact that desiccation did set in across North Africa and may well have had something to do with agricultural innovations south of the Sahara. Climatic changes had taken place, food resources had altered, and one of the alternative human adaptations to gathering was food production.

AGRICULTURE AS DISCOVERY

The most extensively developed model for agricultural origins is that cultivation was an invention or discovery. Because Darwin's theory of evolution has had profound influence on modern biology and anthropology, it is interesting to see how he viewed the subject:

> The savage inhabitants of each land, having found out by many and hard trials what plants were useful, or could be rendered useful by various cooking processes, would after a time take the first step in cultivation by planting them near their usual abodes. . . . The next step in cultivation, and this would require but little forethought, would be to sow the seeds of useful plants; and as the soil near the hovels of natives would often be in some degree manured, improved varieties would sooner or later arise. Or a wild and unusually good variety of a native plant might attract the attention of some wise old savage; and he would transplant it, or sow its seed.
>
> *Darwin, 1896*

Darwin, among others, was convinced that nomadic people could not develop agriculture:

> Nomadic habits, whether over wide plains, or through the dense forests of the tropics, or along the shores of the sea, have in every case been highly detrimental (to "progress"). Whilst observing the barbarous inhabitants of Tierra del Fuego, it struck me that the possession of some property, a fixed abode, and the union of many families under a chief, were the indispensable requisites for civilization. Such habits almost necessitate the cultivation of the ground; and the first steps in cultivation would probably result, as I have shewn elsewhere (above), from some such accident as the seeds of a fruit tree falling on a heap of refuse, and producing an unusually fine variety.
>
> *Darwin, 1909*

Darwin (1909) concluded, however, that "the problem, . . .of the first advance of savages towards civilization is at present much too difficult to be solved."

Elaborations on the theme developed the "happy accident" or "Eureka!" model of plant domestication. No motive is required, only the brilliant revelation that seeds can be sown to produce plants when and where desired. The advantages of producing food on purpose are so obvious that all that was needed was the concept and the development of agriculture was assured.

There are several ideas in the Darwinian view that should be separated for clarity: 1) man must be sedentary before he can cultivate plants; 2) useful plants are most likely to be discovered in manured refuse heaps; 3) useful plants are likely to be first planted in dump heaps; and 4) a wise old savage is required to start the process.

These concepts seem reasonable enough and have provided the basis for several theoretical treatments of the subject. One of the most influential was that of Carl O. Sauer (1952), a geographer whose *Agricultural Origins and Dispersals* has become a classic. He combined the Darwinian views with Eduard Hahn's idea (1896, 1909) that vegetative propagation should precede seed agriculture, and set out to locate the cradle of agriculture on theoretical grounds. He listed six presuppositions as a basis for his search (here condensed):

1) Agriculture did not originate from a growing or chronic shortage of food. People living in the shadow of famine do not have the means or time to undertake the slow and leisurely steps out of which a better and different food supply is to develop in a somewhat distant future. . . .

2) The hearths of domestication are to be sought in areas of marked diversity of plants and animals. . . . This implies well-diversified terrain and perhaps also variety of climate.

3) Primitive cultivators could not establish themselves in large river valleys subject to lengthy floods and requiring protective dams, drainage, or irrigation. . . .

4) Agriculture began in wooded lands. Primitive cultivators could readily open spaces for planting by deadening trees; they could not dig in sod or eradicate vigorous stoloniferous grasses. . . .

5) The inventors of agriculture had previously acquired special skills in other directions that predisposed them to agricultural experiments. . . .

6) Above all, the founders of agriculture were sedentary folk.

The sedentary life, he thought, could best be developed by fishing tribes, and for his purpose he sought them on fresh waters in a mild climate. Fresh water was selected because seaside vegetation has contributed relatively little to agriculture and what has been developed has come late in crop evolution. With these presuppositions in mind, he proposed Southeast Asia as the oldest hearth of agriculture. From there, systems spread northward into China and westward across India and the Near East, into Africa and the Mediterranean region, and finally into northern and western Europe. In the Americas, he located the original hearth in the northwestern part of South America from whence agriculture spread northward into Mexico, then to eastern North America, southward along the Andean chain, eastward to the Atlantic coast of Brazil, and to the Caribbean island chain. He left open the possibility that cultivation might have been transmitted from the Old World to the New World.

Southeast Asia was selected because most anthropologists have felt that agriculture is older in Asia than in the Americas and because that region fits most of his presuppositions best. In particular it had a mild climate and varied terrain, and was rich in fresh water aquatic resources as well as edible plants. People could settle down in permanent villages and develop the arts of cultivation without the pressures of periodic scarcity. The fact that everywhere a different set of plants was domesticated did not bother him. It was the *idea* of cultivation that diffused and that once people were shown the obvious superiority of the system, they would begin to domesticate plants from their own flora even if the rewards were to be found in the distant future.

Edgar Anderson (1954) liked Sauer's view and added some genetic threads to the fabric. He saw weeds as potential domesticates; he also thought that an increase in hybridization, with disturbed habitats, could result in increased variation and new genetic combinations from which useful selections could be made:

> Rivers are weed breeders; so is man, and many of the plants which follow us about have the look of belonging originally on gravel bars or mud-banks. If we now reconsider the kitchen middens of our sedentary fisherfolk, it seems that they would be a natural place where some of the aggressive plants from the river-banks might find a home, where seeds and fruits brought back from up the hill or down the river might sometimes sprout and to which even more rarely would be brought seeds from across the lake or from another island. Species which had never intermingled might do so there, and the open habitat of the rubbish-heap would be a more likely niche in which strange new mongrels could survive than any which had been there before man came along.

Anderson also felt that agriculture began in the tropics on dump heaps and that vegetative propagation predominated at the beginning, but he also left open the question of early transoceanic contact.

Evidence accumulated since the Sauer-Anderson models were suggested has indicated that some of their presuppositions were incorrect. For example, sedentary life is not essential to the evolution of agriculture. In Mesoamerica there is good archaeological evidence that the people remained nomadic long after they were purposely growing plants for food (Flannery, 1966, 1968). In the Near East, there is evidence that a nuclear center developed in an area not in the tropics and by people not necessarily dependent upon aquatic resources. In that region, the people most dependent upon fishing and fowling, the Natufians, were among the last to take up agriculture. Thus, although the Sauer-Anderson models have been widely accepted by many, they are open to question.

Recent reports of early plant remains in archaeological sites in Southeast Asia (Solheim, 1971; Gorman, 1969; Chang, 1970) have revived interest in the diffusionist theories. The diffusion models imply two fundamental conditions: 1) the deliberate cultivation of plants for food is a discovery or invention that is so radical and novel that it could only have occurred once, or at most a few times, and 2) the system is so obviously superior to gathering that people would adopt it even if they had to start with wild races of their own plants and develop domesticated races from them *de novo*. There are some basic problems with these assumptions, as we shall see in the following section.

AGRICULTURE AS AN EXTENSION OF GATHERING

In Chapter 1 it became clear that gatherers of today know all they need to know to develop agriculture. While much of this information may have been recently derived through contact with cultivators, the Australian aborigine at the time of European contact also had ample information. He did not need to discover the concepts of planting; he already had them. We have asked, "Why farm?" We could also ask the question, "Why not farm if you are equipped with all the materials and information to do so?" One approach is to ask a gatherer. During his study of the Bushmen Richard Lee did exactly that, and he received the celebrated reply, "Why should I farm when there are so many mongongo nuts?" (Lee and DeVore, 1968). The aborigines put it in almost the same terms:

> You people go to all that trouble, working and planting seeds, but we don't have to do that. All these things are there for us, the Ancestral Beings left them for us. In the end, you depend on the sun and the rain just the same as we do, but the difference is that we just have to go and collect the food when it is ripe. We don't have all this other trouble.
>
> *Berndt and Berndt, 1970*

We are now beginning to obtain some data to show that the aboriginal opinion is correct. Black (1971) reported on a series of input-output studies of different agricultural systems. For subsistence agriculture where human labor only is expended, he assigned a generalized, arbitrary figure of 150 kilocalories (kcal) of energy expended per hour. The average for 13 systems analyzed showed a return of 17 kcal for each kcal invested although the range was from 3 to 34. Draft animals did not improve the situation and if the energy for maintaining the animals was included, the results would have been negative. However, the by-products of the draft animals (calves, milk, hides, etc.) were also not included. Mechanized societies produce energy deficits. If the energy of gasoline consumed by a tractor is used for the input side of the budget, outputs are within the range of human labor, but the moment one begins to calculate the energy required to mine ore, make steel, manufacture tractors, transport fuel, etc., the system uses far more energy than it produces. Our vaunted, efficient, modern, mechanized agriculture is *not*, in fact, a renewable resource; rather, it consumes energy.

Using the same conversion figure that Black used, my wild wheat harvest in Turkey netted about 50 kcal for every kcal expended, far more efficient than any form of agriculture for which we have input-output data. I am indebted to Lloyd Evans, CSIRO, Australia, for calling this to my attention.

More studies and better data are needed, but we have ample anthropological and ethnographical evidence to show that increasing the food supply through cultivation means an increase in work. In general, the more intensive the agricultural system, the more work is required for a unit of food. Thus, if we are to understand the origins of agriculture, we must visualize situations in which man is willing to expend more energy to obtain food. In this respect, farming is not so attractive that gatherers are likely to take it up on sight or on first contact. Some rather compelling reasons would seem to be required.

In preagricultural times the human population was not regulated by the food supply. If this were the case, Binford (1968) has pointed out that two corollaries would follow: "1) Man would be continually seeking means of increasing his food supply," and "2) It is only when man is freed from preoccupation with the food quest that he has time to elaborate culture." From what we have seen, both are patently false. Populations of hunter-gatherers are regulated well below the carrying capacity of the range, and the environment does not exert pressure on man to change his food procurement systems. Neither agricultural nor industrial man has anything like the leisure time of hunters and gatherers. Therefore, we must look elsewhere for the motivation to carry on agriculture.

What, then, might generate the motives that caused man to domesticate plants (and animals)? A much-cited model in current literature is one based on proposals put forth by Lewis Binford (1968) and Kent Flannery (1968). It attempts to integrate ethnographic and archaeological information and suggests not only reasons for but places where the initiative toward food production might have been taken. Explicit in the Binford-Flannery model is the recognition that gatherers are sophisticated, applied botanists who know their material and how to exploit it. They are prepared to grow plants if and when they think it would be worth the effort. Furthermore, the difference between intensive gathering and cultivation is minimal; recall the square kilometers of Australian landscape pitted by aborigines digging yams.

Binford, in particular, emphasized the fact that one of the general post-Pleistocene adaptations of man was a fuller exploitation of aquatic resources. This is one of the most characteristic features of the so-called "Mesolithic" wherever it can be identified. Canoes, boats, and rafts were developed, and there was a great proliferation of archaeological sites that suggested fairly permanent residence and subsistence by fishing, fowling, and gathering. The sedentary fisherfolk referred to by Sauer and Anderson did appear in many parts of the world; however, Binford suggests that it was not they who began domestication, but groups that budded off from them and migrated into regions already occupied by hunter-gatherers. The argument goes that long before there was a food resource crisis among the fisherfolk, groups would move out and migrate into less well-endowed regions and ecological zones. The fisherfolk population remained stable, but the migrants precipitated a crisis along the interface between the sedentary peoples and the nomadic hunter-gatherers. It was in response to this crisis that people were willing to go to the effort of cultivation.

The Binford model was spelled out in sufficient detail that he could make some predictions to be tested:

1) The initial activities of domestication in the Near East will appear adjacent to areas occupied by sedentary forager-fisherfolk (evidence for this fairly firm at the time of the prediction).

2) Evidence will be found of independent domestications in European Russia and south-central Europe (suggestions coming in that this may be true).

3) Evidence will be found of similar events widely separated over Europe, Asia, and the Americas. (Flannery has provided some evidence from Mesoamerica and the African evidence is compatible with the prediction.)

There may be biological and ecological reasons as well for proposing that cultivation would begin adjacent to the best foraging ranges rather than in them. In the Near East massive stands of wild wheats cover many square kilometers. Harlan and Zohary (1966) have asked, "Why should anyone cultivate a cereal where natural stands are as dense as a cultivated field? If wild cereal grasses can be harvested in unlimited quantities, why should anyone bother to till the soil and plant the seed?" The same arguments could well apply to the African savanna or California, where wild food resources were abundant.

A major implication of the model is that the activities of plant domestication are likely to have taken place independently and probably simultaneously in many areas all over the world. The space-time pattern that would emerge would be almost the opposite of that of the Sauer-Anderson model. It would appear that the differences are testable by archaeological means and that even botanical and genetical evidence could come to bear on the problem.

GEOGRAPHY OF PLANT DOMESTICATION

No consideration of agricultural origins would be complete without mention of Alphonse de Candolle and N. I. Vavilov. Although neither of them maintained elaborate theories about why or how agriculture originated, they were both concerned about the geography of plant domestication and crop origins.

De Candolle lived in Geneva and was one of the foremost botanists of the 19th century. His book, *Origin of Cultivated Plants* (reprinted in 1959), was primarily an academic and intellectual exercise. He was interested in the geography of plants in general and wrote extensively on the subject. He attempted to locate the region of origin of a good many cultivated plants by any means he could. He investigated the distributions of wild relatives, history, names, linguistic derivatives, archaeology, variation patterns, and every other clue he could think of.

In many respects there was not a great deal known in de Candolle's time. Archaeological plant remains were largely confined to materials from the Egyptian tombs and the Swiss lake dwellers. Wild races of a number of plants were not then known, and some of his information was faulty. Nevertheless, his book remains today a model of scholarship and continues to be a useful source of information about the origins of cultivated plants.

N. I. Vavilov was a Russian geneticist and agronomist in charge of an enormous national Institute of Plant Industry. At his disposal were dozens of experiment stations scattered over the Soviet Union, staffed with thousands of professional and subprofessional workers. He proposed one of the most dazzling and ambitious plant breeding programs ever attempted. It was his plan to collect and assemble all of the useful germplasm of all crops that had potential in the Soviet Union, to study and classify the material, and to utilize it in a national plant breeding effort. A vigorous, worldwide plant exploration program was launched, and for the first time a really systematic plan for genetic resource management was established.

Vavilov was interested in origins because he was interested in genetic diversity, and he thought the two were related. In 1926 he wrote an essay, dedicated to Alphonse de Candolle, *On the Origin of Cultivated Plants* (Vavilov, 1926) in which he proposed that one could reliably determine the center of origin of a crop by an analysis of patterns of variation. The geographic region in which one found the greatest genetic diversity was the region of origin. This was especially true if much of the variation was controlled by dominant genes and if the region also contained wild races of the crop in question.

On the basis of such analyses and the evidence accumulated from hundreds of thousands of collections, he proposed eight centers of origin for most of the cultivated plants of the world (Figure 1). Although it has been pointed out many times that a center of diversity is *not* the same as a center of origin (Schiemann, 1939; Gökgöl, 1941; Harlan, 1951, 1969, 1970; Kuckuck, 1962; Smith, 1969; Brücher, 1969; Zohary, 1970), centers of diversity do exist and the concept has been enormously useful in exploring for genetic diversity. The subject of geographic patterns of variation will be treated in Chapter 7.

The concept of centers of origin has evolved since Vavilov's time. Basically, what Vavilov did was to draw lines around areas in which agriculture has been practiced for a very long time and in which indigenous civilizations arose. The geography of crop variation depends upon the geography of human history.

When one actually analyzes origins crop by crop, it soon becomes apparent that many of them did not originate in Vavilovian centers. Some crops do not even have centers of diversity. The pattern is much more complex and diffuse than Vavilov had visualized. In the case of the Near East, we seem to have a definable center in the sense that a number of plants and animals were domesticated within a relatively small region and were diffused outward from the center. In Africa, nothing of the sort is apparent. The evidence seems to indicate that activities of plant domestication went on almost everywhere south of the Sahara and north of the equator from the Atlantic to the Indian Ocean. Such a vast region could hardly be called a "center" without distorting the meaning of the word, so I called it a noncenter (Harlan, 1971). In North China, there is fairly convincing evidence for a center, but nothing of the sort is evident in Southeast Asia and the South Pacific. The pattern may be similar in the Americas with a center in Mesoamerica and a noncenter in South America. My own version of agricultural origins is shown in Figure 2.

I have proposed three independent systems, each with a center and a noncenter. I also visualize some stimulation and feedback in terms of ideas, techniques, or materials between center and noncenter within each system. Since making these proposals I have begun to

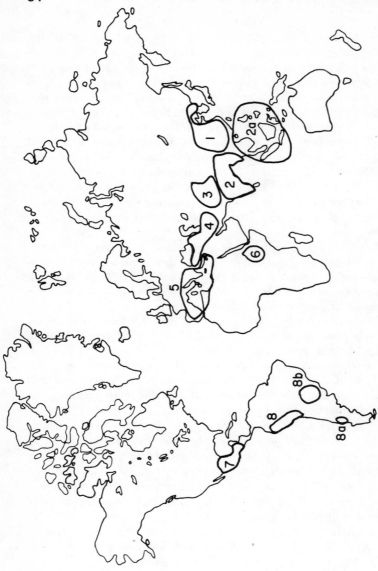

Figure 1
The eight centers of origin, according to N. I. Vavilov (from Harlan, 1971; copyright 1971 by the American Association for the Advancement of Science).

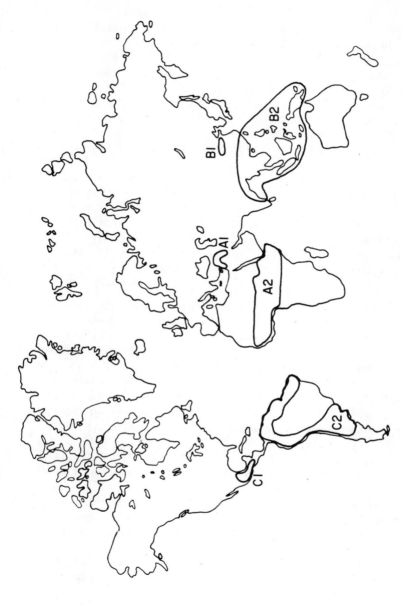

Figure 2

Centers and noncenters of agricultural origins: A1, Near East center; A2, African noncenter; B1, North Chinese center; B2, Southeast Asian and South Pacific noncenter; C1, Mesoamerican center; C2, South American noncenter (from Harlan, 1971; copyright 1971 by the American Association for the Advancement of Science).

wonder if the evidence that gives the appearance of centers may not be so biased and incomplete that it has produced an artifact of sorts. The agriculture that evolved in the Near East, based on barley, wheat, pea, lentil, chickpea, sheep, goats, pigs, etc., was successful and therefore expansive. It spread westward across Europe, eastward to India, and southward to the plateaus of Ethiopia. The fact that it spread may have given the appearance of a center of agricultural origination, but we do not yet know what it was spreading into. Were the Europeans, the Indians, or the Ethiopians entirely without cultivated plants at the time?

The maize-bean-squash[5] complex of Mesoamerica was also expansive, but we have evidence that Indians were growing less efficient plants by the time the complex arrived in eastern North America and northern Chile. The Chinese center requires much more study before sure interpretations can be made. In any case, we have a lot more to learn about where agriculture originated and where a number of individual crops were domesticated. For the time being we shall do the best we can with the three independent systems shown in Figure 2.

It will be noted that the difference between my view and Vavilov's is not enormous. I found more activity of domestication in Africa than he did and less in his regions 2 and 3. In fairness to Vavilov, it should be pointed out that in many cases he was not particularly interested in the center of origin of a crop per se, but was more concerned with centers of diversity of the major races. For example, he was more interested in the origin of deficiens, irregular, two-rowed, six-rowed, or hooded barleys than in the origin of barley itself. This emphasis on the components of a crop led to some misinterpretations of his theory. He was, in effect, saying that Ethiopian wheats originated in Ethiopia and Afghan wheats originated in Afghanistan, which is perfectly true. The ultimate origin of wheat remained to be searched out.

Vavilov had to concede that his method of "differential phytogeography" did not work very well. He invented the concept of secondary centers to account for the fact that centers of diversity are not the same as centers of origin. In fact, the variation in secondary centers is often much greater than in the centers of actual domestication where these can be located on independent evidence.

------

[5] The Latin names of these and subsequent plants are given in Chapter 3, Table 1.

He also developed the concept of secondary crops; these are derived from weeds of older, primary crops. Rye and oats were cited as examples. As agriculture spread from the Near East and Mediterranean centers toward northern Europe, weed rye and weed oats were carried along as contaminants of the barley and emmer fields. In due course domesticated races developed, far removed from the original homeland of rye and oats. As we have seen, Edgar Anderson (1954) favored the idea that crops were often derived from weeds and was strongly influenced by Vavilov's writings.

A NO-MODEL MODEL

Every model proposed so far for agricultural origins or plant domestication has generated evidence against it. It is possible that some plants and animals were domesticated for ritual, magic, ceremony, or religious sacrifice, but only a few out of hundreds of species could be so identified. It is likely that a few cultigens did originate from dump heap weeds, but many show no such inclination. Some crops were derived from weeds and some weeds were derived from crops, but by far the more usual pattern is the crop-weed complex in which both crop and weed are derived from the same progenitors. Some crops arose in the Vavilovian centers, and others did not; many have centers of diversity, but others do not. Some people were sedentary long before agriculture; others maintained a nomadic way of life long after plants were domesticated and agriculture was established. There is no model with universal, or even very wide application; yet most of them contribute, in some degree, to an understanding of the problem.

My own inclination is to recognize the fact that human beings are enormously varied and their motivations are always complex and never simple. It is difficult enough to psychoanalyze a living, speaking human, so how can we expect to analyze people who lived 10,000 years ago and who belonged to cultures we can but dimly imagine? People do similar things for entirely different reasons and they find very different solutions to the same problems.

I am inclined to develop a no-model model which leaves room for whole arrays of motives, actions, practices, and evolutionary processes. What applies in Southeast Asia may not apply at all in Southwest Asia. The patterns in Africa may not be the same as the patterns in Mexico. A search for a single overriding cause for human behavior is likely to be frustrating and fruitless. A humanistic no-model model simply recognizes the likelihood that no single model will explain agricultural origins.

Man did take the initiative in modifying his environment, and plants responded genetically to his activities. He deliberately changed the vegetation with set fires; he sowed seeds; he churned up square miles of land to get tubers, all without developing "agriculture." The development of true agriculture would require more work, but few changes in techniques. It is not even necessary to assume a crisis was always responsible, for the motivations could have been many and various.

The most conspicuous difference between hunting-gathering economies and agricultural ones is in the size of the human populations that can be supported. Farming takes more work, but it can feed more people. Population pressures may or may not have initiated plant domestication, but they have certainly forced the evolution of agricultural economies in a single direction.

Generalizations about human behavior are always hazardous, but there does seem to be a significant difference between agricultural societies and the surviving hunter-gatherers in the role and importance of children. In the agricultural economies, children are an economic asset. They add to the labor force, they create wealth through doweries and bride-prices, and they provide security for the aged. In some societies today, the situation is so intense that childless couples become literally impoverished and may actually starve to death. Even survival sometimes depends upon having children, and the more the better.

The system tends to be self-defeating in the sense that there are strong forces always pressing toward larger populations. More people require more food. More food requires more intensive farming practices which in turn require more work per unit of food. The only way to get more work done is to increase the labor force by having more children. A high value is placed on prolific women and barren ones may be cast out of the society. Subsistence agriculture is not likely to reach equilibrium without external population controls such as disease epidemics, famine, and war.

How far we can push the disequilibrium back towards the beginnings of agriculture has not yet been determined. The economic value of children may have been an important influence very early in the evolution of agricultural societies. Certainly, steady and intense pressures for ever larger populations set into motion trends that are essentially irreversible. Living within the productive capacity of the environment becomes a continual and exhausting struggle. A "hungry time" becomes a part of every year while crop failure means starvation and death. The threat of famine has become a characteristic of agricultural systems; we have no evidence that this was a part of preagricultural systems.

On the other hand, the sample of surviving gatherers is so small and biased that our information may be misleading. The survivors maintain their populations at a fraction of the size that could be supported, but was this true of gatherers in the hearths of agriculture? Perhaps cultivation did begin because of population pressures and degradation of natural resources. How are we to know? Perhaps plant cultivation began in different areas for different reasons.

We have no more facts to support a no-model concept than any other theory, but it does have the advantage of being independent of any set of presuppositions. It is obvious that views of agricultural origins in the past have too often been based on assumptions that have either turned out to be altogether false or that have applied to one situation and not another. The no-model view takes into account the distinct possibility that plant domestication began in different regions for different reasons, and permits us to build theories on evidence as it accumulates rather than on preconceived notions.

The greatest difficulties in understanding agricultural origins trace to a want of information, and no amount of speculation can substitute for evidence. Although we have made some advances in the century since Darwin wrote that the problem was too difficult to be solved, we are still far from determining either the exact regions of agricultural origins or the motivation that brought about such a profound change in human adaptation.

Chapter 3

WHAT IS A CROP?

According to unabridged diction-
aries, the word "crop" has several
meanings. One set of definitions
involves the verbal form of the
concepts of cutting, mowing, grazing, lopping off branches, and so
on. Sheep crop grass closely; a
head of hair or the mane of a

*It is not always easy to distinguish between
wild and cultivated plants in South
America, and there are many intermediate
stages between the utilization of plants in
their wild state and their true cultivation.*

Lévi-Strauss, 1950

horse is cropped. Other definitions involve the material that is harvested, whether it be plant or animal. The forester may speak of a
timber crop, the livestock man of a calf crop or a lamb crop. The
material harvested is referred to as a "crop." In other cases, "crop"
specifies certain kinds of plants that are grown on purpose for a later
harvest. Even so it would be quite appropriate for an American Indian to speak of a "wild-rice crop." Note that in the poem quoted
above, Roscommon speaks of a crop of thorns and thistles. This is
probably not what the Crop Science Society of America had in mind
when it adopted its name.

It is perhaps appropriate that the term "crop" is broad and
somewhat ambiguous because many of the plants we grow for food
are not fully domesticated and the word "crop" covers all that which
is harvested regardless of its status as a domesticate. We must therefore make the distinction between "cultivated" and "domesticated"
as clear as possible. The terms are often used synonymously but actually they have quite different implications.

To domesticate means to bring into the household. A domestic
is one (servant) who lives in the same house. In the case of domesticated plants and animals, we mean that they have been altered
genetically from their wild state and have come to be at home with
man. Since domestication is an evolutionary process, there will be
found all degrees of plant and animal association with man and a
range of morphological differentiations from forms identical to wild

races to fully domesticated races. A fully domesticated plant or animal is completely dependent upon man for survival. Therefore, domestication implies a change in ecological adaptation, and this is usually associated with morphological differentiation. There are inevitably many intermediate states.

To cultivate means to conduct those activities involved in caring for a plant, such as tilling the soil, preparing a seedbed, weeding, pruning, protecting, watering, and manuring. Cultivation is concerned with human activities, while domestication deals with the genetic response of the plants or animals being tended or cultivated. It is therefore quite possible to cultivate wild plants, and cultivated plants are not necessarily domesticated.

Harvested plant materials may be classified as wild, tolerated, encouraged, and domesticated. We have shown in Chapter 1 that a very large number of species has been harvested in the wild, not only by gatherers but by fully established cultivators as well. Examples of tolerated and encouraged plants will be given in the following section.

INTERMEDIATE STATES

Lévi-Strauss' (1950) observation on the distinction between wild and cultivated plants (quoted on p. 63) need not have been restricted to South America. Although the situation occurs generally in the tropics, it applies to many temperate crops as well. We shall examine below a few examples of intermediate states between wild and domesticated.

There is a class of plants that come to be closely associated with man, but without evident genetic modification. One example is the baobab (*Adansonia* spp.), a tree widely distributed through the savannas of Africa, South Asia, and northern Australia. The plant can become very large and is useful in many ways: the fruit can be eaten, the leaves make good pot-herbs, the bark supplies fiber, and the great hollow boles can be used to store water. In Africa there is a fairly close association between village sites and stands of baobab. To what extent the villages are located near baobabs by design or how frequently the trees become established after the village is founded we do not know. Certainly, if fruits are repeatedly brought to a village it would seem that new seedlings would inevitably become established, and since they are recognized and protected, stands would develop.

Another example is the case of *Acacia albida*. The natural habitat of this tree appears to be along ephemeral water courses in the dry savanna, but vast stands have become established over tens of thousands of square kilometers in areas where it would not naturally occur. It is a dominant of certain man-made landscapes of Africa. The tree has the peculiar habit of shedding its leaves at the start of the rains and going dormant through the rainy season. For this reason, it does not compete with interplanted crops and the cultivators believe that crops yield more in association with the tree than without it. Some agronomic studies indicate that this belief is correct (Dancette and Poulain, 1968). At any rate, the tree has prospered enormously by the selective protection of man without any apparent genetic modifications toward domesticated races.

The karité (*Butyrospermum*) is a similar case, except that protection is reinforced by superstition or religious feeling. An edible oil is extracted from the fruit. The plants are individually owned, considered valuable, and almost never cut down. Other trees of the savanna may be cut for firewood, charcoal, house construction and other uses, but the karité (also called the shea butter tree) enjoys the status of a semisacred tree. As a result, vast areas of the broadleaved savanna of West Africa are covered with nearly pure stands of evenly spaced karité trees.

The West African oil palm (*Elaeis guineensis*) is an even more elaborate model in some ways. Wild stands occur near the edges of the forest, but the plant is not sufficiently tolerant to deep shade for it to grow in dense forest. However, as shifting cultivation has reduced the high forest to bush, the oil palm has invaded the forest zone. In the process of shifting cultivation, the farmers slash the bush during the dry season and burn it, reducing the vegetation sufficiently that one or two crops can be grown in the burned area. The oil palm, however, is spared. As a result, the palm is encouraged, and over a period of years, stands become thicker and thicker. In some areas, very extensive stands of oil palm developed without anyone ever purposely planting a seed.

The palm is saved from cutting basically because it is a valuable tree, but this procedure is reinforced by local tradition. There is a belief in some tribes that if an oil palm is cut down there will be a death in the village, so no one among these tribes cuts it.

The fruits of the oil palm are borne in large bunches. At maturity the bunch is cut and fruits the size of plums are beaten off with sticks. There is a belief among some tribes that if this is done in a village, the flying fruits represent people leaving the village. As a consequence, the fruits are beaten off somewhere in the bush, not in the village, thus helping to disseminate the species.

Finally, there is a gene in oil palm that controls the development of the kernel inside the fruit. One allele in the homozygous condition produces a kernel with a very thick shell called the durra type. The other allele in homozygous conditions produces no kernel at all, this type being called pisifera. The heterozygote is called tenera and produces a thin-shelled kernel. The pisifera, having no kernel, is female-sterile, and the gene frequency for that allele would tend to decline except that the people prefer to harvest the tenera and pisifera plants. There is a tendency to tap the durra plants for palm wine instead of harvesting them for oil. Repeated tapping kills the tree, reducing the frequency of the durra genotype and raising the frequency of tenera and pisifera trees.

Here we have a plant that is encouraged, disseminated, harvested, and selected without anyone deliberately planting a seed. Is the oil palm in indigenous agriculture a cultivated plant or not? In this century, it has become a very important plantation crop in the wet tropics, its hectarage is increasing, and the yields of new hybrids are very high. Under plantation conditions, the high-yielding hybrids are domesticated races, but under traditional systems, the status of the plant is very different.

Another example of an intermediate step between wild and domesticated involves the Sago palm (*Metroxylon sagu*). In parts of Melanesia the Sago palm is an important item in the diet. To harvest the tree, it is cut down and split open; the interior is full of a starchy pith which is edible. There are two kinds of Sago: one that is very thorny and difficult to handle and another in which the thorns are absent. It is a simple protoagricultural practice to cut out the thorny trees when they are young and thereby develop a pure stand of the smooth types. Again, man is selecting among wild populations.

Ethiopian oats may be cited as an example of a tolerated species. These rather strange oats are related to the tetraploid *Avena barbata* of the Near East and Mediterranean regions. They arrived in Ethiopia as weeds in barley and emmer fields. Although the Ethiopian cultivators do not grow oats as a separate crop, they do tolerate a mixture of oats in their wheat and barley fields. The oats have responded genetically by producing semishattering and even nonshattering races.

These hold most of their seed until harvest time and the cultivators reap the oats along with their primary crops. No effort is made to clean out the oat contaminants, so a mixture of seeds is sown at planting time. Here, a species has automatically developed some of the genetic traits of a domesticated plant without any deliberate selection by man. It is a case of domestication by indifference.

It is interesting to note that some crops may be partially domesticated and then abandoned and allowed to return to their wild state. Callen (1967) reports archaeological evidence for the domestication of a foxtail (*Setaria*) in Mexico. *Setaria* seeds show up in archaeological sites in some quantity, and it appears that over a period of time they gradually increased in size as though being selected under cultivation. Later they were abandoned when maize became available and replaced *Setaria* as a crop.

Li (1969) gives an account of vegetables in ancient China. Eight of the 32 discussed have now degenerated to the status of weeds.

> The most important green vegetable of ancient China, *Malva sylvestris,* has become completely forgotten and has been relegated to the status of a weed. Its place was taken by *Brassica chinensis,* then a vegetable considered of only secondary importance. The most important tuber vegetable of ancient China, *Brassica rapa,* though still commonly used, has been replaced by *Raphanus sativus,* a relatively unimportant introduced plant in China in former times.

Jacques Barrau (1965) has pointed out that some of the earliest domesticated plants in the South Pacific have been almost abandoned. One of these, the Ti (*Cordyline fruiticosa*), a plant used for religious and magic purposes and a symbol of clan permanence, was once generally eaten. It has been replaced as an article of diet by more desirable plants but lingers on in gardens for its magical and religious uses. In New Guinea the tuberous plant *Pueraria lobata* has been largely displaced by the sweet potato (*Ipomoea batatas*) and the name formerly given to *Pueraria* has been transferred to the sweet potato in relatively recent times.

Throughout the tropics the differences between wild, tolerated, encouraged, and cultivated are much less clear than in temperate zones. Plants are transplanted from the wild, brought into the garden, and escape again into the naturalized state where they are sometimes still harvested. The movement of useful plants from the wild condition to the cultivated and back again is a relatively simple and common occurrence.

The situation is by no means confined to the tropics, however. Weedy escapes from cultivation in temperate zones include spontaneous races of radish, carrot, lettuce, sunflower, Camelina, oats, rye, vetch, and many others. Furthermore, one man's weed is another man's crop. The wild oat may be a serious pest to the California wheat grower, but to the cattleman of the coast and foothill ranges, it may be the most important forage. Johnsongrass may be a hated weed to the Texas cotton farmer, but a valuable hay crop to his neighbor. The weedy watermelon (*Colocynthis citrullus*) is an obnoxious weed in cultivated fields over much of tropical and subtropical Africa, but in the dry season it may be the only supply of water for man and beast alike in the Kalahari Desert. *Brassica campestris* is sufficiently abundant to be damaging to wheat production in parts of the Andean Highlands, but is harvested for livestock feed and pot-herb greens by the Indian cultivators. A man may fight *Cynodon dactylon* with a passion in one field, deliberately plant an improved variety in another field, and nurture still another variety with tender care about his house.

A SHORT LIST OF CULTIVATED PLANTS

For all the difficulties of definition, we can at least identify most of the important species that are cultivated and that usually have domesticated races. The origins are somewhat inconsistent, for, as previously indicated, crops do not necessarily originate in definable centers. A number of those identified with the Near Eastern complex, for example, actually were domesticated in the Mediterranean Basin, northern Europe, or even western Europe. Crops that are added late to a complex well-removed from the center of origin are sometimes called addition crops. Our information lacks precision in all but a few cases that have been intensively studied and may well be faulty in other cases. The list (Table 1) will serve as a basis for further discussion.

Table 1
A short list of cultivated plants and their probable origins.

REGION A₁, THE NEAR EASTERN COMPLEX

Cereals

Avena sativa Linn. — Oats; secondary crop, N. Europe
A. strigosa Schreb. — Fodder oats; addition crop, Mediterranean
Hordeum vulgare Linn. — Barley; primary crop. N.E.*
Secale cereale Linn. — Rye; secondary crop, Anatolian plateau–N. Europe
Triticum aestivum Linn. — Bread wheat; addition crop, Transcaucasia–Caspian
T. dicoccum Schrank — Emmer; primary crop, N.E.
T. monococcum Linn. — Einkorn; primary crop, Turkey
T. timopheevi Zhuk. — Very minor wheat; Soviet Georgia
T. turgidum Linn. — Tetraploid wheat; derived from emmer, N.E.

Pulses

Cicer arietinum Linn. — Chickpea; primary crop, N.E.
Lathyrus sativus Linn. — Grasspea; N.E. crop
Lens esculenta Moench — Lentil; primary crop, N.E.
Lupinus albus Linn. — Lupine; N.E.
Pisum sativum Linn. — Gardenpea; primary crop with addition from Mediterranean
Vicia ervilia Willd. — Bittervetch; N.E.
V. faba Linn. — Broadbean, fava; N.E. or Mediterranean

Root and tuber crops

Beta vulgaris Linn. — Beet, mangel, chard; Mediterranean, W. Europe
Brassica rapa Linn. — Turnip; Mediterranean (also maybe China)
Daucus carota Linn. — Carrot; Mediterranean, widespread
Raphanus sativus Linn. — Radish; wild and weed races widespread

Oil crops

Brassica campestris Linn. — Rapeseed; E. Mediterranean
B. nigra (L.) Koch. — Mustard, mustard oil; E. Mediterranean
Carthamus tinctorius Linn. — Safflower; N.E.
Linum usitatissimum Linn. — Flax, linseed; primary crop, N.E.
Olea europea Linn. — Olive; Mediterranean
Papaver somniferum Linn. — Poppy; possibly primary crop, N.E.

Fruit and nuts

Corylus ssp. — Hazelnut, filbert; Balkans to Caspian
Cucumis melo Linn. — Melon; N.E.
Cydonia oblonga Mill. — Quince; Balkans to Caspian
Ficus carica Linn. — Fig; Turkey-Iraq-Iran
Juglans regia Linn. — English walnut; Balkans to Pakistan
Phoenix dactylifera Linn. — Date palm; Lowland steppes of Near East
Pistacea vera Linn. — Pistachio; Turkey-Iran
Prunus amygdalus Stokes — Almond; Turkey to Pakistan
P. armeniaca Linn. — Apricot; Turkey-Iran
P. avium Linn. — Cherry; Balkans to Caspian
P. domestica Linn. — Plum; Balkans and E. Europe
Punica granatum Linn. — Pomegranate; Transcaucasia–Caspian
Pyrus communis Linn. — Pear; Turkey-Iran

* N.E. = Near East.

P. malus Linn.   Apple; Balkans—Transcaucasia—Caspian
Vitis vinifera Linn.   Grape; Mediterranean

Vegetables and spices

Allium cepa Linn.   Onion; Mediterranean
A. sativum Linn.   Garlic; Mediterranean
A. porrum Linn.   Leek; E. Mediterranean
Anethum graveolens Linn.   Dill; Mediterranean
Brassica oleracea Linn.   Cabbage, cauliflower, Brussel sprouts, kale, kohlrabi, broccoli; addition from W. Europe
Carum carvi Linn.   Caraway; N.E.
Coriandrum sativum Linn.   Coriander; N.E.
Cucumis sativus Linn.   Cucumber; N.E.?, India? (possible domestication in both areas)
Cuminum cyminum Linn.   Cumin; N.E.
Foeniculum vulgare Mill.   Fennel; Mediterranean (also widespread)
Lactuca sativa Linn.   Lettuce; Mediterranean
Lepidium sativum Linn.   Gardencress; Mediterranean
Petroselinum sativum Hoffm.   Parsley; Mediterranean
Pimpinella anisum Linn.   Anise; Mediterranean
Portulacea oleracea Linn.   Purselane; Mediterranean
Trigonella foenum-graecum Linn.   Fenugreek; Turkey

Fiber plants

Cannabis sativa Linn.   Hemp; widespread, Eurasian
Linum usitatissimum Linn.   Flax; primary crop, N.E.

Starch and sugar plant (not root)

Ceratonia siliqua Linn.   Carob, tree with sweet pods; E. Mediterranean

Forage crops

Agropyron spp.   The wheatgrasses; Eurasian, useful types from Turkey and U.S.S.R.
Agrostis spp.   The bentgrasses; W. Europe
Bromus inermis Leyss.   Smooth bromegrass; Turkey to Central Europe
Dactylis glomerata Linn.   Orchardgrass, cocksfoot; Europe, Mediterranean
Festuca arundinacea Schreb.   Tall fescue; Europe, N. Africa, N.E.
Lolium spp.   The ryegrasses; Europe—Mediterranean
Medicago sativa Linn.   Alfalfa; Central Asia, Turkey-Iran
Medicago spp.   The medic clovers; mostly Mediterranean
Melilotus spp.   The sweet clovers; widespread Europe and N.E.
Onobrychis viciifolia Scop.   Sainfoin; Turkey
Phalaris arundinacea Linn.   Reed canarygrass; widespread Europe
P. tuberosa Linn.   Hardinggrass; Mediterranean
Phleum pratense Linn.   Timothy; widespread Europe
Sorghum halepense (L.) Pers.   Johnsongrass; Mediterranean, N.E.
Trifolium spp.   The true clovers; Europe, N.E.
Vicia spp.   The vetches; Mediterranean

Drugs, narcotics, fatigue plants

Atropa belladonna Linn.   Belladonna; Mediterranean
Digitalis purpurea Linn.   Digitalis; Europe
Glycyrrhiza glabra Linn.   Licorice; Mediterranean, N.E.
Hyoscyamus muticus Linn.   Henbane; Mediterranean, N.E.
Papaver somniferum Linn.   Codeine, morphine, opium; Mediterranean
Plantago psyllium Linn.   Psyllium; Mediterranean

REGION A₂, AFRICA

Cereals

Avena abyssinica Hochst. — Ethiopian oats; Ethiopia from *A. barbata*
Brachiaria deflexa (Schum.) Hubb. — Guinea millet; Guinea highlands
Digitaria exilis (Kipp.) Stapf. — Fonio; W. Africa, Nigeria to Senegal
D. iburua Stapf — Black fonio; Nigeria to Togo, Savanna
Eleusine coracana (L.) Gaertn. — Finger millet; Highlands, Ethiopia-Uganda
Eragrostis tef Trott. — Tef; Ethiopia
Oryza glaberrima Steud. — African rice; W. African savanna
Pennisetum americanum (L.) Schum. — Pearl millet; dry savanna Sudan to Senegal.
Sorghum bicolor (L.) Moench — Sorghum; savanna zones Sudan-Chad.

Pulses

Kerstingiella geocarpa Harms — Kersting's groundnut; W. African savanna
Lablab niger Medik. — Hyacinth bean; E. African savanna
Vigna unguiculata (L.) Walp. — Cowpea; W. Africa, forest margins
Voandzeia subterranea (L.) Thouars — Bambara groundnut; W. African savanna

Root and tuber crops

Dioscorea cayenensis Lam. — Yam; Ivory Coast to Cameroun
D. rotundata Poir. — Yam (may be conspecific with *D. cayenensis*); Ivory coast to Cameroun
Dioscorea spp. — Lesser yams; Guinea to Cameroun
Plectranthus esculentus N.E. Br. — Kafir potato; W. Africa
Sphenostylis stenocarpa (Hochst.) Harms — Yampea; W. Africa, forest zone
Solenostemon rotundifolius (Poir.) J. K. Morton — Piasa, becoming rare; W. Africa

Oil crops

Butyrospermum paradoxum (Gaertn.) Hepper — Karité, butter tree; W. Africa, savanna
Elaeis guineensis Jacq. — Oil palm; W. Africa, forest margins
Guizotia abyssinica Cass. — Noog; Ethiopia, highlands
Ricinus communis Linn. — Castor oil; widespread, used Ethiopia-Egypt
Telfairia occidentalis Hook. f. — A gourd; oil from seeds; W. Africa

Fruit and nuts

Adansonia digitata Linn. — Baobab; African savannas
Blighia sapida Koenig — Akee apple; aril eaten (toxic); W. Africa
Colocynthis citrullus (L.) O. Kuntze — Watermelon; dry savanna, S. and E. Africa

Vegetables and spices

Abelmoschus esculentus (L.) Moench — Gumbo, Okra; W. Africa
Aframomum melegueta K. Schum. — Malaguette; W. Africa, Ethiopia
Ceratotheca sesamoides Endl. — Leaves and seeds; savanna
Corchorus olitorius Linn. — Leaves and seedlings; use widespread
Cucumeropsis edulis (Hook. f.) Cogn. — Leaves and fruits; W. Africa
Hibiscus sabdariffa Linn. — Calices and leaves; widespread in savanna
H. cannabinus Linn. — Leaves and seeds; W. Africa
Piper guineense Schum. et Thonn. — Seeds; W. Africa, forest
Sesamum alatum Thonn. — Leaves; savanna
S. radiatum Schum. et Thonn. — Leaves; savanna
Solanum aethiopicum Linn. — Fruits; savanna
S. macrocarpon Linn. — Leaves and fruits; savanna and forest
Solanum spp. — Several "garden eggs" used for fruits and leaves

Fiber plants

Adansonia digitata Linn.   Baobab (bark); savannas, widespread
Gossypium herbaceum Linn.   Old World cotton; Sudan?

Starch and sugar plants

Ensete ventricosa (Welw.) Cheesman   Enset; Ethiopia
Parkia biglobosa (Jacq.) Benth.   Tree with sweet pods; W. Africa, savanna
Sorghum bicolor (L.) Moench.   Sweet sorghum, sorgo; savannas
Tamarindus indica Linn.   Tree with sweet pods; savanna (or India?)

Forage crops

Chloris gayana Kunth   Rhodesgrass; Kenya to S. Africa
Cynodon aethiopicum Clayton et Harlan   A stargrass; Ethiopia to Transvaal
C. dactylon (L.) Pers.   Bermudagrass (several types); widespread
C. nlemfuensis Vanderyst   A stargrass; Kenya to S. Africa
Digitaria decumbens Stent.   Pangolagrass; S. Africa
Eragrostis curvula (Schrad.) Nees   Weeping lovegrass; Tanzania to S. Africa
E. lehmanniana Nees   Lehmann's lovegrass; S. Africa
Hyparrhenia rufa Stapf   Jaragua grass; E. Africa
Panicum maximum Jacq.   Guineagrass; center in Kenya-Tanzania
Pennisetum clandestinum Hochst.   Kikuyugrass; Kenya-Uganda
P. purpureum Schum.   Elephantgrass; widespread, high rainfall
Sorghum bicolor (L.) Moench   Sudangrass and others; savanna zones
                                               Coffee; Ethiopia, forest
                                               Robusta coffee; Lowland forests

Drugs, narcotics, fatigue plants

Coffea arabica Linn.
C. canephara Pierre ex Froehnes
Coffea spp.   A few minor species; forest zones
Catha edulis Forsk.   Chat; leaves chewed; Ethiopia
Cola acuminata Schott et Endl.   Cola; fruits eaten; W. Africa
C. nitida (Vent.) Schott et Endl.   Chewed for caffein; W. Africa
Strychnos spp.   Trees; nux vomica and other uses; widespread

Utility

Lagenaria siceraria Standl.   Bottle gourd; widespread, origin unknown

---

REGION B₁, THE CHINESE CENTER

Cereals and pseudocereals

Echinochloa frumentacea Link.   Japanese millet; E. China
Fagopyrum esculentum Moench   Buckwheat; W. China
F. tataricum (L.) Gaertn.   Tartar buckwheat; W. China
Oryza sativa Linn.   Rice; S. China to India
Panicum miliaceum Linn.   Proso, broomcorn millet; N. China
Setaria italica (L.) Beav.   Italian, foxtail millet; N. China

Pulses

Glycine max (L.) Merill   Soybean; N.E. China
Stizolobium hassjoo Piper et Tracy   Velvet bean; S. China
Vigna angularis (Willd.) Ohwi   Adzuki bean; S. China

Root and tuber crops

Brassica rapa Linn.

Turnip; very important in diet; N. China (Mediterranean? possible independent domestication)

Dioscorea esculenta (Lour.) Burk.
Chinese yam; S. China

Lillium tigrinum Ker-Gawl.
Tiger lily (luxury item); temperate China

Nelumbium speciosum Willd.
Lotus, seeds and tubers eaten

Raphanus sativus var. *raphanistroides*
Chinese radish, very large

Sagittaria sagittifolia Linn.
An elephant ear; S. China

Eleocharis tuberosa Schult.
A sedge with tuber; S. China

Oil crops

Aleurites fordii Hemsl.
Tung oil; S. China

Brassica campestris Linn.
Rapeseed; temperate China

B. juncea (L.) Czern. et Coss.
A mustard seed oil; temperate China

Sapium sebiferum Roxb.
Chinaberry tree; S. China

Fruits and nuts

Canarium album Blanco
Chinese "olive"; S. China

Carya spp.
Chinese hickories; temperate China

Castanea henryi Rehd. et Wils.
Chinese chestnut; temperate China

Chaenomeles spp.
Chinese quinces; temperate China

Corylus spp.
Chinese hazelnuts; temperate China

Eriobotrya japonica Lindl.
Loquat; mountains of S.W. China

Ginkgo biloba Linn.
Ginkgo; N. China; known only in cultivation

Juglans regia Linn.
Walnut; mountains, S.W. China

Litchi chinensis Sonner.
Litchi; S. China

Prunus armeniaca Linn.
Apricot; west temperate China

P. persica Stokes
Peach; west temperate China

Pyrus spp.
Chinese pears; temperate China

Trapa natans Linn.
Water "chestnut"; S. China

Zizyphus sativa Gaertn.
Chinese jujube; west temperate China

Vegetables and spices

Allium bakeri Regel
Chinese shallot; temperate China

A. ramosum Jacq.
Chinese leek; temperate China

Aralia cordata Thunb.
Udo

Benincasa hispida Cogn.
Winter melon or wax gourd; widespread

Brassica cernua Hemsl.
Leafy vegetable; temperate China

B. chinensis Linn.
Chinese cabbage; widespread, temperate China

Cinnamomum cassia Blume
Spice; S. China

Cucumis conomon Thunb.
Pickling melon; widespread

C. sativus Linn.
Cucumber; widespread (probably India as well)

Lagenaria siceraria Standl.
Bottle gourd eaten young; pantropical

Malva verticillata Linn.
The main leafy vegetable of ancient China now a weed

Oenanthe stolonifera Wall.
Oriental "celery"; wet lands

Stackys sieboldi Miq.
Chinese "artichoke"; widespread

Wasabia japonica Matsum.
Horseradish; widespread

Zanthoxylum bungei Planch.
Chinese "pepper"; S. China

Zingiber officinale Rosc.
Ginger; S. China

Zizania latifolia Turcz.
A wild-rice, stems and heads eaten; temperate China

Fiber plants

Abutilon avicennae Gaertn.
Abutilon hemp; S. China

Boehmeria niveae (L.) Gaudich.
Ramie; S.China

Cannabis sativa Linn.
Hemp; central Asia

Drugs, narcotics, fatigue plants

Aralia quinquefolia Decne et Planch.	Ginseng; widespread
Arctium major Bernh	Burdock; temperate China
Camellia sinensis (L.) Kuntze	Tea; S. and S.W. China
Cinnamomum camphora (L.) Nees et Eberm.	Camphor tree; S. China
Rheum palmatum Linn.	Medicinal rhubarb; temperate China

Utility

Arundinaria spp.	Bamboos, innumerable uses; S. China
Bambusa spp.	Bamboos, matting, houses, paper, pipes, etc.
Phyllostachys spp.	Bamboos, some used as food as well
Rhus vernicifera DC	Lac tree for varnish; S. China
Strobilanthes flaccidifolius Nees	An indigo dye plant; S. China

---

REGION B₂, SOUTHEAST ASIA AND PACIFIC ISLANDS

Cereals

Coix lachryma-jobi Linn.	Job's tears, adlay; Indo-China-Philippines
Digitaria cruciata Nees ex Hoof. f.	A millet; hills N.E. India
Oryza sativa Linn.	Rice; E. India to S. China
Panicum miliare Lam.	Slender millet; Himalayas-Upper Burma
Paspalum scrobiculatum Linn.	A millet; Nilgiris of S. India

Pulses

Cajanus cajan (L.) Millsp.	Pigeonpea; origin uncertain (Afro-Indian)
Canavalia gladiata (Jacq.) DC	A jackbean; S.E. Asia
Cyamopsis tetragonolobus (L.) Taub.	Guar; origin in doubt (Afro-Asian)
Dolichos biflorus Linn.	A hyacinth bean; S.E. Asia
Psophocarpus tetragonolobus (L.) DC	Winged bean, also has tubers; New Guinea
Vigna aconitifolia (Jacq.) Verdc.	Mat bean; S.E. Asia
V. calcarata (Roxb.) Kurz	Rice bean; S.E. Asia
V. mungo (L.) Hepper	Urd, black gram; India or S. China
V. radiata (L.) Wilczek	Mung bean, India or S. China

Root and tuber crops

Alocasia macrorhiza Schott.	An elephant-ear; Indonesia-Melanesia
Amorphophallus spp.	Aroid tuber; S.E. Asia
Colocasia esculenta (L.) Schott.	Taro; Assam-Upper Burma
Cyrtosperma chamissonis (Schott.) Merr.	An elephant-ear; Melanesia-Polynesia
Dioscorea alata Linn.	Winged yam; S.E. Asia
Dioscorea spp.	Several minor spp. S. E. Asia to Melanesia
Pueraria lobata (Willd.) Ohwi	A yam-bean; Indonesia-Melanesia
Tacca leontopetaloides Kuntze	Arrowroot; S. Pacific Islands

Oil crops

Brassica juncea (L.) Czern et Coss.	Sarson; N. India
Cocos nucifera Linn.	Coconut; S. Pacific Islands
Sesamum indicum Linn.	Sesame; origin in doubt (Afro-Indian)

Fruits and nuts

Artocarpus communis Forst.	Breadfruit; S.W. Pacific Islands
A. integrifolia Linn.	Jackfruit; S. Pacific and S.E. Asia
Averrhoa bilimbi Linn.	Bilimbi; S.E. Asia

A. carambola Linn.	Carambola; S.E. Asia
Citrus aurantiifolia Swingle	Lime; S.E. Asia and S. China
C. aurantium Linn.	Sour orange; S.E. Asia and S. China
C. decumanus Linn.	Shaddock, pomolo; S.E. Asia and S. China
C. limon (L.) Burm. f.	Lemon; S.E. Asia and S. China
C. medica Linn.	Citron; S.E. Asia and S. China
C. nobilis Lour.	Tangerine; S.E. Asia and S. China
C. paradisi Macfad.	Grapefruit; S.E. Asia and S. China
C. sinensis (L.) Osbeck	Sweet orange; S.E. Asia and S. China
Durio zibethinus Murr.	Durian; S.E. Asia
Eugenia spp.	Jambos, jambolans; S.E. Asia
Garcinia mangostana Linn.	Mangosteen; S.E. Asia
Mangifera indica Linn.	Mango; Indo-Malaysia
Musa acuminta Colla	Banana (A genome); Malaysia-Thailand
M. balbisiana Colla	Plantain (B genome); Malaysia-Thailand
M. sapientum Linn.	Banana (sterile combinations of above); E. India to Borneo
Musa spp sect. *Australomusa*	Fe'i banana; Melanesia-Polynesia
Nephelium lappaceum Linn.	Rambutan; S.E. Asia
N. longana Cambess.	Longan; S.E. Asia

Vegetables and spices

Amaranthus spp.	Leaves and stems eaten; N. India
Curcuma longa Linn.	Turmeric; India-Malaysia
Elettaria cardamomum Maton	Cardamom; S.E. Asia
Syzygium aromaticum (L.) Merr. et Perry	Clove; Spice Islands
Myristica fragrans Houtt.	Nutmeg; Spice Islands
Piper nigrum Linn.	Black pepper; S.E. Asia
Solanum melongena Linn.	Eggplant; India

Fiber plants

Cocos nucifera Linn.	Coirfiber; S.W. Pacific Islands
Corchorus capsularis Linn.	Jute; India to Burma
Crotalaria juncea Linn.	Sun hemp; India-Burma
Hibiscus cannabinus Linn.	Kenaf; origin in doubt (Afro-Asian)
Musa textilis Née	Manila hemp; Philippine Islands

Starch and sugar plants (not roots)

Arenga saccharifera Labill.	Sugar palm; S.E. Asia and S. Pacific
Borassus flabellifer Linn.	Palymra palm; S.E. Asia
Metroxylon sagus Rottb.	Sago palm; S.W. Pacific Islands
Metroxylon spp.	Similar spp; Melanesia
Saccharum officinarum Linn.	Sugarcane; India or New Guinea (both?)
Tamarindus indica Linn.	Tree with sweet pods; Savanna (or Africa?)

Drugs, narcotics, fatigue plants

Areca catechu Linn.	Betelnut; S.E. Asia
Cassia angustifolia Vahl	Senna; S.E. Asia
Croton tiglium Linn.	Croton oil; S.E. Asia
Lawsonia inermis Linn.	Henna; S.E. Asia
Piper betle Linn.	Betel leaf; chewed S.E. Asia
P. methysticum Forst.	Kava-kava; Melanesia-Polynesia

REGIONS C$_1$ AND C$_2$, THE AMERICAS*

REGION C$_1$, MESOAMERICA	REGION C$_2$, SOUTH AMERICA	ELEVATIONS
Cereals		
Panicum sonorum Beal.		
Zea mays Linn.; Indian corn	*Bromus mango* E. Desv.	High
Pseudocereals		
Amaranthus cruentus Linn.; amaranth	*Amaranthus caudatus* Linn.; amaranth,	Med.
A. leucocarpus S. Wats.; amaranth, huauhtli	achis	
Chenopodium nuttaliae Saff. (more used as a vegetable); huaozontle	*Chenopodium pallidicaule* Allen, cañihua	High
Hyptis suaveolens Poit.; chia grande	*C. quinoa* Willd.; quinoa	High
Salvia hispanica Linn.; chia		
Pulses		
	Arachis hypogaea Linn.; peanut	Med.
Canavalia ensiformis (L.) DC; sword bean	*Canavalia plagiosperma* Piper; Jack bean	Low
	Inga feuillei DC; pacae	Low
	Lupinus mutabilis Sweet; chocho	Med.
Phaseolus acutifolius A. Gray; tepary bean		
P. coccineus Linn.; scarlet runner bean		
P. lunatus Linn.; lima bean	*Phaseolus lunatus* Linn.; lima bean	Med.
P. vulgaris Linn.; common bean	*P. vulgaris* Linn.; common bean	Med.
Root and tuber crops		
Bomarea edulis (Tuss.) Herb.; sarsilla	*Arracacia xanthorrhiza* Bancr.; arracacha	Med.
	Calathea allouia (Aubl.) Lindl.; lairen	Low
	Canna edulis Ker.; achira	Low
	Dioscorea trifida L.f.; yam	Low
Ipomoea batatas (L.) Lam.; sweet potato	*Lepidium meyenii* Walp.; maca	High
Manihot esculenta Crantz; manioc	*Manihot esculenta* Crantz; manioc	Low
Maranta arundinacea Linn.; arrowroot		
Pachyrrhizus erosus (L.) Urban; jícama	*Pachyrrhizus ahipa* (Wedd.) Parodi; jícama or ajipa	Med.-High
	P. tuberosus Spreng.; jícama or asipa	Low-Med.
	Oxalis tuberosa Mol.; oca	High
	Polymnia sonchifolia Poepp et Endl.; yacón	Med.
	Solanum tuberosum Linn.; potato	High
	Tropaeolum tuberosum R.& P.; añu	High
	Ullucus tuberosus Caldas; ulluco	High
	Xanthosoma sagittifolium (L.) Schott.	Low
Oil crops		
	Arachis hypogaea Linn.; peanut	Med.
Helianthus annuus Linn.; sunflower		
Gossypium hirsutum Linn.; upland cotton	*Gossypium barbadense* Linn.; sea island cotton	Low

Fruits and nuts

Achras zapota Linn.; sapodilla

Anacardium occidentale Linn.; cashew	Low

Ananas comosus (L.) Merrill; pineapple

Ananas comosus (L.) Merrill; pineapple	Low

Annona diversifolia Saff.; ilama

Annona cherimolia Mill.; cherimoya	Low

A. glabra Linn.; anona
A. purpurea Moc. et Sesse; anona
A. reticulata Linn.; anona
A. squamosa Linn.; sweet sop

A. muricata Linn.; guanábana	Low
A. reticulata Linn.; anona	Low
A. squamosa Linn.; sweet sop	Low
Bertholletia excelsa HBK; Brazil nut	Low
Bunchosia armeniaca (Cav.) Rich.	Med.

Brosimum alicastrum Swartz.; ramón
Byrsonima crassifolia (L.) DC; nance
Carica payaya Linn.; papaya

Carica candicans A. Gray; papaya	Low
Carica spp.; papayas	Low

Casimiroa edulis Llave et Lex; white sapote
C. sapota Oerst.; matasano
Crataegus pubescens (HBK) Steud.; tejocote

Campomanesia lineatifolia Ruiz et Pav.; palillo	Low-Med.
Cyclanthera pedata Schrad.; achocha	
Cyphomandra betacea (Cav.) Sendt.; tree tomato	Med.
C. splendens Dun.; tree tomato	Med.

Diospyros ebenaster Retz; black sapote
Opuntia spp.; prickly pear
Parmentiera edulis DC; caujilote
Persea americana Mill.; aguacate
P. schiedeana Nees; aguacate
Prunus serotina Ehrh.; capulín
Psidium guajava Linn.; guava

Opuntia exaltata Berger; cactus	Low
Passiflora spp.; granadilla	Low-Med.
Persea americana Mill.; avocado	Low
Psidium guajava Linn.; guava	Med.
Solanum muricatum Ait.; pepiño	Med.
S. topiro Humb. et Bonpl. ex Dun.; cocona	Med.
S. quitoense Lam.; lulo	Med.

Spondias mombin Linn.; jocote
S. purpurea Linn.; jocote

Vegetables and spices

Capsicum annuum Linn.; pepper

C. frutescens Linn.; chili, aji

Capsicum baccatum Linn.; pepper	Low
C. chinense Jacq.; pepper	Low
C. frutescens Linn.; pepper	Low
C. pubescens Ruiz et Pav.; pepper	Low

Chenopodium nuttaliae Saff.; huaozontli
Cucurbita ficifolia Bouché; squash
C. mixta Pangalo; squash
C. moschata Duch.; squash
C. pepo Linn.; squash-pumpkin
Lycopersicon esculentum Mill.; tomato
Physalis ixocarpa Brot.; tomate
Sechium edule (Jacq.) Sw.; chayote
Vanilla planifolia Andr.; vanilla

Cucurbita maxima Lam.; squash	Low
Physalis peruvianum Linn.; uchuba	Low

Fiber plants

Agave atrovirens Karw.; maguey
A. fourcroydes Lem.; henequin
A. sisalana Perr.; sisal
A. tequilana Weber; maguey
Gossypium hirsutum Linn.; upland cotton

Gossypium barbadense Linn.; sea island cotton	Low

Forage crops

Centrosema pubescens Benth.; centro	Low
Desmodium spp.; tick clover	Low
Stylosanthes gracilis HBK; stylo	Low
Tripsacum laxum Nash*; guatemalagrass	Low
Paspalum dilatatum Poir.; dallisgrass	Low

Drugs, narcotics, fatigue plants

Agave spp.; alcohol, agave
Datura stramonium Linn.; Jimson weed

Datura spp.; stramonium, Jimson weed	Low
Erythroxylon coca Lam.; cocaine, coca	Low-Med.
Ilex paraguariensis St. Hil.; maté	Low
I. vomitoria A.t.; yaupon	Low

Lophophora williamsii (Lem.) Coult.; peyote

Nicotiana rustica Linn.; tobacco	Low
N. tabacum Linn.; tobacco	Low
Paullinia cupana HBK; guaraná	Low
P. yoco Schultes et Killip; yoco	Low

Theobroma cacao Linn.; cacao, chocolate

Utility

Bixa orellana Linn.; achiote	*Bixa orellana* Linn.; achiote	Low
Crescentia cujete Linn.; tree gourd	*Crescentia cujete* Linn.; tree gourd	Low
Indigofera suffruticosa Mill.; añil	*Indigofera suffruticosa* Mill.; añil	Low
Lagenaria siceraria Standle.; bottle gourd	*Lagenaria siceraria* Standl.; bottle gourd	

* This name is to be changed to *T. andersonii*, but it has not been published yet. The type for *T. laxum* is something else.

There are, of course, hundreds more. I have listed only a few forage crops and have not touched at all on those producing rubbers, gums, resins, essential oils, dyes, poisons, tannins, ornamentals, or useful woods. The lists of fruits, vegetables, and spices are far from complete and many familiar items are omitted. The table does include the most important crops that provide food for the human species and is sufficiently comprehensive that some generalizations can be made.

First, it seems evident that man has searched out the plant kingdom rather thoroughly. The plants listed belong to about 55 families. Although most families contribute very little (e.g., Orchidaceae provides vanilla, Tropoeolaceae presents us with *Tropoeolum*, Passifloraceae with *Passiflora*), an enormous percentage of the food for mankind is supplied by the Leguminoseae and Gramineae. Considering food plants only and discounting forages, drugs, narcotics, fibers, etc., the grass family contributes 29 cereals plus sugarcane to the list and the legume family contributes 41 crops, mostly pulses, tubers, and edible pods. Other strong contributors are Solanaceae, 18 crops (fruits, spices, one tuber); Cruciferae, 13 crops (leafy vegetables, oil, root crops); Cucurbitaceae, 13 crops (squash, pumpkin, fruits, oil seeds); Rosaceae, 11 crops (mostly fruits); Liliaceae, 11 crops (edible bulbs); Umbelliferae, 9 crops (mostly spices and salad vegetables); and Araceae, 8 crops (all tubers).

Another conspicuous feature is the large number of vicarious domestications. If one species proves suitable for domestication, then a similar, related species is likely to be useful as well. There are 40 genera on the list in which 2 or more species were domesticated independently. Some of the more frequently appearing genera are: *Solanum,* 7 spp.; *Brassica,* 6 spp.; *Prunus,* 6 spp.; *Allium,* 5 spp.; *Vigna,* 6 spp.; *Dioscorea,* 5 spp.; *Phaseolus,* 4 spp.; *Annona,* 7 spp.; *Capsicum,* 5 spp.; and *Curcurbita,* 5 spp.

The same kinds of plants were often selected in different parts of the world. Aroid tubers were domesticated in Asia, the South Pacific islands, South America, and possibly Africa (although not on the list). Yams were domesticated in Africa, Asia, and South America. Cotton was domesticated independently in Mexico, in South America, and in Africa, India, or both. In the table, the genera with Old World-New World vicarious domestication are *Amaranthus, Canavalia, Dioscorea, Gossypium, Ipomoea, Lepidium, Lupinus, Prunus,* and *Solanum.*

The table is arranged to point out the remarkable number of vicarious domestications in the Americas. It seems that if the Mexican Indians domesticated a species, South American Indians domesticated a similar species and vice versa.

Sometimes similar plants are put to quite different uses. In the Americas, amaranths were pseudocereals; in Asia they are pot-herbs. *Hibiscus cannabinus* and *Corchorus olitorius* are pot-herbs in Africa and fibers in India. Lepidium is a spicy salad green in the Near East but a root crop in the Andes.

CROPS THAT FEED THE WORLD

While a great variety in food plants adds immeasurably to the quality
of life, it is obvious that most of those listed in Table 1 contribute
relatively little to the nutrition of the world's population. Most of
the food for mankind comes from a small number of crops and the
total number is decreasing steadily. In the United States in the past
40 years, many vegetables and fruits have disappeared from the diet,
and the trend is going on all over the world. More and more people
will be fed by fewer and fewer crops.

It is important to know, then, which crops really feed the world.
The answer is not easy to come by. There are too many ways to
evaluate crops. One may use estimates of total production, hectarage, monetary value, nutritive value, or other criteria. Every year,
my students and I devote a session to discussing the problem. Each
year we come up with a different list. One lesson we learn is that
good statistics are hard to find. Many estimates leave out China,
some omit the Soviet Union, others make wild guesses for many
countries in Africa or tropical America. Crops are often lumped into
classes and cannot be separated, and so on. All we can suggest is that,
if you are interested, you probe to find some of the data and see for
yourself how elusive numbers can be.

Some years ago, Professor Paul C. Mangelsdorf gave the following list as the 15 crops that feed the world: wheat, rice, maize, sorghum, barley, beans, peanut, soybean, sugarcane, sugarbeet, sweet
potato, manioc, potato, banana, and coconut (personal communication). It is a good list, but there are alternatives. Some data, mostly
from FAO sources, are presented in Table 2, for what they are worth.
I have included several crops that are not primarily food crops to give
some perspective. Coffee is not very nutritious, but it does generate
money and one can buy food with money. Cotton not only gener-
ates money, but the seed is edible and a good deal of cottonseed oil
is processed for human consumption. World production of potato is
comparable to that of the most important cereals, but potatoes contain much more water and the nutritive value is less. The production
of maize is about the same as that of rice, but most of the maize goes
into livestock feeds and by the time it is converted to meat and milk,
its caloric value for human food is much reduced. The reader is welcome to draw his own conclusions and to find more accurate figures
as best he can.

Table 2

Some of the most important crops in the world.

Crops	Production, metric tons (millions)	Value, U.S. dollars (millions)	Comments
Wheat	343	21,000	Mostly human food; good protein
Rice	308	15,000	Mostly human food
Maize	308	17,000	Much fed to livestock
Potato	306	17,000	Mostly human food; high in water
Barley	152	7,000	Some fed to livestock
Manioc	92	--	Estimates poor; local consumption
Oats	54	--	Much fed to livestock
Sorghum	49	2,500	Some fed to livestock
Soybean	49	6,000	Much fed to livestock; high protein and oil content
Cane sugar	41 ⎱ 72	6,000 ⎱ 9,000	
Beet sugar	31 ⎰	3,000 ⎰	Low nutritive value
Citrus	37	--	High in water, vitamins
Cotton fiber	11 ⎱ 33	7,069 ⎱ 8,535	
Cottonseed	22 ⎰	1,466 ⎰	Important edible oil
Bean, pea, chickpea	31	--	High nutritive value
Rye	31	--	Some fed to livestock
Banana	28	2,500	Estimates poor; local consumption
Tomato	28	--	High in water, vitamins
Millets	22	1,063	Mostly human food, beer
Sesame	21	--	Mostly human food, high oil
Palm oil	20	4,000	High caloric value
Peanut	18	3,500	High oil and protein
Sweet potato and yams	15	--	Estimates poor
Coffee	4.9	4,000	Cash value; caffeine
Tobacco	4.5	4,900	Cash value; tars and nicotine
Rubber	3.5	961	Cash value; no food
Cocoa	1.5	937	Cash value and food value
Tea	1.3	1,000	Cash value; caffeine

Chapter 4

WHAT IS A WEED?

. . . the history of weeds is the history of man.

Anderson, 1954

When you sow the berries of bays, weed not the borders for the first half year; for the weed giveth them shade.

Bacon
(Johnson, 1827)

Because of the importance of weeds to agriculture and their probable roles in plant domestication, it is important that we have clearly in mind what is meant or implied by "weed." Some of the current definitions used in agronomic instruction, such as "a weed is a plant that does more harm than good," are clearly inadequate. A weed is much more than that, but the implications of the term have changed over the years. The traditional use of the word is well expressed in the Oxford English Dictionary (Murray et al., 1961):

> Weed. 1. A herbaceous plant, not valued for use or beauty, growing wild and rank, and regarded as cumbering the ground or hindering the growth of superior vegetation.

In recent decades, however, it has become clear that identifying weeds by a value judgment is unsatisfactory. Biologists and laymen alike have become more ecologically minded than formerly. The terms "weedy," "weediness" or "weedishness" are commonly used and imply that a weed is a weed because of something it is or does and not simply because it is an object of prejudice. Bacon's line quoted by Samuel Johnson (above) suggests that weeds should not be removed until they stop being useful and so weeds are not always unwanted. Bunting (1960) refers to "the weedy *Digitaria exilis*" as an important crop in parts of West Africa. Thus, if weediness implies unwantedness, then we are dealing with an unwanted crop, which is clearly nonsense.

In an essay on weeds, Harlan and de Wet (1965) assembled a number of definitions of "weed," reproduced in Table 1. The professional weed men are all of the same mind and emphasize the unwanted qualities of weeds. This is understandable since their profession deals with control and eradication. Ecologists take a broader

Table 1
Definitions of weeds (adapted from Harlan and de Wet,
1965).

Source	Date	Definition
	By professional weed men	
Blatchley	1912	a plant out of place, or growing where it is not wanted
Georgia	1914	a plant that is growing where it is desired that something else shall grow.
Robbins, Crafts, and Raynor	1942	These obnoxious plants are known as weeds.
Fogg	1945	any plant which grows where it is not wanted.
Muenscher	1946	those plants with harmful or objectionable habits or characteristics which grow where they are not wanted, usually in places were it is desired that something else should grow.
Harper	1960	higher plants which are a nuisance
Isely	1960	any plant where it is not wanted, particularly where man is attempting to grow something else.
Salisbury	1961	a plant growing where we do not want it.
Klingman	1961	a plant growing where it is not desired; or a plant out of place.
Wodehouse	1960	an unwanted plant.
	By enthusiastic amateurs	
Emerson (in Blatchley)	1912	a plant whose virtues have not yet been discovered.
Cocannouer	1950	...This thing of considering all weeds as bad is nonsensical!
King	1951	Weeds have always been condemned without a fair trial.
	By the ecologically minded	
Bunting	1960	Weeds are pioneers of secondary succession of which the weedy arable field is a special case.
Anderson	1954	artifacts, camp followers.
Blatchley	1912	a plant which contests with man for the possession of the soil.
Dayton	1950	introduced plant species which take possession of cultivated or fallow fields and pastures.
Pritchard	1960	opportunistic species that follow human disturbance of the habitat.
Isely	1960	The prime characteristic possessed by all important weeds is their ability to thrive in land subject to the plow.

| Salisbury | 1961 | The cosmopolitan character of many weeds is perhaps a tribute both to the ubiquity of man's modification of environmental conditions and his efficiency as an agent of dispersal. |
| Rademacher | 1948 | Biologically speaking, weeds are plants that build up associations with useful plants and for which cultivation is beneficial or even necessary. Agriculturally speaking, weeds grow unwanted in cultivated land and there cause more harm than good. |

view of weeds. From this list two basic themes to an understanding of weeds emerge: 1) a weed has certain characteristic ecological attributes, and 2) it is frequently unwanted because of these characteristics. It is the ecological behavior that is paramount. Human opinion has little to do with the ecological behavior of plants, but the ecological behavior of plants can have a lot to do with human opinion. Bunting (1960) put it this way:

> The common definition of a weed—that is a plant in the wrong place—conceals two important implications. Firstly, the word "wrong" implies a human opinion, since right and wrong are human concepts not inherent in nature. Secondly, the word "place" implies some characteristic dependence on environment, or in other words an ecological relationship, and clearly that relationship has to do with man's own botanical activities in farming.

He then defines weeds in ecological terms as "pioneers of secondary succession."

Let us suppose a wheat farm in western Kansas is abandoned, not an unusual event over the last hundred years. For the first year or two after abandonment, the fields are covered with massive stands of sunflowers and Russian thistles (*Salsola kali* L., var. *tenuifolia* Tausch). These two species, the former native and the latter alien, are on everyone's weed list. But, the people have left and gone to town; there is nobody around to dislike them. Have they stopped being weeds? As a matter of fact, the weeds have now become useful plants in stabilizing the soil, preventing blowing, and reducing water erosion. *It is true that weeds are often unwanted, but that is not what makes them weeds.*

Harlan and de Wet (1965) defined a weed as "a generally un-wanted organism that thrives in habitats disturbed by man." Man has probably always caused some disturbance of habitats. Before he knew how to manipulate fire, man's disturbances were probably very minor and more or less limited to the vicinity of cave or camp. After he began to use fire to deliberately alter the vegetation, his disturb-ances were more widespread and more intense. Still, his set fires were relatively casual compared to the habitats he created after de-veloping an effective agriculture in which whole landscapes were churned up and entire floras destroyed and replaced by new vegeta-tion.

The species adapted to the new, artificial habitats are mostly crops or weeds. Man generally wants the crops and tries by various means to encourage them; he does not want the weeds and tries by various means to eradicate them. Because both are adapted to the same habitats, however, practices that tend to favor crops also tend to favor weeds.

Since ecological behavior is the chief criterion for calling some-thing a weed it would be logical to include animal species as well as plants in that category. The house sparrow, the starling, the statuary pigeon, the common brown sewer rat, the house mouse, the fruit fly (*Drosophila melanogaster*), and rabbits in Australia and New Zealand are excellent examples of animal weeds. Indeed, *Homo sapiens* is perhaps the weediest of all species, and the more he dominates the landscape, the more he seems to thrive. If we confine the concept of weeds to species adapted to human disturbance, then man is by definition the first and primary weed under whose influence all other weeds have evolved. One might argue that man is a domesticated animal rather than a weed. But man existed a very long time before he domesticated any other species; he has never seriously or con-sistently attempted to improve the race by selection or breeding as he has with other domesticates; and if we apply the test of unwanted-ness, the current alarm over the population explosion would appear to place man more in the category of weeds than domesticated ani-mals. If man does succeed in controlling his own population size, we shall have an example of a weed becoming domesticated.

INTERMEDIATE STATES

There are, then, two traditions with respect to weeds: one based on ecological behavior and one on man's response to the species in question. As might be expected of biological materials, neither criterion is sharp or clear-cut, and there are gradations between the extremes. With respect to ecological adaptation, the gradients might be diagramed as follows:

→ Increasing intensity of disturbance →

Species adapted to closed, primary habitats	→	Species adapted to open, naturally disturbed habitats	→	Species adapted to range or forest disturbed by man	→	Species adapted to cultivated fields and gardens	→	Species adapted to urban areas

There were, of course, "disturbed" or unstable habitats long before man existed and they occur today in uninhabited regions. Natural disturbances of the kinds that would encourage pioneers of secondary succession or colonizers are common enough but usually do not affect very large areas. Examples would include river banks and frequently flooded areas; the shores of lakes, seas, and oceans; active dunes; areas unstable due to wind or water erosion; land slips; talus slopes; steep cliffs; land covered with volcanic ash or vacated by retreating glaciers; and so on. Species have evolved adapted to all of these naturally disturbed situations.

There are also species adapted to disturbances caused by fires and blowdowns. Fires have always been a part of the natural environment of grasslands, woodlands, and dry forest and were so millions of years before man existed. Species have evolved that are resistant to fire and some even require occasional burning to survive. Some associations are so well adapted to periodic burning that man can cause as much disturbance of the habitat by controlling fires as he can by setting them.

Finally, animals other than man may cause widescale "disturbance," such as overgrazing by herbivores, traffic on game trails, trampling near water holes and bedding grounds, the rooting habits of some species, the burrowing habits of others, migrations in vast numbers of some gregarious species, and the work of termites, ants, and locusts.

Before agriculture, the most widespread disturbance was caused by the Pleistocene glaciation. Most of Europe and great sections of North America were alternately covered and exposed. Pioneer habitats were made available on a vast scale together with ample time for species to evolve adapted to such habitats. Thus, in temperate climates around the world, the chief weeds are Eurasian and North American species that developed in or near the areas of disturbance caused by Pleistocene glaciation.

The Pleistocene disturbance, however, was not nearly so vast or so rapid as that caused by man after the invention of successful forms of agriculture. There is now hardly a spot anywhere on earth untouched by man in some way. Some weedy species might have been rather uncommon before man began to churn up the landscape, but when the agricultural "revolution" reached them their ecological niches were suddenly expanded and they prospered enormously as a result.

Most of our modern weeds and presumably all of our obligate weeds did not exist in their present form before agriculture. New products of evolution, they are dynamic and labile and constitute excellent subjects for the experimental study of evolution. They are products of vast disturbances on a continental scale where whole floras have been uprooted and replaced by imported vegetation and where masses of plants, separated for great periods of time, are suddenly brought together under conditions promoting mass hybridization. Such a global disturbance has probably never occurred before in so brief a time. The result has been the evolution of new plants adapted to the new ecological niches. These are what we call "weeds."

We have seen that whenever we deal with evolution we must deal with intermediates. Some species are weedier than others; some thrive under moderate disturbance but cannot tolerate intensive disturbance. Furthermore, some are disliked more than others. Plants with weedy tendencies may be encouraged as crops; others may be despised or hated. We could, therefore, diagram degrees of human response as we have done with disturbance of the habitat.

$\xrightarrow{\hspace{2cm}}$ Increasing intensity of dislike $\xrightarrow{\hspace{2cm}}$

Domesti-   Encouraged   Tolerated   Discouraged   Hated
cated $\rightarrow$ weed crops $\rightarrow$ weeds $\rightarrow$ weeds $\longrightarrow$ despised, etc.
crops   (noxious)
                                                     weeds

Edgar Anderson (1954) liked to think of weeds as plants that follow man around. Wherever man goes he is soon surrounded by an array of plant companions whether or not he wants them, hates them, or ignores them. In Chapter 3, I mentioned *Acacia albida*, which moved out of its natural habitat along dry washes and spread over extensive areas of the African savanna. The seeds were mostly carried by livestock; the plants were spared by man because he thought them useful. Since the trees were not harvested, one can hardly call the white acacia a crop. The species does thrive under human disturbance, but the protection it receives is deliberate and intentional. The karité and the oil palm have spread and thrived under somewhat similar conditions, but since they are harvested they can be called crops (Portères, 1957).

At the other end of the scale, are the really accomplished weeds that follow man in the face of hostility and outright warfare. Consider the dandelion (*Taraxacum*), for example. Millions of dollars and untold hours of toil are spent each year to reduce dandelion populations in lawns across the United States. Still they come, year after year, bespangling our green carpets with golden yellow blossoms and pushing up naked stems topped with seed heads of lacy gauze. To the unprejudiced eye, the flowers are really beautiful, but there is something in the culture that causes the owner of a lawn full of dandelions to feel guilty if not sinful.

Then there is crabgrass (*Digitaria sanguinalis*), so prolific a seed producer that it was once cultivated as a cereal in central Europe (Körnicke, 1885). Was it cultivated because it was so aggressive or did it become aggressive because it was once cultivated? We can detect no morphological changes in crabgrass that are typical of domesticated cereals. The seeds are small and shatter; European peasants used to cut it "half-ripe" to harvest the seed. The African crops, fonio (*D. exilis*) and black fonio (*D. iburua*), are more or less non-shattering and the seeds are considerably larger than those of wild or weed races of the same species. In common crabgrass, cultivation did not lead to recognizable morphological changes, but it is possible that it led to more aggressive and competitive ecological races.

The most noxious and despised weeds vary from region to region and crop to crop. It seems safe to state that there is no crop that does not suffer some damage from competition with weedy plants, but weeds can occur in nonagricultural land as well. An example of an urban weed is *Ailanthus,* the tree of heaven. It has an astonishing affinity for brick and concrete and is often found growing in cracks in pavement or walls of buildings.

We pointed out in the last chapter that one man's weed is another man's crop and vice versa. Some crops undoubtedly originated from weed progenitors and some crops have degenerated into weed races. Many intermediate states exist. Plants drift in and out of cultivation, are domesticated, abandoned, ennobled, and may degenerate again; they escape, become naturalized, migrate, retreat, build hybrid swarms, and evolve new races. We shall examine a few cases of the genetic interaction between wild, weed, and cultivated races.

CROP-WEED COMPLEXES

The evolution of weeds often parallels the evolution of crops and the same principles apply to both. Both weeds and crops often begin with a common progenitor, as in those complexes where each crop has a companion weed. There are weed and cultivated races of einkorn, barley, sorghum, rice, oats, pearl millet, potato, tomato, pepper, sunflower, carrots, radish, lettuce, and many others. Perhaps most cultivated plants have one or more companion weed races. In some cases, the weed races can be easily distinguished from the wild forms; in others, it is extremely difficult.

The situation in sorghum is quite clear and it can be used as a general model for weed-crop complexes. Massive stands of truly wild races of sorghum can be found widely distributed over the savanna zones of Africa. They are often far removed from human disturbance, and represent truly wild grasses. The same materials can, however, be rather weedy when the habitat is disturbed. With the building of the Aswan Dam, it was necessary to move a rather large number of people out of the area to be flooded by Lake Nasser. People from Wadi Halfa in northern Sudan were moved to an area near Kassala, close to the Ethiopian border. This area was covered with vast stands of truly wild sorghums. The land was leveled, an irrigation project was established, ditches and drains were constructed, and soon irrigated farms covered many thousands of hectares of the Sudanese savanna. The wild sorghum has survived as a weed in the cotton and wheat fields and along the irrigation ditches of this project. There has been no evident genetic change in these populations, and morphologically the field weeds of the Kassala project are identical with the wild material nearby. The people from Wadi Halfa preferred to grow wheat rather than cultivated sorghum so that there has been little or no interaction between the wild sorghum and cultivated sorghum in that region. Although this race has done well as a weed, it is not so aggressive as to be very troublesome and stands on the project are not as dense as those in rangeland not far away.

In other parts of Africa, there is a conspicuous interaction between stands of wild sorghum and cultivated forms. The result is a race, often called shattercane, which is a very serious pest. This weed infests fields of cultivated plants on a massive scale and is extremely difficult to control. It is recognizable morphologically and easily distinguished from the wild races.

The fact that shattercane interacts with cultivated sorghum is clearly shown by the way it mimics the particular race of cultivated sorghum with which it is growing. Shattercane in Sudan and parts of Ethiopia where the durra race is the most common cultivated sorghum tends to have semicompact or even compact heads just like the cultivated kinds. The spikelets shatter and have a typical shattercane morphology. On the highlands of Ethiopia where the cultivated sorghum has a loose, open head, shattercane also has loose, open heads.

Wild sorghums shatter by means of a callus or abscission layer. In the course of domestication, callus formation was suppressed genetically. In most studies this suppression appeared to be controlled by a single recessive gene. Back-mutation is extremely rare, but an alternative shattering device has evolved. Some shattercanes disseminate seed by breakage of inflorescence branches just below the point where the callus would have formed. Thus, the shattered spikelet pair carries a short branch fragment attached. None of the shattercanes that we have been able to examine as escapes in the United States develop calluses. In Africa, where wild species are commonly available for hybrid formation, shattering by callus formation is the mode of dispersal. The branch fragment is an excellent marker to help identify secondarily derived weed races. The evidence is good that weed races can evolve from cultivated races as well as from wild X cultivated hybridizations and in sorghum the two kinds of weed races can be identified morphologically.

Thus, there are four clear-cut and morphologically recognizable categories for sorghum: 1) truly wild races that can tolerate considerable disturbance of the habitat and are mildly weedy, 2) shatter-canes that are derived from wild X cultivated crossing and are serious pests, 3) shattercanes that are derived secondarily from cultivated races and are also serious pests, and 4) semidomesticated to fully domesticated races that are grown under cultivation. The range of variation is not continuous, however. The shattercanes resemble domesticated races more closely than wild races.

We have found no way to prove it, but we suspect that the aggressiveness of johnsongrass in the United States is partly due to the infiltration of germplasm from cultivated sorghum. For one thing, we have not found the American type *Sorghum halepense* anywhere except in the United States. The Mediterranean and Asian races of the species are quite different and are relatively unaggressive. The Mediterranean race is a small, slender, spindly type that grows slowly and is not much of a weed problem. The Indian race (*miliaceum*) is very tall, but does not behave at all like johnsongrass nor does it look much like it. We suspect that wild races become better adapted to field conditions through hybridization with cultivated races. Since johnsongrass is a tetraploid, the genetic infiltration was probably almost all in one direction from cultivated race to weed race. Hybrids are not uncommon and a backcross to johnsongrass quickly suppresses characters of cultivated races. I did find, however, a colony of *S. halepense* in Mexico that shattered by branch breakages instead of by callus, suggesting it had cultivated sorghum in its background.

Extensive genetic interaction between wild, weed, and cultivated races can be demonstrated in African rice (*Oryza glaberrima*) in West Africa. The wild forms are easily distinguished from the weed races that infest the rice fields in that region. Today, most of the rice cultivated in West Africa is of the Asian kind (*O. sativa*) which has almost completely replaced the original native African rice. The African weed rice, however, has persisted better than the cultivated crop and is a serious pest in fields of Asian rice. In addition, the cultivated glaberrima rices were not all fully domesticated and some of them have escaped as weeds of rice fields as well. The populations that build up are sometimes extraordinarily complex.

In Asia, the races are not so clearly recognizable morphological-ly. Weed rices are serious pests of rice fields in India, Burma, and Indochina, and they hybridize a good deal with cultivated types. A number of studies have been made that show that shattering types frequently segregate for characters of cultivated rice (Ramiah and Ghose, 1951; Mitra and Ganguli, 1932; Ghose, Ghatge, and Subrah-manyan, 1956). The agronomic difficulties were described clearly by Bhalerao (1928):

> Due to natural crossing with "wild *Oryza sativa*," every cultivated variety has its own grain shedding type which cannot be dis-tinguished till the last stage of panicle development when all the grains on the panicle shed down in the field below.

In an attempt to solve the problem, some plant breeders de-veloped a series of purple-leaved cultivars so that the farmers could weed their fields before maturity. This seemed like a good idea, for all the cultivators had to do was pull out the green plants and leave the purple ones. In a few years, however, a purple-leaved weed race had evolved and the farmers were no better off than before.

In Near Eastern barley, some races can be identified as wild, but in other races wild and weed forms are confounded. There is a small wadi race that appears to be truly wild. Found in wadi bottoms from the Negev to Afghanistan (Harlan and Zohary, 1966), it is very small, slender, and grassy, and has small ears, small seeds, and short awns. It may often be found far removed from field agriculture. In more mesophytic races of barley, however, it is very difficult to distinguish the weed from the wild. Roadsides, edges of fields, and waste places are often very densely populated with weed barley. However, the same kind of barley may be found in fairly primary habitats and there seems to be no good way to separate them morphologically. The only difference in this case is in their habitats. They are considered spontaneous forms, which means that both wild and weed forms seed themselves without deliberate planting by man.

The genetic interactions among wild, weed, and cultivated races of barley are perhaps less common than those among rice in India, but hybrids and hybrid derivatives can be found. The most con-spicuous are those involving wild or weed two-rowed barley and six-rowed cultivars. Brittle six-rowed types are produced, but they are poorly adapted and soon disappear. More lasting effects of introgres-sion can be detected in seed colors, rough and smooth awns, etc.

Although the wild emmers of the Near East are not particularly weedy, they do come into contact with cultivated wheats sufficiently to cross occasionally. Genetic characteristics have been observed to move in both directions: from wild into cultivated and cultivated into wild (Zohary, 1971).

In the wheats of the Near East, crosses sometimes take place between forms of different ploidy levels. Hybrids between 2x and 4x, 2x and 6x, and 4x and 6x have been observed. The triploids and pentaploids are not always completely sterile and backcrosses can restore fertility through the function of unreduced eggs (Zohary, 1971). These crosses frequently involve weedy species of *Aegilops* and can result in substantial increases in variation.

The races of wild and weed maize have been studied in some detail (Wilkes, 1967). The Chalco race, considered a weed because it grows in cultivated fields only, is said to have more maize characteristics than other races. Races from the Rio Balsas watershed may thrive on steep slopes without cultivation and are considered to be closer morphologically to wild types. Some races from Guatemala are even more extreme in showing a wild-type morphology and an adaptation to less disturbed habitats.

SOME WEED ADAPTATIONS

An interesting adaptation syndrome is one in which the weed mimics the crop sufficiently well that the seed is harvested along with the crop and sown with it at the next planting season. *Camelina sativa*, subspecies *linicola*, is a well-known example; races have developed that resemble particular varieties of flax in stature, posture, and maturity as well as in seed size and weight. *Echinochloa crus-galli* var. *oryzicola* resembles the rice plant very closely throughout its development, from seedling to flowering time (Yabuno, 1961). This makes it very difficult for the cultivator to weed his rice fields in the early stages and at flowering time he is reluctant to walk through the rice fields to pull out the weed. Another example of a weed adaptation is a race of *Bromus secalinus* which retains its spike-like panicle intact at maturity, whereas most races of the species fragment and shatter their seeds. The nonshattering trait insures that the weed will be harvested with the cultivated rye with which it commonly grows.

A race of weed rye that is semibrittle has some seeds that shatter and fall to the ground infesting the soil; the remainder are nonshattering and are harvested along with the wheat crop. These are then planted with the wheat seed the following season. Ethiopian oats has already been described as a crop that originated by the same mechanisms. It seems evident that these adaptations evolved as a result of manipulation by man and are not characteristic of wild plants.

The weed floras of mine dumps have been analyzed in recent decades. Some dumps have such high concentrations of zinc, lead, copper, and other heavy metals that they are very toxic to most plant life, only the most metal-tolerant genotypes of the most tolerant species can grow in such habitats. Genetic studies have revealed striking differences in tolerance among genotypes of the same species. The distribution of tolerant genotypes corresponds to the decimeter with the distribution of toxic concentrations of the poisonous metals (Antonovics, 1971). Heavy applications of salt to streets and highways in wintertime have resulted in strong selection for salt-tolerant genotypes of roadside plants in some regions. Weeds have responded to selection pressures imposed by various other pollutants of the industrial age illustrating, again, that they tend to be genetically labile and capable of rapid evolution.

Most weeds are characterized by enormous phenotypic plasticity. Under favorable conditions a given genotype will be tall, robust, well developed, and highly productive. Under unfavorable conditions the same genotype may be minute and depauperate, live only a short time, and produce few seeds. In a paper entitled "The Weedishness of Wild Oats," H. V. Harlan (1929) described the remarkable behavior of a wild oat population in a barley nursery. The nursery contained winter forms which were still in winter rosettes while spring forms in the same field were tall and heading out, with some of the earliest varieties maturing. In the barley these differences in the growth habits were genetically controlled, but the wild oats with which the field was infested produced phenotypic mimics of all the growth habits. When grown with winter barley, the wild oats produced a low winter rosette; in adjacent rows of spring barley, the wild oats were tall and heading out. As the early barley was maturing, the wild oats were ripening. All stages could be seen on the same day. The capacity for phenotypic mimicry is presumably under genetic control and constitutes an excellent adaptive mechanism for weeds.

Of course, there are many species of weeds that are neither closely related to cultivated plants nor do they mimic them. In many weeds, prodigious numbers of seeds are produced and these have special adaptations that prevent them from germinating at the same time. The seeds are often small and capable of staying viable in the soil for long periods of time. This dormancy may be due to a variety of special adaptations and may be broken in various ways. Light-sensitive seeds buried during tillage may remain viable for a number of years; when the soil is turned again some are brought to the surface and sprout. Some seeds have a cold requirement, others have an inhibitor which breaks down in time or can be leached out, certain seeds are stimulated by specific chemicals, and some will not germinate except in the presence of certain other plants. At any rate, perhaps most annual weeds have an adaptation syndrome involving the production of enormous numbers of seeds with special mechanisms insuring that they will not all sprout at once.

Among perennials, most of the adaptations for weediness concern longevity. Some have rhizomes that not only store food reserves for regrowth but are easily distributed by tillage implements. Some have very deep taproots and many produce buds so deeply that they sprout from below the plow line. Other perennials are woody root-sprouters which are not killed by simply being cut down or burned. Some of the more objectionable weeds are protected by thorns, stinging hairs, or poisons in addition to being persistent. Whatever the adaptations may be, simple or elaborate, they tend to fit the weed to a particular niche of the human habitat, frequently with such success that they cost us dearly in control measures.

WEEDS AND HISTORY

Anderson's statement that the history of weeds is the history of man (quoted on p. 85) needs amplification. In his view, weeds follow man like fruit flies follow a ripe banana or a gourd of unpasteurized beer. Wherever man goes, he is surrounded by his weedy companions because he is a chronic disturber of habitats, and this was going on long before agriculture. If a family or band of hunter-gatherers lived in a cave or an open camp for any length of time, there would be the usual refuse heap, attrition of the local vegetation, and disturbance of the soil opening up a habitat for colonizers. In his dump-heap theory of domestication, Anderson visualized gatherers taking advantage of the dense and luxurious stands of weeds which had themselves taken advantage of the open habitats and enriched soil of the refuse heap (Anderson, 1954). It is a sort of ecological propinquity theory in which man and plants share the same habitats that man himself has created.

It is true that some crops have a dump-heap look about them: chenopods, amaranths, sunflowers, cucurbits of various sorts, etc. We find, in fact, some archaeological evidence that a complex of this sort was being either harvested or cultivated by eastern North American Indians well before the arrival of maize, beans, squash, and other elements of Mesoamerican agriculture (Fowler, 1971). On the other hand, swamp-dwelling plants such as taro (*Colocasia*), *Alocasia*, *Cyrtosperma*, *Trapa*, sago palm, and rice would appear to be poor candidates for such an origin. Wild wheat and wild sorghum occur in denser stands in near-climax formations than on dump heaps. The theory fits some species, but not others.

After agricultural systems had evolved, the role of weeds in human history became more conspicuous and easier to follow. Eloquent testimony is found in pollen profiles now being studied in many parts of the world. The pollen and spores of plants tend to be extremely durable and, under certain conditions, may be preserved as fossils in excellent condition for millions of years. The pollen grains are frequently recognizable morphologically and can be identified as to genus or, occasionally, to species. A good pollen profile yielding a chronological sequence of pollen populations can tell us a great deal about past changes in vegetation. The discipline of pollen studies is called palynology.

Perhaps the best sources of pollen profiles are sediments from lakes and swamps. Wind-borne pollen from the surrounding vegetation is shed and falls on the water year after year. Some of the pollen sinks to the bottom where oxygen content is low and biological activity suppressed. It usually settles along with the clay and silt that reach the lake from upstream, and once buried, may be preserved for long periods of geologic time. Special coring devices have been developed to sample sediments of this kind. Cores must be extracted with care and due precautions against contamination. Sometimes enough organic matter is encountered in a core profile that carbon-14 dates can be determined for various depths of sediment.

Pollen profiles also can be developed from soils, refuse heaps, and archaeological sites. In well aerated soil, however, preservation is not likely to be very good and the number of grains recovered may be small. At any rate, palynological studies have been giving us a good deal of information about changes in vegetation during the Pleistocene and on into the more recent past. A good deal depends upon the volume of studies, and evidence from one or two fragmentary profiles can be misleading.

Palynology is well developed in Europe, and a great deal of information on postglacial vegetation is available. Forests spread over the land as the glaciers retreated. A series of successional changes in the forest populations can be followed by the pollen sequences. Then, in scattered areas, the profiles show a sudden decrease of tree pollen and a dramatic increase in the pollen of field weeds. The Neolithic farmers had arrived and their companion weeds give us the news. The early farmers of Europe practiced some sort of shifting cultivation, opening up the forest with the aid of fire, and in soil profiles, there is sometimes evidence of much burning and alteration of the soil itself (Dimbleby, 1967).

Pollen profiles have helped trace the spread of agriculture in the Near East, eastern North America, and a few other parts of the world. Unfortunately, palynology as a science is not well developed in the tropics and our evidence from some of the most critical regions is meager and tenuous to say the least. Pollen cores from Taiwan suggest possible man-made disturbances of the forests as early as 10,000 B.C., but the evidence becomes more substantial at about 4,200 B.C. (Chang, 1970). Similar disturbances of forest vegetation in Uganda and Kenya are traceable to about 3,000 B.C. (Hamilton, 1972). As more palynological evidence accumulates we should be able to develop a much clearer picture of agricultural dispersals, and the information will be provided in good share by weedy plants.

On a more recent time-scale, the present distribution of weeds may tell us about human activities of the past. Yarnell (1965) reported on a study of plants that occur on or near Pueblo Indian ruins in New Mexico. Some species are common on the ruins, but they are infrequent, rare, or absent away from the site. Almost all of these plants are known to have been used by Indians for some purpose. A few were semicultivated food plants, but a number of them were medicinal or ritual plants, not normally cultivated but weedy enough to become established. Moseley (1930), Gilmore (1930), and others have pointed out cases in which the distribution of species can best be explained by their dispersal by American Indians.

Mayan Old Empire ruins can be spotted all over the Yucatan Peninsula by stands of ramón. The groves are locally called *ramonales,* and commonly include trees of mamey (*Calocarpum mammosum* (L.) Pierre), zapote (*Achras zapota* L.), guayo (*Talisia olivaeformis* (H.B.K.) Radlk.), aguacate, custard apple (*Annona reticulata* L.), and black zapote. Some of these are not found in the wild elsewhere in the region. To what extent these fruit trees were planted by the ancient Maya and to what extent the stands were built up by protection and encouragement, we do not know. In either case the groves were established artificially but have maintained themselves in some cases for a thousand years (Lundell, 1938).

Akihama and Watabe (1970) made a detailed study of the distribution of weed rice in Thailand. They concluded that weed rices were most abundant in regions where rice cultivation was very old. The densest populations seemed to be associated with ancient tanks and irrigation schemes. The weeds have a story to tell if only we knew enough to interpret the evidence properly.

Studies in the biosystematics of *Cynodon* led to an examination of historical dispersals. *C. incompletus* is a species endemic to South Africa, but turns up at wool-cleaning works in Bedfordshire, Worcestershire, and Yorkshire in England and Filburg and Graviers de la Vesdre in Belgium (cf. specimens at Kew). In fact, wool-cleaning stations have developed their own peculiar mini-floras, including plants associated with sheep-rearing from various parts of the world.

Common bermudagrass (*C. dactylon*) is widespread in the Old World, but has sorted out into geographical, ecological, and morphological races. Clones from central Europe, southern Europe, southeastern Europe, the Near East, Afghanistan, East Africa, South Africa, and the wet tropics are all different and most of them recognizable. Materials naturalized and escaped in the United States can often be traced with some assurance to their region of origin by appearance and growth habit (Harlan, 1970; Harlan and de Wet, 1969; Harlan, de Wet, and Rawal, 1970).

The earliest herbarium specimens and records in the United States are from a string of naval stations and ports along the East Coast. It had repeatedly been introduced with ship's ballast, and a good many other weeds found their way to our shores the same way. By the early 19th century, bermudagrass was being extolled for pasture and levee stabilization from Georgia to Mississippi (Spalding, 1844; Affleck, 1844; Moore, 1958). Others were beginning to curse it as "wiregrass" and "devilgrass."

Bermudagrass is one weed that seems to have made its way to practically every island, large or small, in the Pacific Ocean. All of the early specimens we have seen are of the small, turfy race from the tropics. Specimens collected from some of the larger islands during the last half century indicate a very different race, a diploid with very long, fast-growing stolons. It is native to the drier zones from South Africa northward through East Africa to Palestine and southeastward to India. In the city of Honolulu, the small tropical race is found throughout the older part of town. Along the new freeways and in the newly developed suburbs, the diploid race has taken over, and some of the residents have bermudagrass stolons overtopping hedges 2 m high.

Weeds and history are closely associated in the Pacific area. Weedy escapes can help us trace migrations of people at remote periods of time. The seedy fe'i bananas were introduced to Tahiti by Polynesians and became a naturalized element of the flora, and traces of ancient voyages can be detected throughout the Pacific (Barrau, 1963). The island of Guam has a large number of American weedy species that are attributed primarily to the Manila-Acapulco shipping that maintained a regularly scheduled route from 1565 to 1815; Guam was a refreshing station for ships sailing both directions. The land around Manila Bay also has a large number of weedy introductions from America (Merrill, 1922–26).

Sources of weeds can be traced if we know enough about them. Weeds do tell us something about where man has been and what he has done. Anderson was right; the history of weeds is the history of man, but it is an obscure history full of gaps and subject to misinterpretation because we have not taken the trouble to study the most common plants about us.

Weeds are not always passive companions of man; sometimes they alter the human situation. Alang-alang or cogongrass (*Imperata cylindrica*) is an aggressive rhizomatous grass of the Old World tropics. It becomes readily established in fields cleared from the forest. If the fields are cultivated too many seasons in succession, cogongrass may take over completely and make it very difficult to grow crops. Furthermore, the forest tree seedlings and root sprouts may be suppressed, making it almost impossible to employ the bush fallow of traditional shifting cultivation. Large areas of grassland, sometimes called cogonals, may develop in regions of forest climax. With traditional agricultural techniques the cogonals are virtually worthless and people may have to move their villages elsewhere. Forest succession may be very slow in cogonals even with abandonment. As a consequence, there is strong pressure to keep the cropping part of the cycle short in order to avoid cogonal development.

Aggressive, rhizomatous weeds have always caused serious problems in agriculture. Most of the worst ones are grasses and include: cogongrass, kikuyugrass, wild sugarcane (*Saccharum spontaneum*), the African perennial wild rice (*Oryza longistaminata*), johnsongrass, bermudagrass, and quackgrass (*Agropyron repens*). All of these have from time to time forced man to abandon his fields and give up the contest. On the other hand, all but cogongrass and the *Saccharum* can be useful and productive forage grasses.

Sometimes aggressiveness has its virtues. After the conquest of Peru, the Spaniards introduced European livestock which soon caused very severe problems of overgrazing. The South American grasses had not evolved under heavy grazing use and were easily obliterated. The denuded mountainsides suffered enormously from erosion and streams were clogged with sediments. In due time, bermudagrass and kikuyugrass found their way to Peru and have done great service in stabilizing slopes at lower and middle elevations.

The coast and foothill ranges of California provide a celebrated case in which the native grassland component of the flora has virtually been replaced or overwhelmed by an aggressive annual weed flora from the Mediterranean. The wild oats (*Avena barbata* and *A. fatua*), filarees (*Erodium*), mustards (*Brassica campestris, B. nigra, B. arvensis, Sisymbrium officinale, S. altissimum*), bur-clover (*Medicago hispida*), weed radish (*Raphanus sativus*), Klamath weed (*Hypericum perforatum*), white clover, sweet clover, chickweeds, and others are among the most common and conspicuous. It will be noted that most of them are related to cultivated species and several have domesticated races. The California climate is well suited to the production of annuals and the coast and foothill ranges are probably more productive on a sustained basis than they were before the weed flora was introduced.

SUMMARY AND CONCLUSIONS

Weeds are adapted to habitats disturbed by man. They may be useful in some respects and harmful in others. They may be useful to some people and hated and despised by others. There are weed races of most of our field crops and these interact genetically with cultivated races as well as truly wild races. This interaction probably results ultimately in better crops and more persistent weeds. Although some weeds have evolved elegant adaptations under the influence of man, many had weedy tendencies before man existed. Weeds are products of organic evolution; they exist in intermediate states and conditions. They are also genetically labile and phenotypically plastic. Weeds have been constant and intimate companions of man throughout his history and could tell us a lot more about man, where he has been and what he has done, if only we knew more about them.

Chapter 5

CLASSIFICATION OF CULTIVATED PLANTS

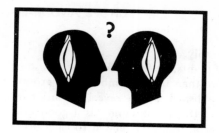

The primary purpose of classification is to reduce the number of items to manageable proportions. If there were only 100 plants on earth, we could assign a name, number, or other symbol to each and deal with them individually. Because there are millions on millions of plants of thousands upon thousands of different kinds, for convenience we group them so that we can deal with a reduced number of categories of plants. Obviously, it would do little good to group plants at random; if the reductional system is going to work, we must group like with like.

Botanists have generally neglected cultivated varieties as beneath their notice.

Darwin, 1897

The hardware merchant puts his bolts into separate bins. For the arrangement to be convenient, he must classify them. First he sorts out the major classes: stove bolts, machine bolts, carriage bolts, and so on. Each class is then divided by diameter and within each of these categories divided again by length. Ultimately, each bin contains items that are essentially identical. Plants are not so easy to sort, but the purpose and the method are about the same. The bins will not contain identical plants, but we would like them to contain individual plants that resemble each other more than they resemble individuals in other bins.

To classify like with like, we must have methods of description. We must decide which characters are useful in grouping plants and which characters are too inconsistent to be helpful. We must not only describe the individual to be classified, but the category to which it will be referred. Botanical description is basic to plant classification, but there is as much art as science to it. Taxonomists differ enormously in their ability to find suitable characters for groups and in their ability to describe simply, clearly, and unambiguously. The introduction of numerical taxonomy and computers has not improved the situation noticeably.

As we describe categories of plants, we inevitably find that some groups resemble each other more than they resemble other groups. Broad genetic affinities are established which reveal evolutionary history in a rather general way. If our taxonomy is a good one, plants assigned to one genus are more nearly related to each other than to plants assigned to another genus, and similarly for plants belonging to a family. No matter how the classification is arranged, however, we encounter intermediates that do not fit well into one group or another and we find anomolous groups that do not seem to belong to any group in particular.

Finally, classification provides an opportunity to give something a name. Names are very important, and most societies have naming ceremonies that are taken very seriously. A given name confers a very special identity upon a person or thing, and verifies its existence.

We found this to be true of plants as well. In studies of the bio-systematics of *Cynodon*, we found out very early that we had in our collection taxa that had not been named. We accumulated a great deal of information about geographic distribution, morphological variation, genetic affinity, chromosome pairing in hybrids, crossability, fertility, sterility, etc., but we could not publish any of it until the taxa were officially described. Botanically, these plants did not exist until names were given.

Classifications, then, lump individuals into groups so that we can deal with categories of plants instead of vast numbers of individuals. They reveal genetic affinity and evolutionary history, and they describe and give names to plants. Taxonomy is, pragmatically, a science of convenience. It makes it possible for man to deal rationally with the vast arrays of variation found in the natural world.

PROBLEMS OF FORMAL TAXONOMY

As Darwin pointed out (see p. 107), botanists have had little to do with classification of cultivated plants. This may not be so much because such plants are beneath their notice as because the traditional taxonomist is bewildered and confused by cultivated plants and doesn't know what to do with them. When botanists do try to classify cultivated plants, remarkably erratic results can be expected.

The inconsistencies and lack of agreement among taxonomists

dealing with the same materials are remarkable, to say the least, and are even more striking when the treatments of different crops are compared. Confusion and disagreement extend over the generic, specific, and infraspecific levels. For example, in the wheats, Percival (1921) listed 2 species, Bowden (1959) 3, and Jackubziner and Dorofeev (1968) 24, but all were classifying essentially the same materials. Snowden (1935) used 31 species of cultivated *Sorghum* alone, in addition to the wild and weedy ones that are fully compatible genetically with the domesticated sorts; Jakushevsky (1969) reduced these to 9 and de Wet and Huckabay (1967) to 1. Bukasov (1933) had well over 200 species in the Tuberarium section of *Solanum*; Hawkes (1963) reduced these to about half that many, yet retained 64 species in *Tuberosa* Rydb, in which the taxa can be intercrossed and in which there is very little genomic differentiation despite a fairly extensive polyploid series. Some taxonomists assign teosinte to the genus *Euchlaena*, some to *Zea,* and some to a race or subspecies of *Zea mays. Aegilops* is maintained as a genus by some and assigned to *Triticum* by others.

The number of examples of this kind can be multiplied many times. Faced with this sort of vacillation and indecision among taxonomists, the people who deal with cultivated plants the most, geneticists, agronomists, horticulturalists, and foresters, have developed their own informal and intuitive classifications, based on experience, as to what constitutes useful groupings. They will continue to use their own systems no matter what the taxonomist does or does not do. However, there is more involved here than the usual differences in judgment between "splitters" and "lumpers." First, cultivated plants *are* different from wild ones and require special taxonomic treatment; and second, there have been no guidelines for consistent groupings of related taxa according to the degree of relationship.

How do cultivated plants differ from wild species? Their variation patterns are different. Darwin (1859) opened his book on the origin of species with a discussion of these differences in both plants and animals. Broccoli, Brussel sprouts, cabbage, and cauliflower do not look much alike, but belong to the same species in a biological sense. They can be crossed readily and their hybrids are fertile. In appearance they are as different as collies, terriers, Great Danes, and chows, and these all belong to a single species as well. Darwin considered the enormous arrays of variation found among domestic breeds of cattle, horses, sheep, pigeons, and chickens, and among wheat, roses, peas, dahlias, iris, carrots, and so on. The morphological differences among genetically related breeds are simply of a different order of magnitude from those which are found in wild species.

The science of genetics was not developed in Darwin's time and he thought that variation was induced by changes in environment, but it is true that the conditions of domestication lead to a wider range of variation. Strange and bizarre forms that might appear in nature are usually promptly pruned out by natural selection, but in cultivated plants the strange and bizarre are likely to be precisely the ones to be selected and propagated. Most of our cultivars are biological "monsters" that could not survive in the wild but are cultivated by man because they please him in some way.

Furthermore, man has been very active in manipulating gene pools through repeated introductions or migrations followed by natural or artificial hybridization. The germplasm of domesticated plants has been repeatedly and periodically stirred (Harlan, 1969, 1970). The environment provided has been artificial, unstable, and often very extensive geographically. Selection pressures have been very strong but biologically capricious and often in diverse directions. The result is an enormous amount of conspicuous variation among very closely related forms.

Faced with this situation, the traditional taxonomist tends to overclassify. He finds conspicuous either/or characters often without intermediates and frequently bases species on them. These characters may be controlled by one or a few genes and have little biological significance. Too many species and too many genera are named and then, to accommodate the enormous variability remaining, unreasonable numbers of infraspecific classes may be established.

De Candolle (1867, 1883) recognized the situation rather clearly and objected strongly to the application of Latin names to "horticultural productions." It is a question of fundamental taxonomy: what are the most useful characters for the separation of groups? In cultivated plants, it is the plant breeders who will make the most use of classifications of their germplasm. The most useful characters will, therefore, be concerned with genetic compatibility; morphological features are useful, but secondary.

THE GENE POOL SYSTEM

To provide a genetic perspective and genetic focus for cultivated plants, Harlan and de Wet (1971) proposed three informal categories: 1) primary gene pool, 2) secondary gene pool, and 3) tertiary gene pool.

Primary gene pool (GP-1)—This corresponds to the traditional concept of the biological species. Among forms of this gene pool, crossing is easy, hybrids are generally fertile with good chromosome pairing, gene segregation is approximately normal, and gene transfer is generally simple. The biological species almost always includes spontaneous races (wild and/or weedy) as well as cultivated races. To make this clear they propose that the species be divided into two subspecies: 1) subspecies A, which includes the cultivated races, and 2) subspecies B, which includes the spontaneous races.

Secondary gene pool (GP-2)—This includes all biological species that will cross with the crop and approximates an experimentally defined coenospecies. Gene transfer is possible, but one must struggle with those barriers that separate biological species. Hybrids tend to be sterile, chromosomes pair poorly or not at all, some hybrids may be weak and difficult to bring to maturity, and recovery of desired types in advanced generations may be difficult. The gene pool is available to be utilized, however, if the plant breeder or geneticist is willing to put out the effort required.

Tertiary gene pool (GP-3)—At this level, crosses can be made with the crop, but the hybrids tend to be anomalous, lethal, or completely sterile. Gene transfer is either not possible with known techniques or else rather extreme or radical measures are required (e.g., embryo culture, grafting or tissue culture to obtain hybrids, doubling chromosome number, or using bridging species to obtain some fertility). The value of GP-3 is primarily informational; it defines the extreme outer limit of potential genetic reach. However, if a cross can be made at all, there is always a chance that some technique will be discovered that will make it possible to use germplasm in the tertiary gene pool. Since very few people have worked at this level, GP-3 is likely to be rather ill-defined, but will be better known as information accumulates.

Perhaps the most powerful tool now known for introducing genes from GP-3 into a crop is the use of complex hybrids. For example, Russian workers under Tsitsin (1962) tried for many years to cross *Elymus* with *Triticum*. After a great many failures they finally obtained a few sterile hybrids by embryo culture techniques (Ivanovskaya, 1946). Later they found that the use of an *Agropyron* X *Triticum* derivative as a female parent permitted a straightforward incorporation of *Elymus* germplasm without special techniques (Soulier, 1945), and similar results were obtained using amphiploid wheat X rye derivatives (Pissarev and Vinogradova, 1945). Hybrids between *Hordeum bulbosum* and *H. vulgare* at both the diploid and tetraploid levels are generally completely sterile, but Schooler (1967, 1968) was able to incorporate germplasm of *H. bulbosum* into *H. vulgare* and recover female fertility by way of a complex cross involving *H. jubatum* and *H. compressum* as well. De Wet et al. (1970), working with *Zea* and *Tripsacum*, were able to incorporate teosinte and *Tripsacum* for the first time only by way of maize X *Tripsacum* hybrids. Previously, Harlan and de Wet (1963) had had similar experiences in wide crosses in *Bothriochloa* and some of the widest crosses in sugarcane have involved complex hybrid materials (Price, 1957).

The secondary gene pool might outline groups that would be acceptable to some taxonomists as generic limits, but the tertiary gene pool may extend too far. Price (1957), after reviewing the wide crosses with sugarcane, remarked:

> The results from hybridizing *Saccharum* species and their allies can be regarded only as fragmentary. Yet they suggest that eventually it may be necessary to return certain species of *Erianthus, Narenga,* and *Sclerostachya* to *Saccharum.* On the other hand, despite the undoubted validity of sugarcane X *Sorghum* crosses and the possibility that hybrids from sugarcane X maize may yet be found genuine, one can scarcely imagine a genus which would include species presently assigned to *Saccharum, Sorghum,* and *Zea.*

Nor is a taxonomist likely to accept a genus including *Triticum, Aegilops, Secale, Haynaldia,* and only some species of *Agrypyron* and of *Elymus.*

Thus, GP-3 describes the extreme outer limit of the potential gene pool of a crop. It is not a taxonomic unit in the conventional sense and the terms primary, secondary, and tertiary gene pools are not proposed as formal taxonomic categories. They are simply guides for placing existing classifications into genetic perspective. The system is shown diagrammatically in Figure 1, with specific examples in Figures 2 to 5.

The figures help to standardize comparisons of different crops and their relatives and at the same time reveal contrasting gene pool structures. Wheat, for example, has a very large GP-2 (over 35 species) and a substantial GP-3, whereas barley has no GP-2 and a rather small GP-3. I have pointed out elsewhere (Harlan, 1966, 1970) that barley is a weakly-buffered, self-pollinated diploid and wide crosses with it are predictably far more difficult than those with a

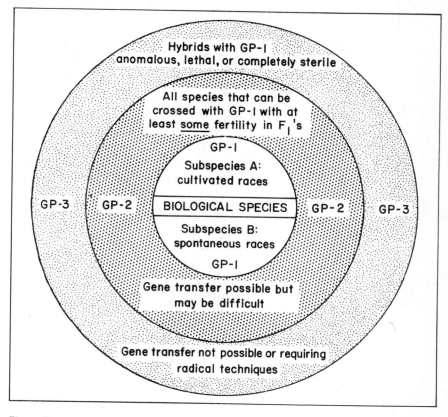

Figure 1
Schematic diagram of primary gene pool (GP-1), secondary gene pool (GP-2), and tertiary gene pool (GP-3) (from Harlan and De Wet, 1971).

highly-buffered polyploid such as wheat. Sorghum is not much different; it also has a very small GP-2. Rice has a substantial GP-2 but no GP-3, and the soybean *Glycine max* has neither a GP-2 nor a GP-3. Some knowledge of gene pool structure is useful to the plant breeder in indicating what species can be crossed and is at the same time important in the understanding of biological taxonomy.

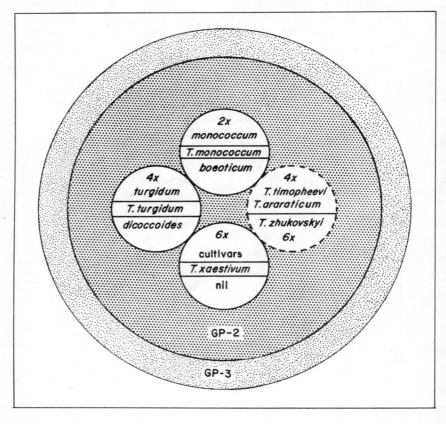

Figure 2
The gene pools of wheat. The secondary gene pool is very large and includes all species of *Aegilops, Secale,* and *Haynaldia,* plus at least *Agropyron elongatum, A. intermedium,* and *A. trichophorum.* The tertiary gene pool includes several species of *Agropyron,* several of *Elymus,* and even *Hordeum vulgare* (from Harlan and De Wet, 1971).

The problem of polyploidy must, of course, be dealt with. There may be no solution that would apply to all crops, but as a general guideline it was proposed that separate gene pools be recognized for different ploidy levels. This would not apply to artificial or induced polyploids; for example, tetraploid barley and tetraploid maize would be included in the diploid gene pools for barley and maize. On the other hand, *Sorghum halepense* would be separated from *S. bicolor*. In wheat, three cultivated gene pools are recognized (Figure 2), representing three ploidy levels. These are separated from the *Triticum timopheevi-T. araraticum* group on the basis of chromosome pairing and sterility barriers. The genetic barriers due to polyploidy are not always strong and gene transfer across ploidy levels may be rather easy. The barriers are there, however, and it is generally useful to indicate their presence by providing separate epithets. For certain crops, like potato and sugarcane, this may not be appropriate and each crop must be treated as a separate case.

Formal taxonomy has failed most conspicuously at the infraspecific level in cultivated plants. Many systems have been proposed and there is little agreement among specialists. There is a strong tendency to overclassify and give formal categories to groups of cultivars that have little or no genetic integrity. In the proposal of Harlan and de Wet, the biological species (GP-1) would first be partitioned into two subspecies, one containing the cultivars, the other including the spontaneous forms. At this point it is recommended that all formal taxonomy be abandoned in order to permit the use of the informal systems used by those who work with cultivated plants professionally. The term "varietas" would be avoided as a botanical term because it is too easily confused with agronomic and horticultural varieties (cultivars) and is not especially appropriate for cultivated plants in any case. The infraspecific categories proposed are:

Species

      1) Subspecies A. The cultivated races
        2) Race
          3) Subrace
            4) Cultivar
              5) Line, clone, genotype
      1) Subspecies B. The spontaneous races
        2) Race
          3) Subrace

A classification of cultivated plants does not require more divisions than this. A reasonable amount of variation must be allowed for both race and subrace, but more infraspecific categories tend to destroy the purpose of classification.

Race—In the classification proposed, it is necessary to have some understanding of what constitutes a race. A race not only has a recognizable morphological identity but is a biological unit with some genetic integrity. A race originated in some geographic region at some time in the history of the crop. As a biological unit it is not as clearly separable as species but has a distinct cohesion of morphology, geographical distribution, ecological adaptation, and frequently breeding behavior.

It is understood, of course, that racial differentiation is not always clear-cut. There are ill-defined races, hybrid races, races in the process of formation, and complex races made up of derivatives of two or more races. This is the very reason that formal categories have failed and why informal systems based on the experience of plant breeders are to be preferred. Ultimately, a race becomes simply a useful group of cultivars, but the group is most useful when it has a biological basis.

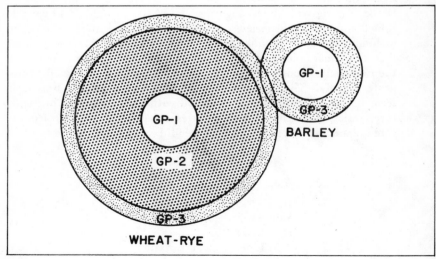

Figure 3
The gene pools of wheat-rye and barley overlap at the tertiary level. Barley has no secondary gene pool, while that of wheat contains 35 species or more (from Harlan and De Wet, 1971).

One may also express the presumptive derivations of groups by very simple combinations of the basic elements of variation. As an example, Harlan and de Wet (1972) classified the cultivated sorghums into five basic races: bicolor, guinea, caudatum, kafir, and durra. There are, however, clearly identifiable, intermediate races involving all combinations of these basic races: kafir-caudatum, most modern American grain sorghums; durra-caudatum, the kauras of Nigeria and similar subraces; guinea-kafir, the common shallu sorghum of India; guinea-caudatum, common in Nigeria, Chad, Sudan; etc. The hyphenated names imply exactly what the races appear to be on a morphological and distributional basis and thus provide useful information.

Subrace—The subrace is simply a convenient division of a race. It must be reasonably recognizable to be convenient and it may or may not be appropriate to divide a race into subraces. In most cul-

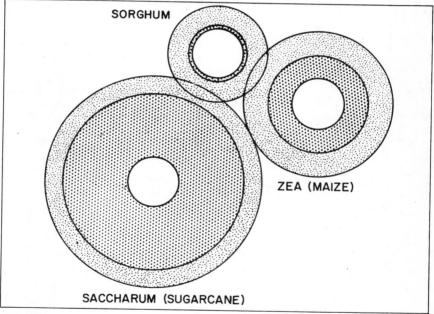

Figure 4
The relationship of three important cultivated plants of the Tribe Andropogonae. Sorghum has a very small secondary gene pool (one species). Maize has a somewhat larger one, while sugarcane has a secondary gene pool containing at least seven species. The gene pools overlap at the tertiary level (from Harlan and De Wet, 1971).

tivated plants there is such a continuous range of variation from sub-race to subrace and sometimes from race to race that there is no use-ful purpose to be served by very fine divisions in the classification.

It must be emphasized that races and subraces are not intended to be formal categories and they are not to be italicized. Racial classi-fications should be flexible and subject to change as more experience becomes available, and it is recommended that rigid rules for their ap-plication be avoided. Indeed the entire system of Harlan and de Wet is without formal terminology in the usual sense. Partitions of the gene pool are designed to give consistency to classifications already available and suggestions for infraspecific categories are designed to permit use of the informal systems that have been found by experi-ence to be useful.

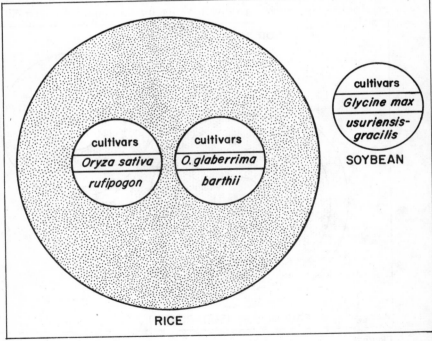

Figure 5
Gene pools of rice and soybean. We have shown the two rice domesticates with separate primary gene pools. The secondary gene pool contains the species of the section *Euoryza*, but we do not know of a tertiary gene pool. The soybean has neither a tertiary nor even a secondary gene pool (from Harlan and De Wet, 1971).

Table 1
Primary and secondary gene pools of the major cereals.

| Crop | Ploidy level | Primary gene pool, GP-1 | | | Secondary gene pool, GP-2 |
| | | Cultivated subspecies | Spontaneous subspecies | | |
			Wild races	Weed races	
Wheats					
Einkorn	2x	*Triticum monococcum*	*T. boeoticum*	*T. boeoticum*	*Triticum, Secale, Aegilops*
Emmer	4x	*T. dicoccum*	*T. dicoccoides*	None	*Triticum, Secale, Aegilops*
Timopheevi	4x	*T. timopheevi*	*T. araraticum*	*T. timopheevi*	*Triticum, Secale, Aegilops*
Bread	6x	*T. X aestivum*	None	None	*Triticum, Secale, Aegilops*
Rye	2x	*Secale cereale*	*S. cereale*	*S. cereale*	*Triticum, Secale, Aegilops*
Barley	2x	*Hordeum vulgare*	*H. spontaneum*	*H. spontaneum*	None
Oats					
Sand	2x	*Avena strigosa*	*A. hirtula; A. wiestii*	*A. strigosa*	*Avena* spp.
Ethiopian	4x	*A. abyssinica A. vaviloviana*	*A. barbata*	*A. barbata*	*Avena* spp.
Cereal	6x	*A. sativa*	*A. sterilis*	*A. sterilis A. fatua*	*Avena* spp.
Rices					
Asian	2x	*Oryza sativa*	*O. rufipogon*	*O. rufipogon*	*Oryza* spp.
African	2x	*O. glaberrima*	*O. barthii*	*O. stapfii*	*Oryza* spp.
Sorghum	2x	*Sorghum bicolor*	*S. bicolor*	*S. bicolor*	*S. halepense*
Pearl millet	2x	*Pennisetum americanum*	*P. violaceum*	*P. americanum*	*P. purpureum*
Maize	2x	*Zea mays*	*Z. mexicana*	*Z. mexicana*	*Tripsacum* spp., *Z. perennis*

An example of how the gene pool system works is given in Table 1. The more commonly used epithets are arranged under primary and secondary gene pools for the more important cereals. An example of infraspecific classification would look like this:

Species: *Sorghum bicolor*

Subspecies: *S. bicolor* ssp. *bicolor*
Race: guinea
Subrace: guineense
Cultivar: Sabba Bibi
Line: a selection from the cultivar
Genotype: an individual plant or homozygous line selected from the cultivar
Clone: an individual plant selected from the cultivar and propagated asexually by cuttings, tissue culture, apomixis, etc.

Evolutionary implications

The system permits us to compare different crops, on a more or less genetically equivalent basis. When this is done, it becomes apparent that most crop evolution takes place within the primary gene pool. Domestication very seldom leads to speciation despite the many classifications that provide separate epithets for domesticates. Genetically, domesticated races belong to the same biological species as their wild progenitors and are fully compatible with them when hybridized. There are very few crops for which wild races have not yet been identified and most of these have been little studied.

Among the cereals, the only exception is hexaploid bread wheat, which is not known in the wild. This gene pool apparently arose after domestication of tetraploid wheat through the addition of the D genome of *Aegilops squarrosa*. It is one of the very few demonstrable cases of a new gene pool being generated under domestication. The cultivated sweet potato is also a hexaploid and may have had a similar origin, but we know much less about it. Various degrees of genomic modification have taken place in other polyploids, such as potato and sugarcane. Nevertheless, with very few exceptions, crop evolution has operated at the infraspecific level.

We know that polyploidy is a form of quantum evolution in that it takes only one or two generations to pass from one ploidy level to another. In the absence of polyploidy, evolution is much slower, and it appears that the processes of domestication have not been operating long enough to bring about speciation. According to our archaeological information we are dealing with between 10,000 and 12,000 generations for our older annual crops and much fewer for perennials. Either this is not enough to establish substantial genetic barriers or the sporadic crossing between wild and cultivated races has prevented establishment of separate gene pools. The morphological modifications in this period of time, however, have sometimes been spectacular.

To be sure, there are some cases of ignorance on our part. We do not know for certain the progenitors of sesame, guar, or the sweet potato, and the status of wild bottle gourds is presently uncertain. No doubt there are others of which we are ignorant, but the number of such crops is small and getting smaller as we study crop evolution more intensively.

On the other hand, we know much less about the role of secondary gene pools in crop evolution. There are reasons to suspect that *Aegilops, Secale, Agropyron,* and *Haynaldia* have contributed something to wheat, that *Oryza longistaminata* has contributed something to African rice and even to Asian rice in Africa (Chu and Oka, 1970), and that *Saccharum spontaneum* has introgressed into sugarcane. It has repeatedly been suggested, but not proven, that *Tripsacum* has contributed to maize evolution. These interactions can be produced artificially, but it is much more difficult to establish their genetic contributions under natural conditions. This is an area in urgent need of serious research.

Whatever infusions of germplasm may have taken place from the secondary gene pool into the primary gene pool, they are of such a nature that new gene pools are seldom formed. Wild and cultivated emmers are fully compatible, as are wild and cultivated rices and teosinte and cultivated maize. From experience with several hundred crop species, it seems that primary gene pools have not been disrupted by whatever contributions might have come from secondary gene pools.

Chapter 6

THE DYNAMICS OF
DOMESTICATION

DOMESTICATION OF SEED CROPS

Cereals

The Greek philosophers were fascinated by the problem of change. How could a thing become something other than what it is—unless it was secretly the other thing all the time? Heraclitus, a philosopher from Ephesus, thought that everything in the universe was in a constant state of flux and that the only way stability could be achieved would be through a balance of opposing forces. This is fundamentally an evolutionary dynamic. In a variable genetic field, populations may become stable only through centripetal selection pressures. If pressures change one way or another, the populations will change accordingly.

Domestication is an evolutionary process operating under the influence of human activities. Since it is evolutionary, we would expect a relatively slow and gradual progression from the wild state to a state of incipient domestication to forms that differ more and more from the progenitors. We would also expect that it would be difficult to separate initial steps in domestication from truly wild or weedy forms, and that it would be impossible to predict how far the process might extend into the future.

We visualize the domestication of cereals as beginning with the harvest of wild grass seeds. We have seen that this was common and widespread among gathering peoples. As long as human activity is confined to harvesting, any genetic effect on wild populations is likely to be negligible. It is the seeds that escape the harvester that produce the next generation, and if there is any selection pressure at all it would be in favor of such wild-type characters as shattering, indeterminate growth with maturation over a long period of time, seed

125

dormancy, etc. As soon as man starts to plant what he has harvested, the situation changes drastically.

Now there are two populations, one spontaneous, the other being harvested and planted, and the selection pressures are in opposite directions. The seeds that are *harvested* are those that contribute to the sown population, and any modification that would enhance seed recovery and competition in the new environment would be selected favorably. Automatic selection for interrelated syndromes of characteristics is set up immediately (Table 1).

Selection associated with harvesting

Of all the adaptations that separate wild from cultivated cereals, the nonshattering trait of cultivated races is the most conspicuous. It is taxonomically the most diagnostic in separating domestic subspecies from spontaneous subspecies and is crucial in establishing the disruptive selection that effectively maintains separation of the two kinds of populations. Most of the seeds that do not shatter are harvested; most of the seeds that shatter escape the harvest.

In most of the major cereals, it seems that shattering is under relatively simple one- or two-gene control. Appearances may be somewhat deceiving. Intermediate semishattering forms are known in all cases but are relatively uncommon. Such a condition is not well adapted to either cultivation or spontaneous conditions. Strong disruptive selection for either one state or the other will produce at least the appearance of simple either-or inheritance. As far as domestication is concerned, however, the establishment of nonshattering traits is genetically one of the easiest and simplest steps in the entire process.

There are cases, however, where semishattering may have some advantage. We have already mentioned the semishattering Ethiopian weed oats and weed rye, where some of the seed falls and infests the ground and the rest is harvested and planted with the crop it infests. The nonshattering races of Ethiopian oats, *Camelina sativa*, and *Bromus secalinus* have also been mentioned as weeds which are adapted to being harvested and planted along with their companion crops even though the farmer may not want them. Such examples seem to indicate that nonshattering is a trait that automatically shows up in seed crops without intentional selection.

Wilke et al. (1972) have suggested that the tough rachis charac-

Table 1
Adaptation syndromes resulting from automatic selection
due to planting harvested seed of cereals (adapted from
Harlan, de Wet, and Price, 1973).

I. Selection pressures associated with harvesting result in:
    A.   Increase in percent seed recovered
        Adaptations: (1) *Nonshattering*
                     (2) *More determinate growth*
                         (a) Growth Habit I: Cereals whose wild races have lateral seed-bearing branches, e.g. maize, coix, sorghum, pearl millet. There is a trend toward apical dominance resulting in *fewer inflorescences, larger inflorescences, larger seed, greater daylength sensitivity,* and *more uniform ripening.*
                         (b) Growth Habit II: Cereals with unbranched culms e.g. barley, emmer, rye, einkorn, rice. There is a trend toward more *synchronous tillering* and *uniform whole plant maturation.*
    B.   Increase in seed production
        Adaptations: (1) *Increase in percent seed set.*
                     (2) *Reduced or sterile flowers become fertile.*
                     (3) *Increase in inflorescence size,* especially in maize, sorghum, pearl millet.
                     (4) *Increase in number of inflorescences* especially wheat, barley, rice, etc.
II. Selection pressures associated with seedling competition result in:
    A.   Increase in seedling vigor
        Adaptations: (1) *Greater seed size*
                     (2) *Lower protein, higher carbohydrate*
    B.   More rapid germination
        Adaptations: (1) *Loss or reduction of germination inhibitors*
                     (2) *Reduction in glumes and other appendages*
III. Selection pressures associated with tillage and other disturbances result in the production of weed races
        Adaptations: (1) Plants competitive with cultivated races, but
                     (2) Retain the shatter habit of wild races.

---

ter might not show up if the North American Indian method of harvesting was used. North American Indians harvested most herbaceous seeds by beating them into a basket with a paddle. This is a radically different treatment from that of cutting with a sickle or stone knife as was done in the Near East, North Africa, and Australia. If the seed is knocked into a basket, the fragile spike would be an advantage instead of a disadvantage. This may explain why few cereals were domesticated in the Americas even though many grasses were harvested and some were planted (Chapter 1).

The well-known "sunflower effect" applies to cereals with lateral seed-bearing branches, such as maize, sorghum, and pearl millet. Wild and weedy sunflowers have many branches bearing a large number of small heads. The ultimate of domesticated types are the mammoth "Russian" cultivars which have single unbranched stalks bearing enormous single terminal heads. Maize has followed the same path. Spontaneous maize (teosinte) has a branching system in the axils of several leaves on each stem and each branching system includes several small two-ranked fragile ears, each enclosed in a husk. Early maize, which is well represented in archaeological sites from the southwestern United States to southern Mexico, apparently had clusters of very small, four-ranked (i.e. eight-rowed), mostly non-fragile ears in the axils of several leaves of each stem. From this condition there was a gradual progressive evolution to fewer and larger ears at a node until the achievement of modern high-yielding Corn Belt cultivars which usually have one ear at a node and average less than two ears per stem.

Evolutionary changes in sorghum and pearl millet are very similar. Wild sorghum tillers well and although seed heads are terminal, the stems are often branched. The most derived of the modern sorghums are likely to have a single stem with a large terminal head. The contrast between the open, lacy panicle of wild sorghum and the heavy, compact, high-yielding heads of modern cultivars is striking. The evolution of pearl millet heads from the numerous, small (1 dm or less) heads of *Pennisetum violaceum* to the most-derived cultivars (over 2 m in length in some cases) is nothing short of spectacular. The process, however, is the same in all these cereals.

The trend from many small inflorescences to a few or a single large inflorescence is usually accompanied by an increase in seed size. There are other selection pressures that favor large seeds, but a part of the increase may come automatically with the increase in size of the inflorescence. The end product of the trend is a monstrous structure completely unadapted for survival in the wild. The head of a commercial cultivar of sunflower, an ear of maize, or a head of modern grain sorghum or grain-type pearl millet are each amazingly different from their wild progenitor forms, yet the evolutionary pathway is essentially the same in all.

Maturity is often closely controlled by daylength sensitivity. Tropical cereals like rice, sorghum, and maize are often extremely sensitive because of strong selection pressures to mature at the end of the rainy season. When these crops are moved into more temperate regions, adaptation involves a decrease in sensitivity to short days. Maturation over a long period of time has a selective value for wild plants but is detrimental to cultivated races. The disruptive selection for this trait reinforces that established by the shattering versus non-shattering characteristics.

The small grains all have terminal inflorescences, and there is no sunflower effect. An increase in uniformity of maturation is obtained by tillering over a short period of time. The life cycle of cultivars is more rigidly controlled over time than that of wild races. At a given stage, tillering essentially ceases and there is a tendency for the whole plant to mature at once. This response may also be strongly conditioned by daylength sensitivity but tillering in wheat, barley, rye, and oats is strongly influenced by temperature as well as moisture, soil fertility, and daylength. Whatever the mechanisms involved, selection pressures are strong in the direction of uniform maturity and maximum seed recovery at harvest.

Perennial wild grasses are notoriously poor or erratic seed setters. For them, survival does not depend upon annual seed production and a full set of seed is an uncommon event. Wild annual grasses, however, set seed much better and would not survive without rather abundant yearly seed production. This phenomenon has only peripheral interest to the cereals under consideration. Only rice and rye might have come from perennial progenitors. In Africa, it is very clear that African rice was domesticated from the wild annual species *Oryza barthii*. In Asia, the picture is not as clear. *Oryza rufipogon* has both annual and perennial races and the origin of Asian rice may be more complex. I suggest that it is most likely that the domesticated strains were selected primarily from the annual races, but the evidence at present is tenuous.

A perennial progenitor has been claimed for rye. If this is true, then a considerable improvement in seed set has occurred in the course of domestication. Again, it is more likely, for this and other reasons, that cultivated rye was selected out of a weed rye which in turn was derived from a wild annual progenitor, all in the species *Secale cereale*.

In the course of evolution in the Gramineae it is not uncommon for florets of a spikelet to become sterile and/or reduced and for spikelets to become male, neuter, reduced, or entirely suppressed. Such reduction series are to be found in most of the tribes of the family. It is not uncommon under domestication for that which has been suppressed to be restored.

In *Hordeum* there are three spikelets at a node, the central one fertile, the lateral ones male or neuter. Throughout the entire genus, the wild barleys are two-rowed. In the cultivated six-rowed barley, the sterile lateral spikelets are fertile. The change is rather simple genetically in that a single recessive mutation is adequate to transform a two-rowed barley into a six-rowed one. There are at least two loci involved with an allelic series at each controlling various intermediate forms (Harlan, 1968).

In sorghum, there are cultivars with two seeds per spikelet. A suppressed floret has become fertile. These twin-seeded lines are seldom very productive and have not attracted much attention. The inheritance of the character appears to be controlled by a single dominant gene.

In wheat, the number of fertile florets varies greatly and is to a considerable extent under genetic control. Some genes cause the lower florets to become sterile and the upper ones fertile; other genes reverse the arrangement. Of particular interest is the fact that even the lower glumes that are "always" sterile can be made to bear seeds under certain genetic circumstances. Four doses of the Q gene are required, but it is evident that organs once suppressed can be restored upon genetic command (Wright, 1958; Frankel, Shineburg, and Munday, 1969).

In wild maize (teosinte) spikelets are borne in pairs, one pedicellate, the other sessile. In the male inflorescence both spikelets produce anthers; in the female inflorescence the pedicellate spikelet is suppressed. An early step in maize evolution was the restoration of the pedicellate spikelet to fertility, making four rows of a two-ranked ear and eight rows of a four-ranked ear. Inheritance of this character is said to be under single gene control (Collins, 1919; Rogers, 1950; Langham, 1940), but some stocks give ambiguous ratios and the matter needs further study. Paired fertile spikelets are independent of rank number. In addition, the female spikelets of the American Maydeae have two florets, the lower one reduced to small scales and the upper one fertile. In a few races of maize, the sterile floret is restored to fertility and each spikelet has two seeds. The cultivar 'Country Gentleman' is a familiar example.

Increase in size of the head or ear is closely related to the reduction in number of inflorescences, but selection in this direction is reinforced by selection for increased seed production. The plant that contributes the most seed to a harvest is likely to contribute more offspring to the next generation. Selection is automatic in this respect, but is likely to be still further reinforced by human selection for apparent yield. All of these selection pressures go in the same direction and away from wild-type progenitors. Maize, sorghum, and pearl millet are more affected than the other cereals concerned.

In wheat, barley, rye, oats, and rice, increased yield is achieved through an increase in tillering. Head size may also increase under selection pressure for greater seed production, but not as spectacularly as in maize, sorghum, and pearl millet.

Selection associated with seedling competition

The cultivated field is a very different environment from a wild habitat. The seedbed is favorable for germination and competition with other species is reduced. The competition between seedlings of the same species, however, can become extremely intense. The first seeds to sprout and the most vigorous seedlings are more likely to contribute to the next generation than the slow or weak seedlings. Within species, large seeds have more vigorous seedlings than small seeds (Kneebone and Cremer, 1955).

Selection for highly competitive seedlings results automatically in selection for larger seeds, but the plant that produces the greatest number of seeds also has an advantage and this factor may not be compatible with the production of large seeds. Eventually, a balance is reached in which selection is continuous for a large number of seeds yielding competitive seedlings. This balance can be easily changed by human activities. Deep planting, for example, may result in strong selection pressure for large seeds, while shallow planting may have little effect. Great variation in seed size may, therefore, be expected in cultivated cereals, but the seeds are usually (not always) larger than those of the wild races.

A trend toward lower protein and higher carbohydrate content of cereals is automatic in that most of the increase in seed size is due to an increase in endosperm. The embryo is richer in protein and oil, but does not increase in the same proportion as the endosperm. This type of selection results in increased seedling vigor.

Most wild grasses have some sort of seed dormancy, which breaks down with time. The dormancy prevents premature germination and, when it lasts for several years, helps to maintain a seed supply in the soil. There is an obvious selective advantage for this adaptation in wild plants. Wild oats, einkorn, and emmer in the Near East have an elegant adaptation to the erratic rainfall of the region. In all three wild grasses, there are two seeds in each spikelet, one without appreciable dormancy and the other sufficiently dormant that it will not normally sprout for a year or more after shedding. The nondormant seed of the pair is usually about twice as large as the dormant one. The nondormant seeds germinate with the first rains in the fall and must compete with dense populations of other annual plants. Large seed has a selective advantage under these conditions and some races of wild barley, emmer, and oats have seeds larger than some cultivated races. If the rains fail after this first emergence and the plants die without producing seed, there is still a reserve of dormant seeds which can sprout the following year.

While dormancy has adaptive value for wild and weed races, it is nonadaptive in cultivated races unless it is of short duration. Some cultivars lose dormancy altogether, but in regions where rainfall at harvest time is likely, seeds may sprout in the ear and so be lost. A dormancy that breaks down between harvest and planting time may have selective value under some conditions. Automatic selection pressures are very strong for seeds that come up when planted; therefore, dormancy is much reduced in cultivated races.

Man has, no doubt, selected intensively for less chaff, but there are certain automatic selection pressures set up in the same direction. Dormancy is often controlled by inhibitors in the enclosing glumes, lemmas, and paleas. Selection for reduced dormancy may act to reduce these structures. An increase in seed size also has the feature of reducing the relative amount of chaff in the material harvested. The various selection pressures are all interlocking and tending in the same directions.

Selection associated with crop-weed interaction

When man tills the soil and prepares a seedbed for his crops, he also provides an environment favorable for wild species with adaptations that can take advantage of the new situation. The cereals have responded with weed races adapted to the conditions of cultivation. The morphology and adaptations of the weed races are generally intermediate between the wild and cultivated races. The weeds are adapted to disturbed environments, but retain the shattering habit and, frequently, the dormancy and seed appendages of the wild races.

There is good evidence that the companion weeds of cultivated plants have played important roles in crop evolution. Wherever the crop and weed occur together on a massive scale, hybrid swarms and evidence of introgression can be found by diligent search. The barriers to gene flow are always rather strong, and hybridization does not occur on a massive scale. One population is not going to be swallowed up by the other. Instead, we have two separate populations growing side by side and maintaining their own heredities, but occasionally and locally they do cross and germplasm is exchanged. A differentiation-hybridization cycle is set up and potential variability is released.

In crosses between wild and tame races of cereals, either morphological type can be quickly recovered in backcrosses. The small, two-ranked, fragile ear of wild maize is strikingly different in appearance from the large, multirowed, nonfragile ear of cultivated maize, yet both morphological types can be recovered in a single F_2 population (Beadle and Galinat, unpublished data; Galinat, 1971): either only a few genes are involved or the genes that are involved are tightly linked on only a few chromosomes. Similar crosses in other cereals give about the same results, which is expected considering the observed interaction between spontaneous and cultivated races in the field.

Although gene flow can be easily detected as we have shown by the mimicry of weed races and the infusion of cultivated traits into them, intermediate morphologies are rare. Fragile six-rowed barleys are encountered as a by-product of spontaneous X cultivated crosses in the Near East (Zohary, 1959, 1963, 1971), but are nonadapted and quickly disappear from hybrid swarm populations. I have collected both shattering caudatums and shattering guinea sorghums in Africa, but plants of this morphology are rare and probably ephemeral as well. Even in interbreeding populations, the morphologies are either spontaneous or cultivated.

The system is a remarkably elegant evolutionary adaptation. Too much crossing would degrade the crop, and the weed and cultivated races would merge into one population, possibly resulting in abandonment of the crop. Too little crossing would be ineffective. The barriers to gene flow must be strong but incomplete for the system to work, and the fact that crop-weed pairs have evolved in so many crops is an indication that natural selection has operated to adjust the amount and frequency of hybridization to a range somewhere near the optimum evolutionary efficiency.

Differentiation hybridization cycles

Cultivated plants have the capacity to evolve rapidly. Rapid bursts of evolution are possible only through some variation on the theme of the differentiation-hybridization cycle in which variability already accumulated can be exploited. The ultimate source of variability may be mutation but it must operate in many populations over a long period of time in order to accumulate sufficient diversity for great change in a short period of time.

The crop-weed interaction is only one system by which differentiation-hybridization cycles can be set up in cultivated plants. Another is more or less automatically built into the traditional agricultural system. Farmers are basically sedentary. They settle down in an area and occupy it for long periods of time. This results in an array of varieties adapted to that particular area. Occasionally, farmers move, taking their seed stocks or other planting materials with them. In the new location there is an opportunity for the transported varieties to cross with the local sorts. Populations separated geographically and differentiated ecologically are thus brought together, crosses occur, and a cycle is completed. The past movement of certain races of maize can be traced today from Mexico to South America, where the races were modified by introgression with South American races; then this material returned at a later date to Mexico where it introgressed anew with Mexican races (Wellhausen et al., 1952). An analysis of the great diversity in Turkish popcorns by Anderson and Brown (1953) indicated that the irruption of variability could be traced to two different races introduced into Turkey by different routes. The same authors have presented evidence to the effect that Corn Belt maize is derived from the interaction of northern flints and southern dents brought together unintentionally by white settlers moving into the Corn Belt. The migration of identifiable races of American cottons and their periodic introgression have been documented by Hutchinson (1959).

Patterns of this nature can be traced in a number of crops. Populations of cultivated plants are far more mobile than populations of wild species because they are transported by man and go with him on his wanderings over the face of the earth. This can readily result in the separation of plant populations by geographic isolation and the breakdown of isolation by bringing populations together again. There can be little doubt that these movements and migrations have profoundly affected the evolution of cultivated plants by exposing populations to infusions of germplasm from other domesticated races as well as from various wild relatives of the crop.

Cycles may also be set up by cultural practices. In many parts of West Africa, sorghum is transplanted like rice in Asia. Seedlings are grown in a sandy seedbed, pulled up by the roots, and planted in deep dibble holes in the field. This is done as waters recede after the annual flood of a river or as wet areas dry up at the end of the rains. These cultivars must mature seed on residual moisture only and must be ephemeral, short-season types. The same cultivator may grow full-season types during the rainy season. The transplant race may mature in 90 days; the rainfed one may take 180 days. Such practices set up separate populations that have little chance of interacting with each other; one population matures while the other is in the seedling stage.

The most common rainfed race is guinea and the most common transplant race is durra. We have, however, detected some guinea-durra interaction (Harlan and Stemler, in press). This can come about by late summer or fall planting of a mixture of the two races when the shortening days may bring them into bloom together. Mixtures of this kind may occur through careless handling by the cultivator, but are more likely through seed purchase at the local market.

Thus, populations are fragmented by human activity and often kept apart by agricultural practice. Such barriers leak, and differentiation-hybridization cycles are set up that enhance variability and broaden the base for plant selection.

For differentiation to take place, populations must be fragmented in some way and kept apart genetically. Several isolating mechanisms among cereals are well known: geographic and ecological separation, differences in time of blooming, self-fertilization (barley, wheat, oats, rice, sorghum), translocation races (rye), polyploid races (wheat, oats), gametophytic factors (maize), cryptic chromosomal differences (rice), and meiotic irregularities (wheat). No one scheme is necessarily better than another. Any barrier to gene flow will permit populations to fragment and accumulate genetic differences among the subpopulations. Sometimes a combination of several mechanisms can be demonstrated. The only qualification is that if the differentiation-hybridization cycle is to function, the isolation can not be absolute or permanent. Sooner or later, the separated populations must be brought together again to permit some hybridization.

The appropriate degree of differentiation depends on the amount of buffering in the genetic system. By genetic buffering, I mean essentially the amount of redundancy of genetic information. A self-fertilizing diploid would be presumed to be weakly buffered. Crossing between cultivars should result in a rather major release of

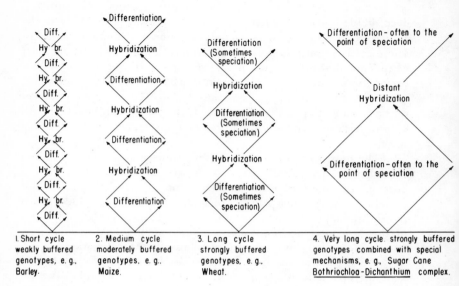

Figure 1
Schematic diagram of differentiation-hybridization cycles
depending upon the degree of buffering of genotypes in
cultivated plants (Harlan, 1966; reprinted from *Plant
Breeding*, Kenneth J. Frey, editor, copyright 1966, by
Iowa State University Press, Ames, Iowa).

potential variability; the variability should be largely oligogenic in
which relatively few genes have conspicuous effects and truly wide
hybridizations should be disastrous, if at all possible. The system is
rather well illustrated by barley (Figure 1).

A cross-fertilizing diploid such as maize should be somewhat
better buffered through carrying many genes in a heterozygous condition. Narrow crosses should have less obvious effects and wider
crosses should be tolerated. Variation should still tend toward the
oligogenic, at least when compared to a polyploid like wheat. Hexaploid wheat is better buffered than tetraploid wheat since the redundancy in genetic information is greater. The elaborate and elegant chromosome engineering of E. R. Sears (1969) could not have
been carried out among tetraploids, for example. At the hexaploid
level, narrow crosses have relatively little effect and decidedly wide
crosses (e.g., with *Aegilops, Secale,* and *Agropyron*) are tolerated.

Finally, the most highly buffered system in the scheme is the case of a high polyploid propagated vegetatively so as to escape the penalities of sterility. Such systems can withstand the shock of distinctly alien germplasm and the widest crosses are thereby tolerated.

Although there are, of course, many gradations between the illustrations given above, all of the systems work. Barley with its short cycle was probably the most important cereal crop on earth at one time. It is still important and conspicuously variable, and has a rather high yield potential. The variability may be somewhat deceiving because of the oligogenic nature, but there seems to be no great advantage or disadvantage to either a long or a short differentiation-hybridization cycle. In each case, the variability accumulated during the differentiation phase is exploited by hybridization at the appropriate stage of differentiation. Natural selection appears to have operated to adjust the length of the cycle to the degree of buffering. If the cycle is too short, there is little effect; if the cycle is too long, it cannot be completed.

Other selection pressures

Throughout the process of domestication, deliberate human selections have been superimposed on automatic selection pressures. In many cases, they are in the same direction and reinforce each other. In selecting for apparent yield, man will also select for larger heads, larger seeds, more seeds, better seed set, more determinate growth, daylength sensitivity, easier threshing, etc. Deliberate selection adds new dimensions to the process, for human selection may be more intense and absolute and is often biologically capricious or even whimsical.

Without deliberate selection a given genotype may have a certain statistical chance of contributing offspring to the next generation. It is a component of a population and even if it is not among the best fitted to the environment, elimination may be relatively slow. However, most cultivators in what we call "primitive agriculture" are very particular about the seed they sow. Each year at harvest time, they carefully choose certain heads of sorghum or ears of maize and seed from these *only* will be planted for the next generation. To be sure, this procedure is less universal among the small grains, but individual head selection is still common.

This practice provides a new order of selection pressure. The population becomes an array of deliberately chosen components. It may still be rich in variation because cultivators of traditional agriculture have an appreciation for mixtures, but the mixtures will conform to whatever an individual selector chooses. The total potential range of variation will be fragmented into landrace populations or primitive cultivars. Different cultivars will be grown for different purposes or to fit different ecological niches of the agricultural system.

Man selects for color, flavor, texture, and storage quality. He selects maize for popping, boiling, eating off the cob, flour quality for making hominy, and for ceremonial purposes in religious rites. He selects sweet sorghum for chewing, white-seeded types for bread, small dark red-seeded types for beer, and strong-stemmed, fibrous types for house construction and basketry. He selects glutinous rice and nonglutinous rice, long-grained rice and short-grained rice, red rice, white rice and aromatic rice. He selects barley for food, barley for beer, and barley for livestock feed. He selects grains that grind well or that process well in a mortar. Man delights in bright colors and curious and unusual variants, and he may select for several different types. High yield is seldom a factor in traditional agriculture, but consistent and reliable yield is absolutely essential; man knows his materials well because survival depends on it.

Man in traditional agriculture has an intuitive feeling for nutritive value. Certain cultivars are said to be good for pregnant women, others for nursing mothers. Many cultivars are prized as food for young children and some are said to be "strong" and reserved for periods of heavy work in the field. Without chemical analyses or laboratory rats for testing, the intuitive feeling usually has considerable nutritional merit. Under automatic selection, the fact that a line of sorghum makes good dumplings confers upon it no particular fitness for survival, but under human selection, fitness may be total. The line survives only because man plants it.

Other seed crops

The principles described for cereals apply in general to other seed crops. The differences are largely in specific details. In leguminous and cruciferous seed crops, for example, indehiscent pods and siliques evolve instead of nonfragile rachises. In the pulses, this may be a rather major change.

A legume is a one-celled pod with two sutures. In many legumes, the pod has a specialized inner layer that contracts at maturity. When the pressure is sufficient and the sutures sufficiently weakened, the legume opens explosively. The inner tissues contract and the halves of the pod roll up into a spiral. The pop is clearly audible even on small pods and the seeds are often snapped several meters from the plant. The legumes of some large tropical tree species pop open with a sound like a small firecracker and seeds are disseminated with considerable force.

The inner layer that operates the mechanism may be suppressed in cultivated races of legumes. This is the most diagnostic difference between wild and domestic races and has been used to identify cultivated beans and lima beans from an Ancash archaeological site in Peru dated to about 6000 B.C. (Kaplan, Lynch, and Smith, 1973). Where seeds are contained in pods and capsules, nonshattering evolves through indehiscence in a way analogous to nonshattering in cereals, although different tissues are involved.

Other evolutionary trends are also similar: we may expect larger seed, loss of dormancy, more determinate growth, more flowers, and larger inflorescences. They are similar because the selection pressures are similar. Weed races are likely to appear as well. Some crops may be less disposed to the evolution of weeds than the cereals are, but among annuals there are few exceptions.

Genetic principles

A few genetic principles seem to be applicable to seed crops in general and are presented below in condensed form:

1) Disruptive selection encourages polymorphisms (Mather, 1955; Doggett and Majisu, 1968).
2) Polymorphisms are maintained even in self-pollinating populations despite high inbreeding coefficients (Allard, Jain, and Workman, 1968; Jain and Allard, 1960).
3) Maintenance of polymorphisms is associated with chromosome segments and linkage (Jain and Allard, 1960, 1966).
4) There is a distinct advantage in the tight linkage of all genes concerned with balanced polymorphism (Fisher, 1930).
5) Linkage between morphology and fitness genes is a general feature of the genetic architecture of plant species (Grant, 1967).

6) Under strong selection pressure, a tight linkage of fitness
   genes results in a rapid initial increase in fitness but a slower
   rate of fitness increase in later generations (Lewontin,
   1964a, 1964b).
7) The highest fitness is reached when there are combinations
   of loosely linked genes and tightly linked blocks of genes for
   fitness (Lewontin and Hull, 1967).

Fitness for primary habitats is one thing; fitness for the cultivated field is another. We would expect a considerable linkage of the
genes that control these differences as well as those genes controlling
wild-type vs cultivated morphologies.

The tight linkages, epistatic effects, or both have caused difficulty in understanding the differences between wild and cultivated races.
The differences have accumulated by degrees over many generations,
but on genetic analysis they often seem to be governed by only a few
major genes.   In wheat, for example, speltoidy is associated with
modification, inactivation, or deletion of the Q locus. A speltoid is
not exactly a wild wheat; it does have many of the morphological
features of spontaneous wheat, but a very small segment of chromosome 5A is involved. The even more bizarre *Triticum vavilovianum*
morphology is associated with the same segment. The C or club gene
has such an effect that taxonomists formerly assigned the epithet *T.
compactum* to genotypes with the club-headed morphology. Thus,
radical morphological differences can appear to be under rather simple genetic control.

Despite the spectacular arrays of variation in cultivated plants,
the genetic differences between wild and cultivated races do not appear to be enormous. Biological speciation hardly ever occurs, unless
polyploidy is involved; strong genetic barriers have rarely developed.
The number of genes controlling wild vs cultivated morphologies is
often rather small, and these are likely to be linked into a few blocks.

At this point I would like to mention some personal experiences
with attempting to domesticate native American grasses. It was intended that these would be used for forage and revegetation of abandoned farmlands. The species chosen were climax perennials, not
weedy, and with inherently poor seed production characteristics.
Even though forage production was the ultimate use, seed and seedling characteristics were the most critical factors in domestication.

Seed set, seed retention, seed size, seedling vigor, and stand establishment were critical in developing something useful. Sources of wild populations were from the southern Great Plains. In most species, substantial progress was made in reducing shattering, increasing seed production, and developing larger seed and more seedling vigor. Several species were capable of yielding in the range of 600 to 700 kg/ha, which is within the range of cereals, such as wheat, rice, and maize, under conditions of subsistence agriculture with depleted soils and no fertilizer supplements.

Forage crop breeding, in general, is very new and many of the materials in use are simply selected from naturally-occurring, adapted populations. The ladino type white clover, the southern smooth bromegrasses and the many landraces of alfalfa, such as 'Flamande,' 'Ladak,' 'Semipalatinsk,' 'Indian,' California, Oklahoma and Kansas commons, are examples. In weeping lovegrass, standard, 'Ermelo,' and 'Morpa' strains are introduced populations from different parts of Africa. 'Greenfield' bermudagrass is a selection from spontaneous populations and 'Coastal' was a chance nursery hybrid. Pangolagrass is apparently a naturally-occurring sterile hybrid. Numerous other examples might be cited. The point is that there is a great deal of variation in natural populations available for immediate exploitation. Domestication is not as difficult as one might think.

DOMESTICATION OF VEGETATIVELY REPRODUCED CROPS

Among root crops, yams might be taken as models because so many species have been cultivated over widely separated parts of the world. Table 2 shows that man has had a rather extraordinary interest in digging tubers of *Dioscorea* out of the ground. Between 50 and 100 species have probably been used for human food, although a good many of them must be detoxified to make them safe.

Yams have uses other than food and we have no way of knowing what it was that first attracted man to these plants. The vines are used for cordage. Many of the African and Asian species contain water-soluble alkaloids that can be extracted and used as poisons against fish, monkeys, insects, tigers, and humans. Steroidal poisons occur in yams of both the Old World and the New and have been used for arrow and fish poisons and against lice (Coursey, 1972).

Table 2
The more important species of *Dioscorea* used for human
food (adapted from Coursey, 1972).

	Asia	Africa	America	Australi
Major spp.	*D. alata* L.	*D. rotundata* Poir.	*D. trifida* L.f.	*D. bulbifera* L
	D. esculenta (Lour.) Burk.	*D. cayenensis* Lamk.		*D. hastifolia* F
Secondary spp.	*D. bulbifera* L.	*D. dumetorum* (Knuth.)	*D. altissima* (Lamk.)	*D. transversa* F
	D. hispida Dennst.	*D. bulbifera* L.	*D. convolulacea* Cham. et Schlecht.	
	D. pentaphylla L.	*D. preussii* Pax		
	D. nummularia (Lamk.)	*D. praehensilis* Benth.		
	D. opposita Thunb.	*D. sansibarensis* Pax.		
	D. japonica Thunb.	*D. colocasiifolia* Pax.		

In any case, the vines and leaves of *Dioscorea* are easily recognized
and the tuber is readily located at the base of the vine. Preagricultural
people knew about them wherever they occurred in the wet tropics.

The species that have attracted man are primarily adapted to
savanna zones with a pronounced wet and dry season. The tuber is a
storage organ adapted to such a regime. At the onset of the rains, the
tubers sprout and the vines grow with remarkable vigor; virtually the
entire contents of the tuber are mobilized and translocated upward.
At the end of the rains, the process is reversed and nearly all of the
food stored in the vines is translocated downward and the tuber grows
very rapidly. The vine dies and the tuber remains dormant through
the dry season. The life cycle is geared toward survival in climates
with sharply contrasting wet and dry seasons.

This poses a problem of exploitation. Premature digging will
kill the plant and net very little. The tuber is formed in a rush at the
onset of the dry season. We have mentioned previously the religious
sanctions of yam eaters in Australia, the Andaman Islands, and West
Africa. People learned long ago that premature harvesting is disastrous to the crop, and this knowledge was woven into their religious
systems. We have also called attention to the practice of planting the
head back at harvest time, which existed even among Australian
aborigines and Andamanese who otherwise practiced no horticulture.

A practice of "protoculture" was described by Chevalier (1936)
in the Ubangui-Chari region of equatorial Africa. Here the people
were harvesting *D. dumetorum* in the wild. They used what they

needed immediately and planted the surplus near camp for future use. In other cases it has been observed that wild yams are brought to camp where the woody heads are cut off and discarded. These may sprout at the proper time of year. The step from precultural and protocultural practices to fully cultural practices is a small one. In the case of yams it merely meant the storage of tubers from harvest time to planting time, and some kinds of yams store very well.

The domestication of manioc was perhaps even easier. *Manihot* is better suited to the wet tropics, although it is also very drought-resistant and has a wide ecological amplitude. It can be reproduced by stem cuttings. All that is necessary is to cut off a branch and stick it in the ground during the rainy season and tubers will be produced. More important, a plant produces a number of tubers and harvesting can be done all year long. There is no need to protect the plant for part of the year.

Among vegetatively propagated plants, selection is absolute and the effects immediate. If clones should be found that are better tasting, less poisonous, more poisonous, more productive, etc., they can be propagated and cultivars are developed immediately. In both yams and manioc, many clones have lost the power to reproduce sexually. They may not bloom at all, or the flowers may be deformed and sterile. These clones are fully domesticated and entirely dependent on man for survival. In manioc, this seems to occur more frequently in the most poisonous types, suggesting that man has actually selected for increased prussic acid. In the wet tropics especially, this affords some protection against insects and wild mammals. Methods of detoxification are laborious but well worked out.

Loss of sexual reproduction is well known in the triploid and tetraploid bananas and plantains. Presumably, hybrids between *Musa acuminata* and *M. balbisiana* occurred naturally through the function of unreduced eggs, resulting in sterile triploids. Undoubtedly, this happened a number of times to the delight of tropical agriculturalists of Southeast Asia and neighboring islands, because the diploid bananas are often very seedy and banana seeds can crack your teeth. Sterile diploid mutations have also occurred and have been propagated vegetatively.

The ease with which vegetatively propagated plants can be brought under domestication is one argument advanced in support of the idea that tropical "vegeculture" is older than seed agriculture. There can be no question of its simplicity nor of its potential for instant domestication. Firm evidence of its greater antiquity remains to be developed, but there is considerable logic in the argument.

The invention of grafting techniques has extended the advantages of vegetative propagation to many crops otherwise propagated by seed. Some of these have been domesticated in recent times and we have full records of the process. The American grape is one example. No doubt, the American Indians knew of some of the more fruitful and palatable vines, but I know of no evidence that they ever tried to cultivate them. Early selections by Europeans were all from wild and weedy populations. To be sure, the behavior of European settlers had some influence on native populations of grapes. The fox grape (*Vitis labrusca*) is well adapted to the edges of woods, fence rows, etc. where birds disseminate the seeds. When settlers began to make farms out of forests, the forest margin habitat was increased enormously under conditions that favored hybridization. It is from these variable populations that some of our better known American grapes were selected. The 'Concord' cultivar, perhaps the most popular of all, was selected by Mr. E. W. Bull, of Concord, Mass., from his pasture. The cultivar 'Catawba' was selected by Major Hadley in Georgetown, District of Columbia. 'Isabella,' 'Rebecca,' 'Niagara,' and many other well-known cultivars were selected over the decades. A work by Charles Downing, published in 1869, lists 144 selected varieties of American grapes. Almost all of these came from wild and weedy populations and only a few from artificial breeding attempts. Several different American species contributed cultivars. Repeated attempts were made to introduce European grape (*V. vinifera*) germplasm by selection and by crossing with American species. The early attempts were largely failures and direct selection of spontaneous seedlings seemed to give the best cultivars early in the 19th century.

Most improved clones of pecan were simple selections from native bottomland stands of wild trees. Many individual trees contributed to the class called "paper shelled." Pecan fanciers and nurserymen searched through the natural stands and when they found a tree bearing nuts to their liking (thin-shelled, good flavor, large size, etc.), they simply cut off some bud-wood and grafted it onto seedling stocks. This, again, is instant domestication. Similar procedures have led to cultivars of hickories, wild plum, mulberry, hazelnut, and many others.

The *Hevea* rubber tree was domesticated in this century. There is great variation in yield of rubber among individual genotypes. Frequently, the most productive trees are highly susceptible to foliage diseases, but a long breeding program was unnecessary. The technique is to graft a high-yielding clone onto selected seedling stocks, then top-work these with disease-resistant clones. Each plant in the plantation consists of three genotypes with the tapping panel the only part of the tree with the high-yielding genotype. Vegetative propagation is a very powerful tool, especially where it can be combined with sexual reproduction.

Finally, there is a large class of recent domesticates consisting of ornamentals. Many of these are perennials and can be propagated vegetatively. This means that the sterile hybrids of wide crosses can be used, and some of our most striking garden flowers have such complex origins. Wild forms are much in demand for breeding stock, and the most elequent testimony to this is the scandalous smuggling of wild tulips from Turkey. Wild tulips are protected by law, but large numbers of bulbs are dug up yearly and are smuggled out of the country.

These examples demonstrate not only the ease with which vegetatively propagated crops can be domesticated, but also the great variability of natural or spontaneous populations. Strikingly superior types can be found by screening large natural populations. Furthermore, selections that would perish under natural conditions can be salvaged for later use. The navel orange, for example, is seedless and could not have reproduced itself. Seedless grapes are in the same class, to say nothing of the thousands of sterile clones of bananas, yams, manioc, and other crops already mentioned.

CONCLUSIONS

Heraclitus was right; the joining together of unlikes and the operation of "strife" or selection pressures have resulted in the production of domesticated races of plants. Natural populations of many species are variable and one can go a long way toward domestication simply by selecting and propagating desirable types already available. In seed crops, *planting* is the key operation. This practice alone sets up an entire syndrome of interlocking automatic selection pressures. Superimposed on the automatic pressures are those of deliberate selection; these are extremely powerful, very artificial, and often capricious. The result is the preservation of types entirely incapable of survival without the care of man.

Human activities, often unintentionally, establish fairly effective plant breeding systems. Migration, trade, cultural practices, or even deliberate manipulation have brought about repeated stirring of the gene pools and the development of differentiation-hybridization cycles.

These dynamics have resulted in great morphological changes without substantial change in the genetic background; speciation rarely occurs under domestication. The parts of the plant that show the greatest morphological alterations are the parts most valued by man. [This was noted by both Darwin (1859) and de Candolle (1959).] Mutations and gene combinations that cause striking morphological modifications are relatively common, but man must intervene and propagate them or they will be pruned out by natural selection. Under domestication, modification can build on modification until the end products are radically different in appearance from their wild progenitors.

Chapter 7

SPACE, TIME AND VARIATION

. . . some species can indeed be said to have had a single and sudden origin, localized and capable of being located. With others, however, the origin is no origin at all but a gradual transformation extending over wide areas and long periods and shifting its focus in the course of time. Between the two is every gradation.

C. D. Darlington and
E. K. Janaki Ammal, 1945

KINDS OF PATTERNS OF VARIATION

Geographic patterns of variation have historically been used to trace the origin and evolution of cultivated plants. We have seen that Vavilov (1926, 1949/50) thought that areas of maximum genetic diversity represented centers of origin and that the origin of a crop could be identified by the simple procedure of analyzing variation patterns and plotting regions where diversity was concentrated. It turned out that centers of diversity are not the same as centers of origin, yet many crops do exhibit centers of diversity. The phenomenon is real and requires explanation.

What causes variation to accumulate in secondary centers is not too well understood, but some observable factors are: 1) a long history of continuous cultivation; 2) ecological diversity, many habitats accommodate many races; 3) human diversity, different tribes are attracted to different races of a crop; and 4) introgression with wild or weedy relatives or between different races of the crop. There may be other causes, but the reasons for secondary centers are human, environmental, and the internal biological dynamics of hybridization, segregation, and selection.

A crop by crop analysis shows the situation to be much more complex than that conceived by Vavilov. Many crops did not originate in Vavilovian centers at all, and some do not have centers of diversity; several can be traced to very limited and specific origins, and others seem to have originated all over the geographical range of the species. It seems evident that if a crop originated in a limited area and did not spread out of it, the center of origin and the center of whatever diversity there may be would coincide. Both space and time are involved, and different crops have different evolutionary patterns. The main patterns can be classified as follows:

Endemic—Crops that originated in a limited area and did not spread appreciably. Examples: *Brachiaria deflexa* in Guinea (Figure 1), *Ensete ventricosa* in Ethiopia, *Digitaria iburua* in West Africa, *Setaria geniculata* in ancient Mexico (Callen, 1967), and *Panicum sonorum* in modern Mexico.

Semiendemic—Crops that originated in a definable center and with limited dispersal. Examples: *Eragrostis tef* and *Guizotia abyssinica* are Ethiopian domesticates; both are grown on a limited scale in India. Basic to the Ethiopian diet, they are not important elsewhere. African rice (*Oryza glaberrima*) is another example (Figure 2); the center of origin is probably the flood basin of the central Niger (Portères, 1956) whence it was distributed to Senegal, southward to the Guinea coast, and eastward as far as the Lake Chad area. Some of the minor tubers of the South American highlands, such as *Oxalis tuberosa, Ullucus tuberosus,* and *Tropaeolum tuberosum,* would also fall into this class (Léon, 1964).

Monocentric—Crops with a definable center of origin and wide dispersal without secondary centers of diversity. Examples: Arabica coffee and hevea rubber. Crops of this class are mostly new plantation or industrial crops. Ancient widespread crops usually develop secondary centers, but this takes time.

Oligocentric—Crops with a definable center of origin, wide dispersal, and one or more secondary centers of diversity. Examples: the whole Near East complex of barley, emmer, flax, pea, lentil, oats, chickpea, *Brassica* spp., etc.; all have secondary centers in Ethiopia and some also have centers in India and/or China.

Noncentric—Crops whose patterns of variation suggest domestication over a wide area. The suggestion may be misleading, of course, but centers are either not apparent or anomalous. Examples: sorghum, common bean, banana, and *Brassica campestris*.

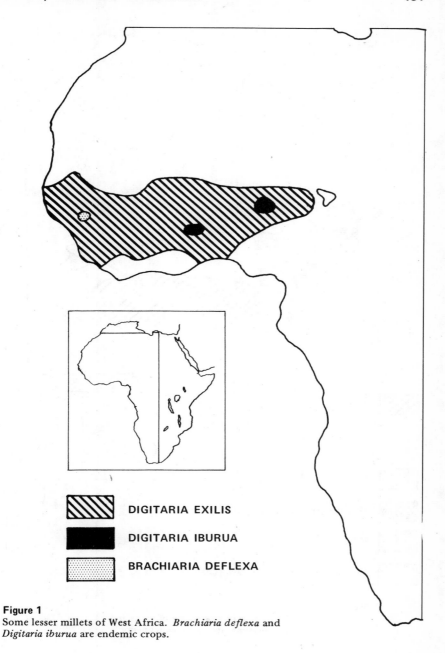

Figure 1
Some lesser millets of West Africa. *Brachiaria deflexa* and
Digitaria iburua are endemic crops.

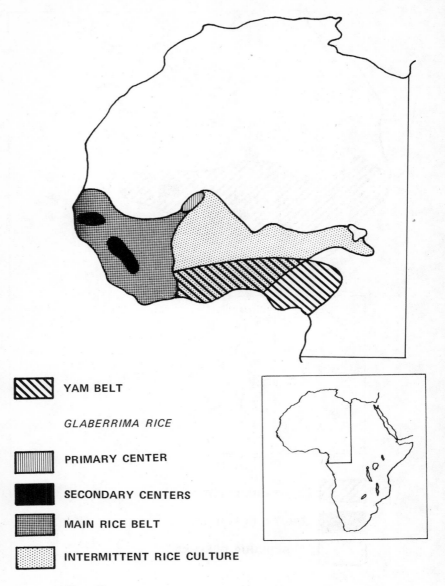

YAM BELT

GLABERRIMA RICE

PRIMARY CENTER

SECONDARY CENTERS

MAIN RICE BELT

INTERMITTENT RICE CULTURE

Figure 2
Distribution of major areas of cultivation of yams and
African rice. The glaberrima rice has a semiendemic
variation pattern.

NONCENTRIC CROPS

Aside from the subjective questions of how endemic is "endemic" and how widespread is "widespread," the categories are clear and self-evident except for the one called "noncentric." It seems to me that some crops simply do not have centers, and the concept of centers of either origin or diversity as universal phenomena can be called into question.

Sorghum is selected as an example of a noncentric crop; i.e. neither a center of diversity nor a center of origin is evident from the distribution of variation alone. Vavilov had indicated that Ethiopia was a center of diversity-center of origin for sorghum, but he did not know sorghum well and did not understand African crops. To some extent, Ethiopia is a center of diversity for the durra race and is certainly the main center of diversity for the durra-bicolor race, but these are only 2 of the 15 races according to a new classification by Harlan and de Wet (1972). All other cultivated races are rather poorly represented in Ethiopia.

The region from eastern Nigeria through Chad and western Sudan is a center of diversity for the caudatum, guinea-caudatum, and durra-caudatum races, but not for the races of Ethiopia. The region from western Nigeria to Senegal is the center of diversity for the guinea race, and while there are some durras in the drier zones, other races are poorly represented. The area from Tanzania to South Africa is the center for the kafir race and although guineas and guinea-kafirs are found, they are not especially variable. There is no area in Africa where the diversity of even several races is highly concentrated.

Snowden (1936) suggested that the several major races of sorghum had been ennobled separately from distinct wild races. This may, indeed, have been the case, although we have yet to see much evidence either for or against the theory. Multiple ennoblements are probably common, however, and must be dealt with by geographers and students of plant domestication.

The distribution of the races of sorghum in Africa is shown in Figures 3 to 6. The patterns are remarkably consistent and clear-cut and presumably mean something with respect to the origin and evolution of sorghum. Harlan and Stemler (in press) attempted to reconstruct the history of sorghum domestication using this and other distributional information. The results are shown in Figures 7 and 8.

While we show a center of origin labelled Early Bicolor in Figure 7, this region was not selected because of any clues given by variation patterns in modern cultivated sorghum. It was chosen because 1) archaeological evidence suggests African agriculture originated north of the equator, 2) the West African race of wild sorghum is a forest grass with an adaptation quite different from that of the crop, and 3) the region outlined includes the most massive stands of wild sorghum adapted to a savanna habitat north of the equator.

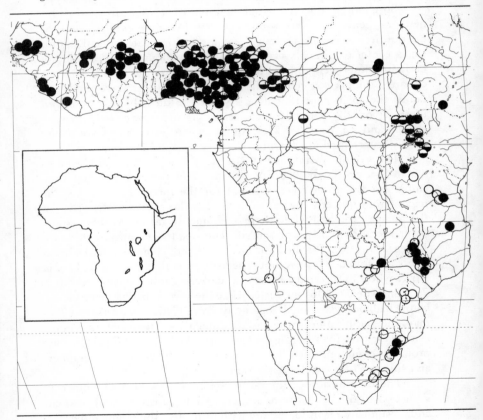

Figure 3
Distribution of guinea and half-guinea sorghums in Africa: guinea, solid circles; guinea-kafir, open circles; guinea-caudatum, upper clear, lower solid; guinea-durra, upper solid, lower clear.

Today, the most common cultivated race in the region is caudatum, which we consider to be a relatively new race. One could describe the pattern in terms of a series of secondary centers, e.g. West
Africa for guinea, southern Africa for kafir, Sudan-Chad-Uganda for
caudatum, and Asia-Ethiopia for durra, but these are not centers of
diversity for sorghum; they are centers for only certain races of sorghum. Some crops clearly have centers and others do not. Variation
patterns must be analyzed in each crop separately before generalizations can be made.

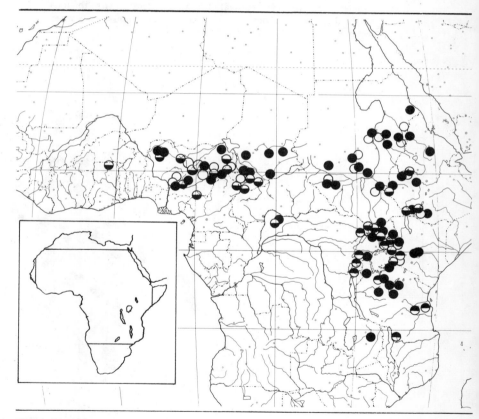

Figure 4
Distribution of caudatum and half-caudatum sorghums in
Africa: caudatum, solid circles; durra-caudatum, open
circles; guinea-caudatum; upper clear, lower solid;
kafir-caudatum, upper solid, lower clear.

The idea of a noncentric crop is not new and was well documented by a distinguished member of Vavilov's professional team. E. N. Sinskaya (1928) wrote a monograph on some of the cruciferous crops; she made the following observation about *Brassica campestris*:

> The geographical distribution of the forms of colza, as it may be pictured on the basis of data available at the present time, points in no way to the existence of a special centre of diversity. To every region corresponds a definite ecotype. The introduction into cultivation has taken place, and is still taking place, in every region independently of any "centre." The cultivated forms are identical with the local weeds; the local climatical ecotype being first distributed as a weed, becomes afterward a cultivated crop.

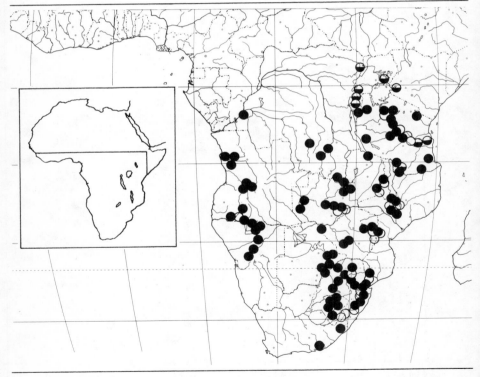

Figure 5
Distribution of kafir and half-kafir sorghums in Africa:
kafir, solid circles; guinea-kafir, open circles, kafir-caudatum,
upper clear, lower solid.

Nothing since has been found to change that impression. Indeed, the introduction of the weed into cultivation, having taken place over most of Eurasia, appears to be once again in process in the Andean highlands of South America (Gade, 1972).

The common bean has a pattern rather similar to the examples just given. In South America, wild races are found along the eastern slopes of the Andean chain at midelevations from Argentina to

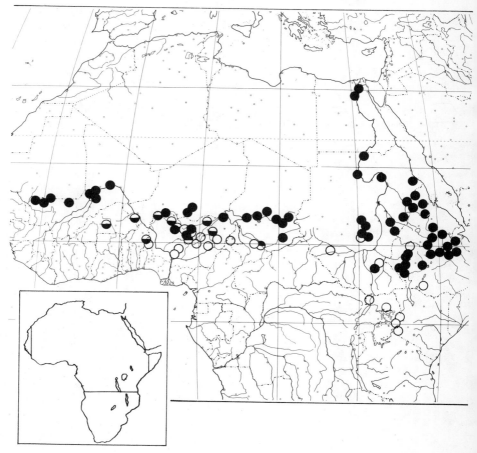

Figure 6
Distribution of durra and half-durra sorghums in Africa:
durra, solid circles; durra-caudatum, open circles;
durra-guinea, upper clear, lower solid.

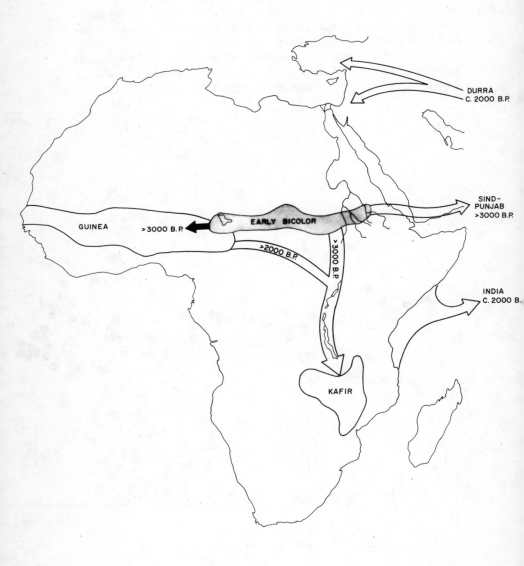

Figure 7
Suggested early movements of sorghum. Initial domestication
in shaded area (from Harlan and Stemler, in press).

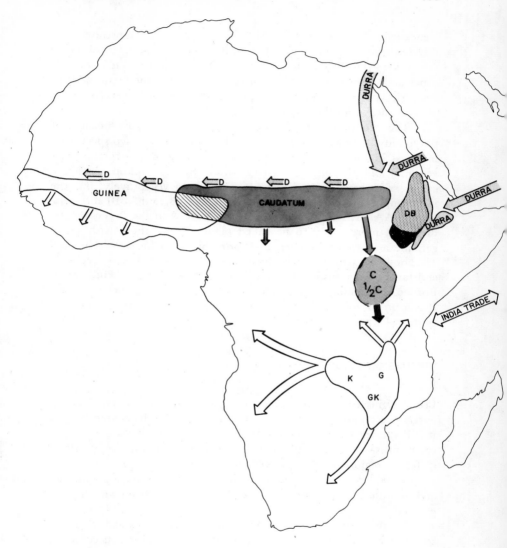

Figure 8
Suggested later movements of sorghum (from Harlan and
Stemler, in press).

Venezuela, about 5,000 km. Brücher (1968) has demonstrated that different races were domesticated at different places and at different times along this distribution. Gentry (1969), however, has shown another area of bean domestication centers in south and western Mexico. Altogether, the area of domestication stretched over 7,000 km with a series of local domestications.

The situation in bananas can be unraveled, in part, because of polyploidy. The wild bananas are diploid and seedy. Two species are involved in the evolution of the true bananas, *Musa acuminata* (A genome) and *M. balbisiana* (B genome). Sterile, diploid, parthenocarpic races have evolved and are propagated vegetatively, but the more important types are triploids (AAA, AAB, and ABB) and tetraploids (AAAA, AAAB, and AABB). Those with the B genome are drier and more likely to be called plantains and those with the A genome are sweeter, juicier, and more likely to be called bananas. The zone over which such evolutionary events took place is very wide and ranges from eastern India across Southeast Asia, the Philippines, Borneo, Indonesia, New Guinea, and perhaps still further eastward. It is a broad zone of domestication rather than a center in the conventional sense of the word.

DIFFUSE ORIGINS

Crop origins can be diffuse in both space and time. Even if a crop enters the domestic fold in a limited area, it may change radically as it is dispersed from its center of origination. As it spreads, it may receive infusions of germplasm from its wild relatives, and people in different regions may apply very different selection pressures. The most highly derived end products may be far removed geographically and morphologically from the wild progenitors from which they evolved.

To the best of our knowledge, maize was domesticated first in southern Mexico and spread slowly in all directions from its center of origin. At the time of European contact, it was being cultivated from southern Canada to southern Argentina (about 43°S) and Chile and throughout the Caribbean Islands. Each region had its own characteristic array of races. Some rather large areas had only a few races, and these were relatively uniform; other, much smaller regions were characterized by many races, some of which were highly variable. These areas of diversity occurred in southern Mexico, Guatemala, parts of Colombia, and Peru. In fact, Peru is noted for extreme diversity in maize. The giant-seeded Cuzco, forms with "interlocking" cobs, cultivars with extremely long and flexible cobs, etc. are among the unique races of the region. These innovations are not found in the center of origin, but far removed from it.

All the available information indicates that barley was first domesticated in the Near East, and the present distribution of wild barley together with archaeological evidence point to a rather specific part of the region (see Chapter 8). It has become, perhaps, the most widely grown of major crops, being cultivated from above the Arctic Circle to southern Argentina and Chile as well as in tropical latitudes. The progenitor is the wild two-rowed *Hordeum spontaneum,* and the earliest barleys from archaeological sites are two-rowed. Two-rowed barleys are still common throughout the region and are grown in the drier zones under rainfed conditions. The irrigated barleys are usually six-rowed.

Variation is not notable in the center of origination, and most of the races of barley occur elsewhere. Each geographic and ecological region has its own set of cultivars with characteristic concentrations of particular genetic traits. The Ethiopian plateau is especially favorable for the development of leaf diseases, and the barleys have responded over the centuries by developing high frequencies of genes for resistance. Genes conditioning irregular (seed formed in some of the lateral spikelets) and deficiens (lateral spikelets suppressed) head types are also common in Ethiopian barleys. Barleys of Tibet and adjacent highlands show high frequencies of the gene for naked seeds and some are hooded. Chinese and Japanese barleys have their own peculiar characteristics.

But Ethiopian barleys originated in Ethiopia, Tibetan barleys in Tibet, and Chinese barleys in China. All of them differ considerably from the primitive two-rowed barleys first cultivated by man in the Near East. In this case, we have a center of origin that can be located within reasonable limits, but it is obvious that most of the evolution of barley took place elsewhere. To say that barley, as we now know the crop, originated in the Near Eastern nuclear area is misleading, to say the least.

Wheat is an even more extreme example, for what originated in the center of origin was not wheat as we know it, but einkorn and emmer, crops that are now obsolete. There is good reason to believe that hexaploid bread wheat originated outside of the nuclear area where einkorn and emmer were first cultivated. Again, we have a crop dispersed over vast geographic areas and evolving new arrays of locally adapted cultivars as it spread. Wheat is relatively uniform over extensive parts of its range of distribution, but in specific local regions there are nodes of variation or centers of diversity.

Variation in a crop may be increased considerably if the crop is used for different purposes by different people. The common bean, for example, may be selected for green beans or for dry beans. The garden-pea may be selected for green peas, dry peas, or edible pods. The mung bean is ground into flour in India and sprouted in China. *Corchorus olitorius* is a vegetable in Africa and a fiber in India. Roselle is a food in Africa and a fiber in India. Some people grow flax for fiber, some for edible seeds, and some for industrial oil. Hemp is grown for fiber, edible seeds, and narcotics. Most cereals have multiple uses and special races are developed accordingly. The variation patterns of crops are largely artifacts resulting from human activity; therefore, the larger the number of people who grow a crop and the greater their diversity, the more variable the crop is likely to be.

MICROCENTERS

Even within centers of diversity, it is not unusual for a crop to be reasonably uniform over extensive areas and to show enormous diversity in very small regions. This is the microcenter phenomenon which I described many years ago (Harlan, 1951). Later the term was used in a very different sense by Zhukovsky (1968). Microcenters, as I originally observed them, are relatively small regions, 100 to 500 km across, in which may be packed an astonishing variation of one to several crops. I have observed microcenters for wild plants as well (Harlan, 1963a, 1963b), and they appear to be fairly common in the variation patterns of plant species.

Variability is of such an order that microcenters can be spotted easily in the field, and it contrasts sharply with the amount of variation in adjacent regions. The pattern has not been investigated as much as it deserves, but in the microcenters that I studied, the source of variability appeared to involve introgression between contrasting populations.

As of 20 years ago, one could still detect microcenters scattered across the Near East: Turkish Thrace, Transcaucasia with adjacent parts of Turkey, parts of Iran, and Afghanistan. Some of them have been destroyed, and the rest are threatened by replacement with modern cultivars. Most of them were located outside of the Near Eastern nuclear area and the source of variation was attributed to current evolutionary activity rather than to any relationship to crop origins.

LANDRACE POPULATIONS

For people accustomed to modern agriculture, it seems necessary to describe landrace populations. It is only within the last century or less that landraces have been replaced by uniform, true-breeding cultivars or special hybrids of controlled parentage. Traditionally, field crops consisted of landrace populations rather than cultivars in the modern sense. Landraces are still grown, of course, wherever traditional agriculture is practiced.

Landrace populations are often highly variable in appearance, but they are each identifiable and usually have local names. A landrace has particular properties or characteristics. Some are considered early-maturing and some late. Each has a reputation for adaptation to particular soil types according to the traditional peasant soil classification: e.g. heavy or light, warm or cold, dry or wet, strong or weak. They may also be classified according to expected usage; among cereals, different landraces are used for flour, for porridge, for "bulgur," and for malt to make beer, etc. All components of the populations are adapted to local climatic conditions, cultural practices, and diseases and pests.

Genetic variation within a landrace may be considerable, but it is far from random. The various component genotypes have survived in a region for a long period of time or else they are offspring of lines that have undergone local selection for many generations. The genotypes are not only adapted to their environment, both natural and man-made, but they are also adapted to each other. A landrace population is an integrated unit and the components have adjusted to one another over the generations. Landraces are adapted to conditions of traditional agriculture, they are adapted to low soil fertility, low plant populations, and low yield. On the other hand, the genetic variability provides some built-in insurance against hazards. Really devastating disease epidemics are unlikely, because the populations contain such an array of resistance genes that no single race of pathogen can build up to epidemic proportions. Some genotypes would be affected each year, but not all of them.

Seedlings of landraces can emerge from a wide range of planting depths. Landraces usually produce something despite drought, standing water, insects, hail, or diseases. In traditional agriculture, high yields have never been necessary, but a crop failure means famine and death. Landraces may not yield much by modern standards, but they tend to be dependable.

The composition of landraces is frequently deliberately manipulated by cultivators. In Africa, the first step at sorghum harvest time is the selection of seed stocks for the next planting season. The farmer walks through his field and carefully chooses heads to be saved for seeding. Sometimes the heads are rather similar; sometimes a remarkable array of head and seed types is assembled. I have often asked the reasons for choosing a particular type. There is always a reason, but it may have little relation to the answers I receive. When a farmer selects a really variable range of material, the reason given is usually to the effect that a mixture of types is more nutritious than uniform strains. This could well be true. On one occasion I noticed that a farmer had selected crook-necked types from his field. On inquiry he replied that they are easier to hang from the tukel roof. [It is common to store the stock seed inside the house (tukel) above the hearth where the smoke from the kitchen fires provides some protection from weevils.]

Similar procedures are used by traditional farmers for maize. Ears are carefully chosen for stock seed and set aside. The reasons for selecting this or that are complex and deserving of serious anthropological and genetic study. Wellhausen et al. (1952) suggested that the very intense pigmentation of highland *elote* maize came about because of the usage of these races for roasting ears rather than because of some esthetic appreciation of colored seeds. Mexicans prefer floury endosperm in roasting ears, and it is easier to keep stocks pure for floury if the more intensely pigmented types are selected. In Peru some deeply pigmented races are selected for the production of a red, nonalcoholic beverage. Anderson (1954) noted that some farmers in Mexico sow an occasional seed of red-eared maize in their fields of white or yellow races "for luck." Wilkes (personal communication) has observed Mexican peasant farmers actually building hybrid races by interplanting selected parental types. The practice might well be very ancient. The genetic consequences of these behavior patterns have not been seriously studied.

Whatever the reasons for the choice and whether the selections tend to be uniform or variable, all components are from adapted materials. Landraces are built up and the components are selected, reassorted, recombined, and rearranged, but the local materials are constantly being adjusted to local conditions. The great variability of landraces makes them good sources of genes for modern plant breeding, but otherwise they are of little use in modern agriculture. They are not adapted to high fertility, high plant populations, or high production.

IMPLICATIONS FOR PLANT BREEDING

Analyses of variation patterns of crops are essential in order to understand the germplasm that went into their evolution and to make efficient use of the available variability in plant breeding. Typical variation patterns include: 1) wild populations that are often highly variable, especially when they cover a considerable geographic range and/or ecological amplitude, 2) landrace populations which are balanced, integrated mixtures of genotypes adapted to a region and to cultural practices in vogue, 3) weed populations, frequently derived from genetic interaction between wild and cultivated races, 4) microcenters in which enormous diversity is found in a restricted geographic area, usually due to genetic interaction between cultivated races and/or spontaneous races, and 5) secondary centers in which great variation has accumulated in certain special geographic regions, usually with considerable isolation from other regions for long periods of time. Depending on the age and distribution of the crop, the variation may have an endemic, semiendemic, monocentric, oligocentric, or noncentric pattern.

Geographic patterns of variation help direct plant exploration and germplasm assembly for breeding programs. Collecting is most rewarding in centers of diversity and in microcenters when they can be found. We now know that certain geographical areas may have concentrations of genes for multiple disease resistance. Other useful traits have been plotted, and we know enough about variation patterns in some crops so that reasonably systematic collections can be made. Not all of the useful genes are found in centers of diversity. Cultivars being grown near the climatic or ecological limits of a crop may have special attributes. Sorghum on the high plateaus of Ethiopia are especially cold tolerant, pearl millet in southern Chad growing under higher rainfall than pearl millet usually receives is particularly resistant to leaf diseases, barley from high elevations in the Himalayas is more resistant to frost damage at flowering time than other races, etc.

In theory, plant explorers and collectors assemble the raw materials and plant breeders maintain the collections for use. Several gene banks have been established for long-term storage. In practice, collection and maintenance have seldom been done systematically. There is no really complete collection, although some are much better than others. Maintenance has ranged from good in a few cases to virtually nil in others. In past decades, the maintenance of collections was generally casual, it was too routine to be interesting, there was no prestige in it; it was a lot of work for little reward, and one could always go out and make a new collection anyway.

Times have changed. The old centers of diversity are disappearing, and some have already gone. New, modern cultivars are replacing the old landraces, and microcenters are being wiped out. In some crops, even the weed races are being lost due to modernization of agriculture, and the wild populations are being plowed or grazed out in many parts of the world. Genetic erosion is far advanced in some regions and accelerating everywhere. The sources of variation for plant breeding are drying up and genuine alarm is being expressed in many quarters. To date, there has been more alarm than action, but some steps are, at last, being taken with some of our most important food plants.

The time will probably come when essentially all the variation available for plant breeding will come from two sources: 1) collections maintained in gene banks and their satellite working collections maintained by plant breeders, and 2) cultivars in current production. In crops that are grown on a large scale worldwide, such as wheat, rice, and maize, the second resource is of considerable value. The traditional sources of variation, however, appear to be doomed. Gene centers and microcenters are very fragile, and landraces are easily replaced by uniform cultivars. We know that these sources of breeding materials are disappearing in many parts of the world, and future generations would have the right to be unforgiving if we fail to assemble a good sampling of crop germplasm while it is still available.

The subject of plant genetic resource management has been treated in a variety of ways in recent years. For the interested reader, I would suggest at least a perusal of the following references: Frankel and Bennett, 1970; Frankel, 1973; Bakhteyev, 1969; Plant Genetic Resources Newsletter, FAO, Rome, Italy; Plant Introduction Review, CSIRO, Canberra, Australia; Burgess, 1971; and National Academy of Sciences, 1972.

Chapter 8

THE NEAR EASTERN CENTER

Why has Ea caused man, the unclean
To perceive the things of Heaven and
Earth
A mind cunning has he bestowed upon
him
And created him into fame.
What shall we do for him?
Bread of life get for him; let him eat.

Akkadian Epic,
third millennium B.C.
(Langdon, 1931)

In the last two decades a considerable research effort has been concerned with an attempt to understand the shift from hunting-
gathering economies to a food-
producing economy in the Near
East. Archaeologists, anthropologists, prehistorians, zoologists, botanists, geneticists, palynologists,
geologists, and others have col-
laborated in a team effort to assemble evidence bearing on the
problem. The research has resulted
in a generalized framework of
evidence which establishes a se-

*I kept alive Hefat and Hormer . . . at a
time when . . . everyone was dying of
hunger on this sandbank of hell. . .
All of Upper Egypt was dying of hunger
to such a degree that everyone had come
to eating his children, but I managed
that no one died of hunger in this nome.*

Inscription on tomb of Ankhtifi, a
nomarch of Hierakonopolis and
Edfu, ca. 2000 B. C.
(Bell, 1971)

quence of events and developments and the geographic regions in
which they took place. As more and more information is accumulated, however, it is becoming increasingly clear that the process of
developing an effective food-producing system was immensely complex and involved. The initial steps might have easily grown out of
intensive gathering economies, but the end results were a complete
revolution in food procurement systems. A completely new ecological adaptation is not likely to be easily achieved.

The focus of the problem can be stated simply by beginning
with the end products we know the most about. High civilizations
did emerge in the Near East in Mesopotamia and in Egypt. These
were not only the first of the high civilizations we know about, but
because they provided the roots for Western civilization they have
always been intensively studied and other civilizations have been
measured, at least by Western man, according to the development of

various elements found in the Near Eastern civilizations. The emergence of towns and cities, monumental buildings, professional classes, stratification of economic and political power, centralized government, priestly castes, standing armies, writing, and metallurgy are components of the criteria used to compare the Near Eastern civilizations with other civilizations.

During investigations of the emergence of Near Eastern civilizations it became obvious that they were based on agriculture. City dwellers are consumers, not food producers, and agriculture is a prerequisite for any high civilization. To understand the origins of these civilizations then, one must understand how food production came into practice in the area. Furthermore, an economic analysis of the historical period as well as earlier prehistoric communities showed that the bulk of the food produced and consumed came from four domesticates: wheat, barley, sheep, and goats. There were other domesticated plants and animals, of course, but a high proportion of the caloric intake came from these four, and the story of Near Eastern agriculture is largely their story.

Where traditional subsistence agriculture survives today this situation still holds true. Cattle are used for work and milk; meat is a tertiary consideration and is more likely to be sold to city dwellers than consumed in the village. Domestic pigs are raised but are never much competition to sheep and goats as a source of food. Locally, dates, olives, and leguminous grains are important, but almost never replace the cereals as the staff of life.

In domesticating plants like wheat and barley, one presumably begins by harvesting the wild progenitor. Figures 1, 2, and 3 show the distribution of known sites for wild barley, wild einkorn, and wild emmer, respectively. Stands of wild cereals can be extremely abundant today, and all three cereals may occur on extensive areas in patches as thick as a stand of cultivated grain. The wild emmer is abundant today in the Palestine area but is found in Turkey, Iraq, Iran, and the Soviet Union in only thin scattered stands. Experiments with harvesting the wild cereals have shown that it can easily be done with a flint-bladed sickle and that the effort would be rewarding in terms of food obtained per hour spent in harvesting (Harlan, 1967). Extensive natural stands of wild cereals would surely have been an attractive source of food for hunting-gathering people.

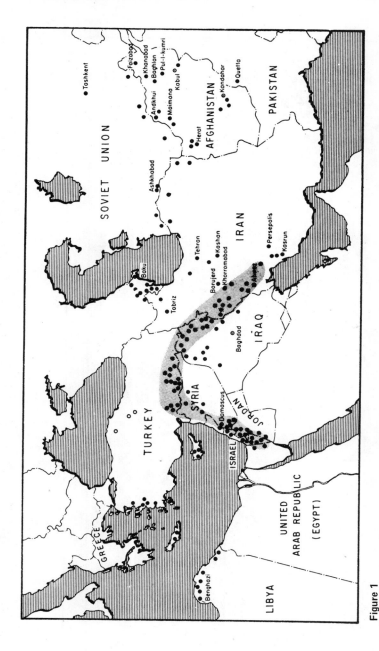

Figure 1

Distribution of known and reasonably certain sites of wild barley. Massive stands in fairly primary habitats may occur within the shaded area. Elsewhere, wild barley may be abundant, but confined to highly disturbed habitats (from Harlan and Zohary, 1966; copyright 1966 by the American Association for the Advancement of Science).

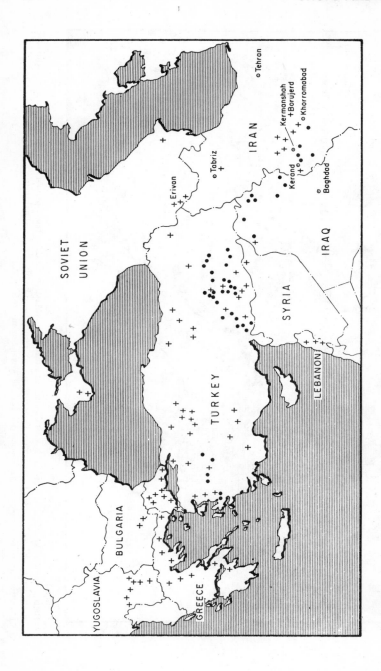

Figure 2
Distribution of known and reasonably certain sites of wild einkorn wheat. Solid circles, fairly primary habitats; crosses, definitely segetal habitats (from Harlan and Zohary, 1966; copyright 1966 by the American Association for the Advancement of Science).

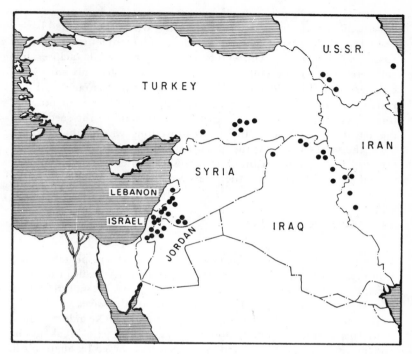

Figure 3
Distribution of known and reasonably certain sites of wild
emmer (from Harlan and Zohary, 1966; copyright 1966
by the American Association for the Advancement of
Science).

The archaeological problem, then, is to find out when and where
the wild cereals were being harvested and when and where the first
evidences of cultivated forms appear. Cereals are most likely to be
found in archaeological sites in the form of carbonized grains or impressions in lumps of clay, mud walls, or adobe brick. Impressions
and scraps of epidermis are not uncommon in pottery, but since the
primary cereals were domesticated in prepottery times, this helps
only in understanding later evolutionary events. The most useful
specimens are usually the carbonized grains, although changes in size
and shape due to carbonization often cause problems in precise
identification.

The most useful criterion in distinguishing wild from domesticated cereals is the articulation of the seeds or spikelets. Wild barley

has a fragile rachis that shatters at maturity, whereas cultivated barley has a tough rachis that may remain more or less intact even after the seeds are threshed off. The wild wheats also have fragile rachises, but cultivated emmer and einkorn have rachises that are only somewhat tougher than the wild ones. The head will remain intact until harvested, but on threshing breaks up at the joints just as in the wild forms. Additional processing is required to remove the seeds from the enveloping glumes. In the free-threshing wheats that evolved later, the rachis is tough, the glumes are more or less deciduous, and the seed falls free when threshed. This character is a certain indication of domestication, as is the six-rowed character in barley.

ARCHAEOLOGICAL PRELUDE

The archaeological record of man in the Near East is respectably long, although not nearly as long as that for Africa. Acheulean man apparently wandered over the whole region and Neanderthal man (Mousterian tool tradition) occupied many of the caves in the hilly or mountainous areas. After the disappearance of Neanderthal man from this region, about 35,000 years ago, there is a break in the evidence of human activity until caves were reoccupied by anatomically modern man (*Homo sapiens*), somewhat more than 20,000 years ago. The artifacts left behind by modern man are Upper Paleolithic in nature and tend to show rather striking regional differentiation. The older Paleolithic stone tool assemblages were very generalized and easily recognizable over vast areas of Europe, North Africa, and western Asia, but the new post-Mousterian assemblages soon differentiated by region and tended to vary considerably from valley to valley and even from site to site.

There was also an increasing tendency to depend more on local small animals and probably more on wild plant productions as well. Snail shells, clam shells, bird, fish, lizard, snake, and tortoise remains become more abundant relative to the traditionally hunted animals such as deer, onager, wild ox, wild sheep, wild goat, and gazelle. There is some indication the sites were occupied most of the year if not year-long. Boulder mortars, pestles, and grinding stones appear, suggesting processing of coarse plant foods. Some of these artifacts were large and heavy and relatively nontransportable. The local environment was evidently being exploited more intensively, a prelude to plant and animal domestication.

ARCHAEOLOGICAL SEQUENCE OF VILLAGE SITES

By the early part of the ninth millennium B.C., village sites that have a direct bearing on the problem were established. These will be discussed briefly by name; their locations are shown in Figure 4.

Zawi Chemi Shanidar in Iraq, excavated by Ralph Solecki, is an open-air village or campsite in the same valley as the famous Shanidar cave. It is dated about 8850 B.C. and the artifacts have clear ties to some of the upper layers in the cave. Probably the same people lived both in and out of the cave. There are remains of rock dwellings, boulder mortars, and many flint blades. Most significant about the site, however, is that an analysis of the bones by Dexter Perkins (1964) shows a rather dramatic shift from goat to sheep and at the same time an increase in the percentage of young animals. Throughout the time range studied, the percentage of young goats was more or less constant at 25% of the goats, while in the upper layers of Zawi

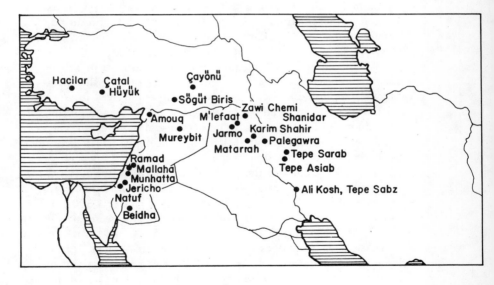

Figure 4
Early farming village sites, 7500 to 6500 B.C. (from Harlan, 1971; copyright 1971 by the American Association for the Advancement of Science).

Chemi young sheep represented about 50% of the sheep. The evidence is slender and tenuous but does suggest that the people of Zawi Chemi Shanidar had considerable control over the sheep population whether or not they were actually herding. Other sites of a similar time range and typology are Karim Shahir in Iraq and Asiab in Iran.

To the west near the Mediterranean, the Natufian culture flourished throughout the ninth millennium. Their lithic industry was first discovered in 1928 by Dorothy A. E. Garrod in Shouqbah cave and is now known from 20 or more sites from Beidha in the southern Jordan highlands to basal Jericho to Mallaha near Lake Houleh and westward to the coast. There are recent indications that the Natufian culture might have ranged from Turkey to Egypt, but always rather near the coast. Of particular interest here is the presence of sickle blades in large numbers, sickle handles, and even some intact sickles. The sickle blades often have a sheen which is taken to indicate that they had been used to harvest cereals. Grinding and pounding equipment, stationary and mobile, was also abundant. At Mt. Carmel, hollows were cut into solid rock to form mortars. At Mallaha, rather elaborate well-made mortars were produced, and sometimes decorated. Large quantities of stone pestles, grinding slabs, and handstones were also found (Perrot, 1966).

All the equipment for cultivating cereal grains is present in the Natufian industries, but there is no indication that either plants or animals were domesticated. The Natufian people lived in an area in which wild wheat and wild barley are abundant today and presumably were abundant at the time. The actual grains have not yet been found, but it seems likely that the Natufians depended to a considerable extent on wild cereal harvests.

Toward the close of the ninth millennium (about 8000 B.C.) we do actually find the grains of wild cereals at Tell Mureybit on the Euphrates about 85 km east of Aleppo in Syria. Over 1,800 grains of wild einkorn were found in the excavation and were studied by Willem Van Zeist and W. A. Casparie (1968). An interesting feature is that wild einkorn does not occur in the area today. Either the climate was sufficiently different 10,000 years ago that the species could live in the vicinity of Mureybit or the people harvested the seed 100 to 150 km to the north and imported it to Mureybit. Wild barley seeds were also found, although in much less abundance. Mureybit is, however, within the present range of wild barley. The site of Ganji-Darreh in Iran is typologically similar, but plant remains have not yet been reported.

The first clear indication of domesticated plants and animals at the present time comes from the basal Bus Mordeh phase of Tepe Ali Kosh in Iran (Figure 4). The dating of the basal layers of the mound is suspect because of groundwater and carbon contamination, but the best present information indicates the village was founded not later than 7500 B.C. and could well be older. A hornless, female sheep skull indicates the presence of domesticated sheep. Goat remains are much more abundant, and an exceptionally high proportion came from young males, again indicating domestication had occurred (Hole, Flannery, and Neely, 1965).

Plant remains in the Bus Mordeh phase were abundant and included large numbers of small, wild legume seeds, some cultivated emmer, a little einkorn, wild and tame, and barley with a fragile rachis. Hans Helbaek (1966), who studied the plant remains, is inclined to use the term "cultivated wild barley," which means that barley with a fragile rachis was grown deliberately, but not until it evolved a tough rachis could it be called a domesticated plant. Regardless of the interpretation, it seems likely that sheep, goats, and both kinds of early wheat were domesticated by the middle of the eighth millennium B.C. and probably earlier.

People continued to live at Ali Kosh until about 5600 B.C. when the village was abandoned. During this time the ratio of sheep to goats increased substantially and the goats developed twisted horns typical of modern domesticated goats of the region. Barley became fully domesticated (hulled, two-rowed), lentils were added, and the use of small-seeded wild legumes was discontinued. Pottery came in about 6000 B.C. and tools for processing cereals increased considerably. Later developments were recorded in the nearby site of Tepe Sabz (Hole et al., 1965).

The site of Çayönü in southeastern Turkey, dated to approximately 7000 B.C., indicates the presence of domestic sheep, pig, dog, and probably goats. The plants included wild and tame emmer and einkorn, pea, lentil, bitter and wild vetch, pistachio, and almond. Flax, chickpea, and *Lathyrus* occurred in small quantities (Van Zeist, 1972).

As we move into the seventh millennium B.C., evidence becomes more abundant. One of the most famous of the farming villages is Jarmo in Iraq, studied for three seasons by R. J. Braidwood and his team of specialists (Braidwood and Howe, 1960). Domestic goat, sheep, pig, and probably dog were present together with cultivated two-rowed barley, emmer, and einkorn. Çatal Hüyük on the Konya plain of Turkey, dated to about 6500, had domestic cattle. This is the earliest evidence now available for domestic cattle, although there is some evidence for them in Nea Nicomedia in northern Greece by 6200 B.C. Seeds of cultivated einkorn, emmer, six-rowed barley, free-threshing wheat, pea, vetch, and bitter vetch have also been identified at Çatal Hüyük but at layers dated approximately 5800 to 5600 B.C. The nature of the site implies that full-scale agriculture was carried on when the site was first established (Helbaek, 1964).

Ramad, a site near Damascus, may go back as early as 6500 B.C. Plant remains from near the base include two-rowed barley, emmer, einkorn, club wheat (free-threshing), lentil, and vetch. Above the Natufian culture at Beidha was a second occupation by people who cultivated emmer wheat, harvested barley with a fragile rachis, and probably herded goats. The site has been dated as early seventh millennium, about 6750 B.C. (De Contenson, 1971).

Meanwhile, some sites seem to have remained in a backwater. The site of Munhata, excavated for three seasons by Jean Perrot, is in the Jordan Valley, 15 km south of the Sea of Galilee. Levels 3 to 6 are dated as slightly earlier than 6000 B.C. There were houses of un-baked brick and plastered floors, sickle blades with sheen, mortars, grinders, querns, and all the accepted equipment for handling cereals, but no other evidence of either plant or animal domesticates. The animal bones are all from wild and not even of domesticable kinds. The site went unoccupied for about 15 centuries and level 2 is dated 4500 to 3500 B.C. Even in the second occupation the animals were not domesticated.

Another well-known site of the seventh millennium B.C. is the prepottery Neolithic B of Jericho (Hopf, 1969). Typologically it shows relationships to Ramad I and II, Munhatta levels 3 to 6, and Beidha II to IV. Plant remains include einkorn, emmer, two-rowed barley, pea, lentil, and vetch.

By 6000 B.C. agriculture was established. By this time we can find within the nuclear area primary evidence for domestic sheep, goat, cattle, pig, emmer, einkorn, barley, pea, vetch, bitter vetch, lentil, chickpea, and flax. Six-rowed barley and free-threshing wheat had appeared. Pottery was in general use and irrigation was either in practice or imminent. Large towns were about to be founded. Food production as an ecological system had been established.

The picture that emerges, however, is rather like a moving picture, with over 90% of the frames on the film blank. This is not surprising since over 90% of the sites have not been excavated. Not only have too few sites been excavated but the primary evidence is not always preserved and not always recovered. The Natufians probably harvested wild cereals throughout the ninth millennium, but not until about 8000 B.C. do we find the actual grains at Mureybit. Cultivated emmer appeared in Ali Kosh, Jarmo, Beidha, and Çayönü before it appeared at Munhatta in the very region where the wild form is most abundant today. Our present evidence indicates domestic sheep first at Zawi Chemi Shanidar, goats at Ali Kosh, cattle at Çatal Hüyük, and pig at Jarmo and Çayönü. So far our first evidence of domesticated wheat is at Ali Kosh and Çayönü, whereas the earliest barley is reported from Jarmo, Jericho, and Ali Kosh (Table 1). An excellent review of the evidence is presented by Ucko and Dimbleby (1969) and Renfrew (1969).

THE NUCLEAR AREA

While the evidence that emerges provides a reasonably good general framework, there are many details that elude us or are bothersome. At present, we have no primary evidence for domestication of plants before the middle of the eighth millennium; yet a number of farming village communities have been identified that seem to belong to the end of the eighth or early seventh millennium. It would be absurd to suppose that we have found, or ever will find, the earliest plants grown purposely for food, but as more sites are excavated we may expect the dates to be pushed back considerably.

Differences in relative development are already becoming clear. There is said to be domesticated emmer at Ali Kosh and Beidha while the barley still had a brittle rachis. Both sites are within the range of wild barley today but outside the range of wild emmer. The people of Munhata lived in an area where wild emmer is extremely abundant today but there is no evidence that they grew emmer at all. In fact, emmer was cultivated elsewhere at a time when the people of Munhata presumably harvested it from the wild. Harlan and Zohary (1966) suggested that domestication might be more likely outside of the regions where the wild forms were most abundant:

Table 1

Finds of domesticated plants and related species from the Near East and Europe before 5000 B.C. (adapted from Renfrew, 1969).*

Sites	Dates, B.C.	Wild einkorn	Einkorn	Wild emmer	Emmer	Bread wheat	Wild 2-row barley	Hulled 2-row barley	Naked 2-row barley	Hulled 6-row barley	Naked 6-row barley	Oat	Millet	Pea	Lentil	Vetch	Flax
Ali Kosh (B.M.)†	7500–6750	x	x	–	x	–	x	–	x?	–	–	–	–	–	–	–	–
Ali Kosh (A.K.)	6750–6000	–	–	–	x	–	–	x	–	x	–	Wd	–	–	–	–	–
Ali Kosh (M.J.)	6000–5600	–	–	–	x	–	–	x	–	–	–	Wd	–	–	–	x	x
Çayönü	7500–6500	x	x	x	x	–	–	x	–	x	–	–	–	x	x	x	x
Tepe Sabz (Sabz)	5500–5000	–	–	–	–	x	–	x	–	x	–	–	–	x	x	x	–
Tepe Guran	6200–5500	–	–	–	x	–	x	x	–	–	–	–	–	–	–	x	–
Tell es-Sawwan	5800–5600	–	x	–	x	x	x	x	–	x	x	–	–	–	x	x	x
Tell Mureybat	8050–7542	x	–	–	–	–	x	–	–	–	–	–	–	–	–	x	x
Jericho, prepottery Neolithic	ca. 7000	–	x	–	x	–	–	x	–	–	–	–	–	x	x	x	–
Beidha, prepottery Neolithic B.	ca. 7000	–	–	–	–	–	x	x?	x?	–	–	Wd	–	x	x	x	–
Jarmo	ca. 6750	x	x	–	x	–	x	x	–	–	–	–	–	x	x	x	–
Tell Ramad	ca. 6500	–	x	x	x	C	x	x	–	–	–	–	–	–	–	x	–
Matarrah	ca. 5500	–	–	–	x	–	–	x	–	–	–	Wd	–	–	–	–	–
Amuq A	ca. 5750	–	–	–	x	–	–	B	–	–	–	–	–	–	–	–	–
Mersin, Early Neolithic	ca. 5750	–	–	–	–	–	–	–	–	–	–	–	–	–	–	–	–
Çatal Hüyük, VI–II	5850–5600	–	x	–	x	x	x	–	–	x	x	–	–	x	x	x	x
Aceramic Hacilar	ca. 7000	x	–	x	x	–	–	–	–	–	x	–	–	x	x	x	–
Ceramic Hacilar	5800–5000	–	x	–	x	x	–	x	–	x	x	–	–	x	x	x	–
Can Hasan, Late Neolithic	ca. 5250	–	–	–	–	–	–	–	–	x	–	–	–	–	–	–	–
Knossos, Stratum X	ca. 6100	–	–	–	W	x	–	B	–	x	–	–	–	x	x	x	–
Aceramic Ghediki	ca. 6–5000	–	x	–	x	–	–	x	x	–	–	–	–	x	x	x	–
Aceramic Sesklo	ca. 6–5000	–	–	–	x	–	–	x	–	–	–	–	–	x	–	–	–
Aceramic Argissa	ca. 6–5000	–	x	–	x	–	–	–	–	x	–	–	x	–	–	–	–
Aceramic Achilleion	ca. 6–5000	–	–	–	W	–	–	–	–	–	–	Wd	–	–	–	–	–
Nea Nikomedeia	ca. 6200	–	–	–	W	–	–	B	–	–	–	–	–	x	x	x	–
Karanovo I	ca. 5000	–	x	–	x	–	–	–	–	–	–	–	–	–	x	–	–
Azmaska Moghila, Early Neolithic	ca. 5000	–	–	–	x	–	–	–	–	–	–	–	–	–	x	–	–

* W = Wheat unspecified; B = Barley unspecified; Wd = Wild form; C = Club wheat.
† B.M. = ... ; A.K. = ... ; M.J. = ...

Why should anyone cultivate a cereal where natural stands are as dense as a cultivated field? If wild cereal grasses can be harvested in unlimited quantities, why should anyone bother to till the soil and plant the seed? We suspect that we shall find, when the full story is unfolded, that here and there harvesting of wild cereals lingered on long after some people had learned to farm, and that farming itself may have originated in areas adjacent to, rather than in, the regions of greatest abundance of wild cereals.

There are many other details that remain to be worked out, but the general pattern that is coming into focus implies that the nuclear area is rather large and must be taken as a whole unit. A comparison of Figures 1 and 5 shows that our earliest primary evidence for both plant and animal domestication falls within the area where wild bar-

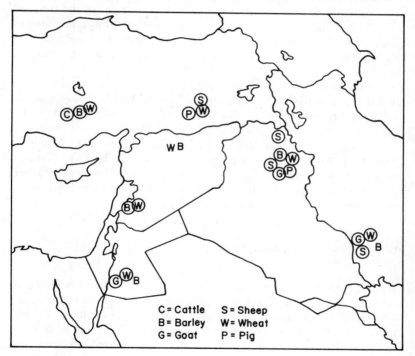

Figure 5
Early finds. Circles indicate domesticated races.

ley is abundant today and where it may be found in rather primary habitats. The shaded area of Figure 1 may serve to outline the nuclear area of early plant and animal domestication in the Near East. It is true that the earliest evidence of domestic cattle falls slightly outside of the region indicated, but the nature of the site shows clearly that agriculture had been well established before the founding of Çatal Hüyük.

The nuclear area must be understood as a unit because it is becoming apparent that events in one part of the area were not without influence on other parts. Agriculture did not arise full-blown in one spot but as a synthesis of practices and techniques that had different origins. Some people concentrated on sheep and goats, others on pigs or cattle. Emmer, barley, and einkorn were probably introduced into cultivation by different people in different subregions of the area and at different times. There were probably multiple domestications of both plants and animals. It was the integration of several practices and techniques that established food production as an ecological system.

One concrete evidence of contact across the nuclear area is the distribution of obsidian tools, mostly blades. Within this region, obsidian occurs only near Lake Van and central Anatolia in Turkey. By 7500 B.C. there is already evidence for an obsidian trade extending throughout the nuclear area (Wright and Gordus, 1969). People of Beidha or Ali Kosh had some sort of contact with the Lake Van area in order to obtain the obsidian found in these sites. The trade reached preagricultural sites as well. By early seventh millennium there might even have been some trade in native copper.

QUESTIONS OF CLIMATIC CHANGE

While the correspondence of the present distribution of wild cereals and the archaeological evidence for plant and animal domestication is very good, it is legitimate to ask: "Was the distribution of wild cereals 11,000 years ago the same as today? Has there been a significant change in climate that would alter their distributions?" These questions have led H. E. Wright, Jr. (1968), Willem Van Zeist (1969), and others to attempt a study of climates in the critical time range, 15,000 to 7000 B.C. The study has been hampered by a scarcity of suitable lakes from which sediment cores could be extracted for pollen analyses, but the evidence that has emerged is consistent in showing that a considerable change in climate did, in fact, take place.

Dated pollen sequences indicate that in 12,000 B.C. there may have been an *Artemisia* steppe vegetation in the Zagros Mountains where an oak woodland exists today. At about 9000 B.C. oak pollen begins to appear in some abundance and increases steadily until about 6000 B.C. when there is a more rapid rise in relative abundance. By about 3500 B.C. oak pollen accounts for 50 to 70% of the pollen rain; this is approximately the present situation in the oak woodland belt. Evidently the climate of 9000 B.C. was considerably different from that of today. Wild emmer is today closely associated with the oak woodland and if that formation was not present in the Zagros, perhaps the wild emmer was not present either.

A study of Figures 1, 2, and 3 shows that all three wild cereals have discontinuous distributions. The implication is that the distributions were once continuous and later became discontinuous as a result of a change in climate. If, as a result of late Ice Age influence, the life zones had been displaced downslope and toward the south, all three species might have had continuous ranges. The outpost of wild einkorn in the Lebanon might have been connected with the major range of the species and this may well account for the wild einkorn found at Mureybit where wild einkorn does not occur today.

The same displacement of life zones may have brought the presently disjunct races of wild emmer together. If so, then both Beidha and Ali Kosh might have been within the natural range of wild emmer at 7000 B.C. Both sites have been assigned cultivated emmer largely because they are now out of the natural habitat of the wild forms. Such an interpretation would bring the first known domestic wheat and barley into the Jarmo-Çayönü time range.

The present discontinuity in wild barley stretches from Sinai to Cyrenaica. A past displacement of life zones, sufficient to bring these populations together, would imply that wild barley was once in the delta of lower Egypt and distributed at least along the Mediterranean coast to Libya. Indeed, the flood zone of the Nile would seem to be an ideal habitat for a rather ephemeral, large-seeded annual grass, at least where the annual silt deposits were not too thick. Pollen identified as barley has been found in southern Egypt in archaeological contexts, but grass pollen is notoriously difficult to identify positively.

Finally, one should also bear in mind that the present distribution of wild cereals may be misleading to the archeobotanist because of the evolution of weed races whose ranges have expanded since the invention of agriculture. All of these problems need further study before a full understanding of the nuclear area of Near Eastern agriculture can be developed.

SPREAD OF AGRICULTURE OUT OF THE NUCLEAR AREA

The spread of agriculture out of the nuclear zone was charted by J. G. D. Clark in 1965 and Figure 6 shows an adaptation of his map.

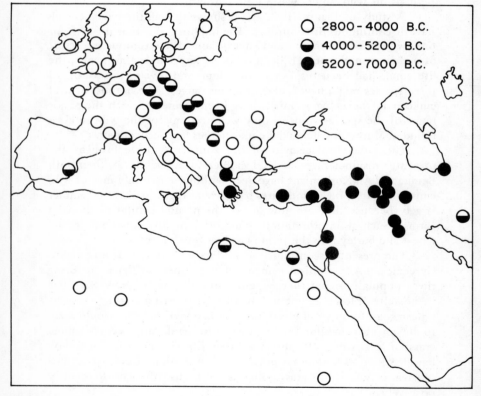

Figure 6
Early farming settlements.

Agricultural sites in the sixth millennium are found in Greece. An early thrust by farming people up the Danube and into the forests of Europe established farming on the lower Rhine at about 4000 B.C. An impressive amount of evidence for prehistoric agriculture in Europe has been assembled in Murray (1970) and Tringham (1971). To the east, the site of Djeitun in Soviet Turkmenistan suggests a farming community of the sixth millennium, although the site has not been precisely dated. We do not know when agriculture reached Pakistan and India but the Mohenjo-daro and Harappa civilizations seem to have been based on a wheat and barley culture. They arose in the early and middle third millennium B.C. Wheat and barley did not seem to reach China before the second millenium B.C. (Ho, 1969).

The Near Eastern crop complex also reached the Ethiopian highlands at a fairly early time, but there is as yet no primary evidence to estimate the date. The Near Eastern crops have been in Ethiopia long enough to develop centers of diversity (Harlan, 1969) and to have evolved unique varieties that are not found elsewhere. The emmers of Ethiopia, however, are more closely related to those of southern India than to those of Europe.

RECORDED HISTORY

The historic time range is too late to tell us much about the origin of the primary crops and agricultural development, but it is not without interest. In the Mesopotamian Valley, where writing appears to have originated, barley was the chief crop. In the south especially, barley almost completely displaced wheat as the cereal crop by 2300 B.C. This is taken to be not so much from preference as from necessity since there is independent evidence that the irrigated lands were salting up. Barley is much more salt-tolerant than wheat. However, even before this shift to a near monoculture, barley was apparently the more important of the two (Adams, 1958).

Barley also held a dominant position even into classical Greek times. It was the food of the poor and the ration of the soldier. It is not an attractive cereal from a dietary and culinary point of view. The covered sorts, especially, are very high in fiber and difficult to digest. The culture of naked varieties improves the diet considerably, but even naked barley is less desirable than wheat. Helbaek claims to have identified naked six-rowed barley in Çatal Hüyük and Tepe

Sabz, which indicates it was available. Much of the grain recovered in Mesopotamia, however, was covered and some sort of special processing may be implied.

In the cuneiform literature of Mesopotamia generally, barley is mentioned much more often than wheat. There is a myth concerning the divine origin of barley but not a corresponding one for wheat. The relative value as indicated by price, taxes, or rations shows barley and emmer (probably in the glume) about equal and about half the value of naked wheat. Yields at about 2400 B.C. were calculated by R. M. Adams (1958) from a number of records and show: barley, 2,537 liters/ha; emmer, 3,672 liters/ha; and wheat, 1,900 liters/ha. The emmer was presumably in the glume and, therefore, about 75% as heavy as wheat. The yields are quite respectable but similar computations only a few centuries later indicate a sharp decline that, again, may be attributed to salinization. By 2100 B.C. the yield of barley was only 1,460 liters/ha and wheat had virtually disappeared as a crop in the southern region (Jacobsen and Adams, 1958).

In Egypt where salting was less of a problem, emmer was the preferred cereal for bread, and naked free-threshing types were not grown until the Greek occupation after Alexander the Great. When Herodotus visited Egypt in the fifth century B.C., he wrote that the Egyptians ate emmer and considered it a disgrace to eat (naked) wheat. Under Greek influence, however, they did change to bread wheat after a big export market opened up in Rome.

Einkorn apparently never reached Egypt, Ethiopia, or India. It moved with the early agriculturalists up the Danube and into western Europe, but seems to have been a relatively minor crop almost everywhere it was introduced. Records indicate it was important to Schwabia and is still grown in mountainous regions of Switzerland, Italy, and Germany. In recent years it has been reportedly grown on a small scale in France, Spain, Morocco, and the Balkans. The only place that it is grown on a large scale today is in Turkish Thrace where it is used as livestock feed.

CONCLUSIONS

Long before recorded history, the people of the Near East had become completely and utterly dependent upon agriculture for their food. There was no possible way to return to gathering economies.

The threat of famine was ever at hand. If the rains failed, starvation stalked the land. Biblical literature makes repeated reference to years when the heavens were shut up and the rains did not come. While the Israelites were still pastoralists, they were forced by drought to move to Egypt, but even Egypt could suffer hard times. There is evidence that the Old Kingdom went into eclipse because of a series of years with low floods. The inscription on the tomb of Ankhtifi (see p. 171) was written during this first "dark age" of Egypt when the Old Kingdom came to a close and before the rise of the Middle Kingdom. The full text is starkly eloquent.

Another commentary of the time is the lament of the Egyptian prophet Ipuwer, which reads, in part:

> Plague stalketh through the land and blood is everywhere . . . Many men are buried in the river . . . the towns are destroyed and Upper Egypt is become an empty waste . . . the crocodiles are glutted with what they have carried off. Men go to them of their own accord. Men are few. He that layeth his brother in the ground is everywhere to be seen . . . grain hath perished everywhere . . . the storehouse is bare, and he that hath kept it lieth stretched out on the ground . . .
>
> *Erman, 1927*

What, then, did it profit man to domesticate barley, wheat, sheep, and goats? What was gained by the development of effective food-producing systems? Obviously, it was not an assured or stable food supply. But when the system works well, large numbers of people can be supported and civilizations can emerge from an agricultural base. The pyramids were all built before Egypt's first dark age, and the splendor, wealth, and power of the Old Kingdom were unmatched anywhere in the world in early third millennium B.C. The ancient civilizations of the world are the visible fruits of the evolution of agricultural economies.

Chapter 9

INDIGENOUS
AFRICAN
AGRICULTURE

While the developments we have recorded were taking place in the Near East, something was going on in Africa south of the Sahara, but we know little about it. Contact between the Mediterranean world and sub-Sahara Africa was extraordinarily tenuous from the beginnings of recorded history until the rise of Islam, and the Western world did not learn much of Africa until Portuguese explorations in the 15th century. Among the masses of beautifully preserved plant materials found in ancient Egyptian tombs there is not a single indigenous African crop, although some of the wild native plants were collected. Egypt and the whole of North Africa looked northward; their culture and their agriculture belonged to the Mediterranean world.

An indigenous African agriculture was developed in Africa, by Africans domesticating African plants. An agricultural system evolved with a farming village pattern and spread over much of the continent. It was adequate to support the high cultures of Mali, Ghana, Nok, Ife, and Benin. The system was complete with cereals, pulses, root and tuber crops, oil crops, vegetables, stimulants, medicinal crops, and magic and ritual plants. This much we know: when, where and by whom and under what circumstances remain to be established.

---

[1] Anywhere in Black Africa was "Ethiopia" to the Greeks and "Sudan" to the Arabs.

The number of plants domesticated is impressive (Chapter 3, Table 1). The most important of these from a world view are coffee, sorghum, pearl millet, oil palm, watermelon, cowpea, and finger millet. The most important to the Africans as food are sorghum, pearl millet, African rice, yams, oil palm, karité, cowpea, bottle gourd, finger millet, tef, enset, and noog. Other crops of considerable importance to Africans are fonio, cola, chat, okra, roselle, *Voandzeia,* and *Corchorus olitorius.*

In addition to these are some of uncertain origin which may have been domesticated either in Africa or Asia. These include sesame, "Asian" cotton, tamarind, pigeonpea, and guar. In the case of sesame, cotton, and guar, the nearest relatives of the cultivated subspecies appear to be African, but we are not sure that these plants were domesticated in Africa. Guar is not grown in Africa; cotton may have been domesticated in Asia, and while the genus *Sesamum* is essentially African, the species most genetically compatible with sesame are Indian.

ARCHAEOLOGICAL PRELUDE

The prehistory of man extends farther back in time in Africa than anywhere else on earth. The evidence, as we now understand it, indicates that the genus *Homo* originated in Africa well over 2 million years ago and most of human evolution has taken place in this arena. In this sense we are all Africans, and Africa is the home of the human race, but studies of our own origins are concerned with a time range far too early to be of help in understanding the origins of African agriculture.

The time range of concern to us begins with the terminal phase of the glaciation in Europe, about 12,000 to 13,000 B.C. Evidences for changes in climate in Africa are not as subtle as those in the Near East. Any observant amateur can recognize stabilized dune formations in the broad-leaved savanna regions both north and south of the forest zones. Fossil lake shorelines and fossil streams are conspicuous. The levels of lakes Chad, Rudolph, Afrera, Nakuru, Naivasha, Magadi, Victoria, and Katwa changed rather radically within this time span. Lake Chad was once 10 times its present size, and Lake Rudolph was once so deep that it overflowed into the Nile watershed. A series of terraces along the Nile indicate a succession of rather spectacular rises and declines of the river level.

The several surveys that have been made involving geology, hydrology, and palynology all agree that the changes in climatic patterns have been complex and difficult to interpret. The rises and declines in the lake levels have not been synchronous; long-term trends were interrupted by short-term countertrends. The details are too complex to deal with here, but the most general shifts in climate can be sketched (Clark, 1967).

Basic to any interpretation is the fact that north and south Africa are subject to cyclonic weather patterns and have winter rainfall regimes. Closer to the equator, tropical monsoon patterns prevail, with a single summer rainy season toward the tropics and two rainy seasons in the equatorial belt. In addition to increases and decreases of temperature and rainfall, there has evidently been expansion and contraction of the cyclonic belts.

At about the middle of the 13th millennium B.C., the Nile rose significantly and began a phase called the Sahaba aggradation which lasted until after 10,000 B.C. During the flood stage, water infiltrated across the flood plains and established shallow, temporary lakes, many of which dried up before the next flood. The Sahaba silts reached a thickness of over 20 m above the modern flood plain at Wadi Halfa.

In association with the temporary lakes is a series of sites, named Tushka after a village now beneath the water of Lake Nasser. Occupation seems to have ranged from about 12,500 to 10,500 B.C. Among the standard Upper Paleolithic tool kit are found numerous grinding stones and a number of blades with apparent sickle sheen. Wendorf, Said, and Schild (1970) interpret these items as indicating the use of ground grain. No actual seeds have been found, but the tools do suggest the harvesting and grinding of grass seeds. Similar grinding equipment is found at Kom Ombo, which is about 200 km farther north, at about the same time, although no sheen is found on the blades. Still further to the north at Isna, near Luxor, more settlements were found with both grinding stones and blades with gloss. Other examples associated with the Sahaba aggradation have also been reported.

The occurrence of grinding stones and blades with sickle sheen becomes very spotty after the Sahaba, perhaps because the people went elsewhere or perhaps because we have not searched enough. A few specimens found in Nubia are dated about 7400 B.C. but it is not until 6500 B.C. that the evidence becomes more abundant. By the end of the fifth millennium B.C., evidence of the Near Eastern complex becomes apparent in Egypt with barley, emmer, flax, pottery, and a tool kit quite different from any previously known in Africa.

Conditions in the Sahara between 12,000 and 4000 B.C. are suggested by pollen analyses in the Tibesti and Haggar massifs. In the plain below the Tibesti, vegetation was apparently grassland with some acacia and tamarisk along the water courses. Higher in the mountains was a woodland of myrtle, oak, hackberry, and olives and still higher up juniper and pine trees. Several pollen analyses scattered across the Sahara and showing the presence of pine, juniper, ash, and a number of other species of the Mediterranean woodlands indicate that the zone of winter rainfall had expanded over much of the Sahara. Most of the regions that are now desert appeared to have been perfectly hospitable to man at that time.

There is a sprinkling of so-called Neolithic sites across the Sahara region to the Maghreb, some of which show evidence of grinding equipment and sickles by 10,000 B.C. (Clark, in press). By 5000 B.C. pottery, sheep and goat herding were prevalent in the region. From 6000 B.C. the economies in the central Sahara seemed to have been based on hunting and grain collecting. This continued with pastoralists, who moved in about 5000 B.C., until desiccation forced them out in the third millennium B.C. Despite the abundance of sites and the long occupation of the Sahara, there is no direct evidence that a plant agriculture was practiced at all (Clark, 1970).

Direct evidence from archaeology has been of very little help in Africa to date. Sorghum has been found in abundance in east and southeast Africa and at the site of Daima in Nigeria, but all the samples are more recent than 500 A.D. By this time, the crop was already known archaeologically in India, so the later finds are of little help in understanding origins of African agriculture. A study by Munson (1968, in press) in Mauritania is more significant, however, in that he found a series of sites that seemed to indicate a switch from a dependence on gathering wild grass seeds to the cultivation of pearl millet. The sites were associated with a shallow lake system, now dried up, and the people herded livestock, fished, hunted, and collected grass seed. The main grass harvested at the beginning was *Cenchrus biflorus* which is a sandbur and a very uncomfortable grass to handle. It is called kram-kram in much of western Africa and is still harvested for food from time to time. The chronology is shown graphically in Figure 1. These data were taken almost entirely from impressions in potsherds. The date, a little before 1000 B.C., again is of little help because pearl millet is known archaeologically in India by that time. Nevertheless, the study gives us insights into how people may change their subsistence over a period of years and take up agriculture when it had not been practiced before.

By the middle of the third millennium B.C., the Sahara was beginning to dry out and the process accelerated sharply about 2,000 B.C. There was a marked reduction of prehistoric sites and people apparently were moving out of the region at this time.

It has been suggested that some of the African crops might have been domesticated in the Sahara during the time it was occupied by rather sedentary herding-fishing-hunting people. The shallow lakes apparently provided a considerable portion of the diet in the form of fish, hippopotami, and the like and the back country provided game and grazing for sheep and goats. Since the lakes occupied flat pans, they enlarged during the rains and shrank during the dry season. This may well have been an ideal situation to learn the techniques of "décrue" agriculture so characteristic of many parts of West Africa.

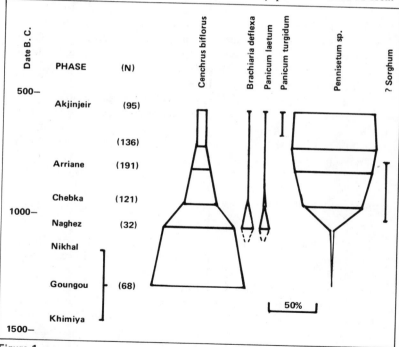

Figure 1
Percentages of identified grain impressions per phase (from Munson, 1971).

"Crue" means "flood" in French; "décrue" means the time when the flood waters subside. There is no convenient English word, so we have borrowed the French. In décrue agriculture, planting is done in the moist soil as the flood waters go down or as ephemeral pools of the rainy season dry up. This tends to be at the onset of the dry season so that the crops must grow and mature on residual moisture. To speed up the life cycle the farmers often resort to transplanting. Both sorghum and pearl millet are transplanted in décrue systems. Today décrue agriculture has achieved a highly sophisticated form in the Bend of the Niger region and along other rivers of western Africa (Harlan and Pasquereau, 1969).

There are also other possibilities. A considerable number of sites that could be referred to the Neolithic period have been identified along the forest-savanna margins. The Kintampo culture of Ghana is one that shows some cohesion and has been sufficiently studied to be characterized in a general way (Flight, in press). Direct evidence for agriculture includes bones of domestic goats and seeds of cowpeas. Cereals were probably also grown although seeds have not yet been found. The culture flourished in the second millennium B.C. and must have had antecedents before that. We have seen that the pollen evidence suggests human disturbance of the forests of East Africa in the third millennium B.C. (Hamilton, 1972).

So far, archaeological studies have not been sufficiently detailed nor systematic to tell us very much. We must rely more than is desirable on evidence from the crops themselves and the people who grow them. For a review of such evidence as we do have at this time see Thurstan Shaw (in press).

A SAVANNA COMPLEX

Unlike the Near Eastern agricultural complex, African crops lack cohesion. Many have very limited distributions; some are found only in Ethiopia, some only in limited areas of west Africa. There is no apparent center of plant domestication and activities of domestication seem to have ranged over a vast area from the Atlantic to the Indian Ocean, south of the Sahara and north of the equator. African agriculture is, however, basically a savanna agriculture. Sorghum is a savanna crop, not well suited to the high rainfall of the forest zones. Pearl millet is one of the most drought-resistant of all the crops and becomes the dominant one near the fringes of the Sahara (Figure 2).

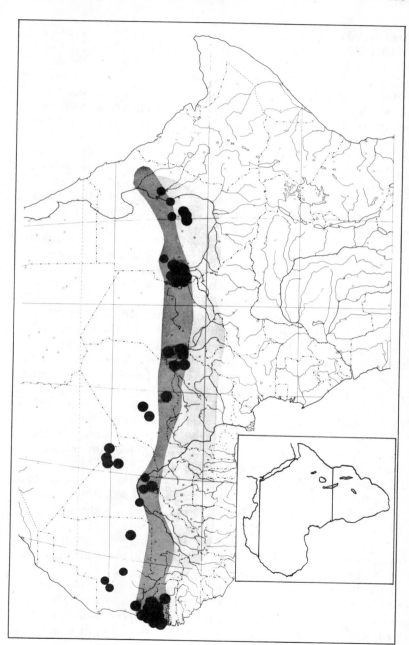

Figure 2
Known distribution of wild pearl millet (*Pennisetum violaceum*), solid circles. The northern pearl millet belt is shown by heavy shading. The crop is grown in the zone of light shading, but sorghum is more important there. There is a southern millet zone in association with the South African deserts, but it is less clearly defined.

African rice was domesticated from an annual wild rice, *Oryza barthii*, which is a plant of water holes in the savanna zone (Figure 3). In fact, the truly wild forms do not occur in the forest zones or in the derived savanna today, even though a derived weed type does infest rice fields in the high rainfall belt. The *Voandzeia* or Bambara ground nut is a highly drought-resistant savanna plant. Even the yams, which are the staff of life of the tribes of the forest belt from central Ivory Coast to Cameroon, are basically savanna plants. Their large tubers are adaptations for storage enabling them to survive the dry season and periodic burning. Karité, baobab, tamarind, and *Parkia* are all savanna trees. The oil palm was originally a tree of forest margins since it is not tolerant of deep shade. It has spread into the forest and thrives under the disturbance of shifting cultivation, but this is not its natural habitat. Wild cowpeas and hyacinth beans are also forest margin plants. Fonio, roselle, *Corchorus olitorius,* bottlegourd, and watermelon are all savanna plants. Tef, enset, noog, and finger millet are plants of the cool East African highlands. The only true forest plants of the African agricultural complex are cola, coffee, malaguette, and a few other minor plants.

The African savanna complex did spread out of its hearth in a way similar to the Near East agricultural complex. The system spread southward along either side of the rift into southern Africa. Sorghum, pearl millet, finger millet, cowpea, and hyacinth bean went to India and became very important there, and cotton, sesame, guar, pigeonpea, and tamarind are perhaps more important in India than in Africa. Roselle and *Cochorus olitorius* are vegetables in Africa but fiber plants in India. Noog is grown on a small scale in India but may have been introduced rather recently. The most important of these African plants to the Indians are the drought-resistant cereals, sorghum and pearl millet; they are the staff of life for millions in the drier sectors of India. Archaeological finds in India suggest that these crops may have arrived in the second millennium B.C. (Vishnu-Mittre, 1968, in press). There are Sanskrit words for pearl millet and finger millet but not for sorghum.

From the evidence we do have, I conclude that agriculture in Africa is basically noncentric, that plants were domesticated throughout a broad zone from the Atlantic to the Indian Ocean and primarily within the Sahel and Guinea savanna zones. From the savanna, it slowly encroached into the forest through practices that often produced derived savanna. Parts of the complex spread southward into East Africa and also reached India by the second millennium B.C.

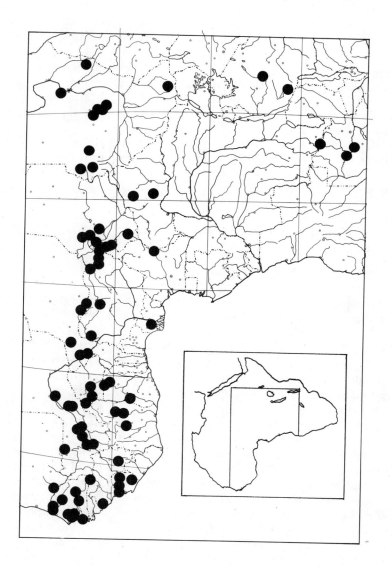

Figure 3
Known distribution of wild African rice (*Oryza barthii*), solid circles. The grass is native to the savanna, and colonies within the forest zone appear to be recent introductions.

When this all began is still a matter of conjecture. The grinding stones along the Nile and out into the Sahara are a common tool of hunter-gatherers and are used by Australian aborigines today. The sickle sheen implies the use of small grains like barley rather than sorghum or pearl millet. If a winter rainfall regime prevailed at the time, this is only reasonable. Barley pollen has been tentatively identified in the Sahaba phase along the Nile and stands of wild barley occur today in Cyrenaica. It appears that the zone of wild barley harvesting may have once been much larger than we had thought, but as of now, we have no evidence of barley domestication in Africa.

When, then, were the African plants domesticated? We have no concrete evidence, but I suggest that the process went on over a period of several millennia and that some indigenous agriculture was being practiced by 4000 B.C.

CROP COMPETITION AND DISTRIBUTION

The distribution of African crops and cultures may suggest a sequence of events even if the exact dates of the events are not yet known. The very sharp demarkation between rice-eating tribes and yam-eating tribes has attracted much attention. In Ivory Coast, people on the right bank of the Bandama River eat rice, people on the left bank eat yams (Chapter 7, Figure 2). Each crop is very deeply enmeshed in the culture of the people. Rice-eaters do not feel they have eaten a meal unless rice is served. Yams are central not only in the diets of yam-eating tribes, but also in their ceremony, ritual, myth, and folklore (Coursey, 1972).

The most reasonable explanation of the very sharp separation of cultures appears to involve a series of events. African rice had to be domesticated in the savanna zone, since that is where the progenitor is found (Figure 3). Cultivars were developed that could be grown under high rainfall on upland areas in the forest zone. This permitted the rice-eating tribes to expand to the Guinea coast. Rice cultures tend to be expansive, but when these people reached the yam belt they found an agricultural system already established. In fact, the social structures of the yam cultures are very strong and more systematically organized than those of other tribes in West Africa. The implication, then, is that yam agriculture and rice agriculture had independent origins and that the yam cultures may have been the

older (Coursey, 1972).   At least the yam cultures were well en-
trenched when the rice cultures arrived in the adjacent forest zone.

    In Ethiopia, evidence of crop-culture competition takes on other
forms. The bulk of Ethiopian agriculture is based on the Near East
complex of barley, wheat, grain legumes, flax, safflower, etc. This
imported agriculture apparently met an indigenous system already in
place when it arrived. The locally domesticated crops are tef, noog,
ensete, finger millet, chat, coffee, etc. The two systems have blended
to some extent in that tef occupies the largest area of any crop in the
country, while barley is second. Noog is widely grown over most of
the country, but ensete is the staff of life for a number of tribes in
the central and southern highlands. There is a genuine ensete culture
distinct from those that depend on seed crops.

    Finger millet is largely grown in Ethiopia and Uganda, but has
spread westward to Lake Chad or a little beyond.   There it encountered the West African millet, fonio, and went no further. Other
examples could be cited, but it seems evident that crop distributions
in Africa depend more on the distribution of tribes and cultures than
on the ecological adaptation of the plants.

    The introduction of crops from the Americas has had a profound
impact on African agriculture. Manioc is now more important in
Africa than in the New World where it originated. Maize has displaced a great deal of the sorghum acreage in South and East Africa.
In West Africa, maize is more of a garden crop than a field crop.
Capsicum peppers are absolutely basic to much of the African cuisine.
Other American crops that have become important are sweet potato,
cotton, peanut, tomato, papaya, and tobacco. All have been received
well and have competed successfully with indigenous counterparts.

RECORDED HISTORY

Written history is, of course, too late to tell us anything about agricultural origins, but it is worthwhile to call attention to one event
recorded about 1500 B.C. During the 18th dynasty of Egypt, Queen
Hatshepsut sent an expedition to Punt, thought to be somewhere on
the horn of Africa. It was the first government-sponsored plant exploration expedition in recorded history. She had built a temple at
Deir El Bahari and wished to establish incense trees on the terraces
(see inscription, p. 193). Five ships were dispatched to Punt and were
greeted by the inhabitants. Scenes on the temple walls show round,

thatched houses on stilts with ladders reaching to the doors. The people had cattle and donkeys and were able to supply goods in quantity (Naville, 1898). Incense trees were potted into huge tubs and loaded on board. The cargo from Punt included much incense, gums, resins, ivory, jewels, metal rings, hides, leopard skins, ebony, and other items. Despite serious defacing and vandalism of the temple a fascinating glimpse is presented of sub-Sahara Africa of the middle of the second millennium B.C. (Figure 4). It shows as well that plant exploration and introduction are venerable activities and can receive governmental support from time to time.

Figure 4 (at right)
Two ships from Queen Hatshepsut's expedition are being loaded with the produce of Punt. Incense trees are being carried on board in tubs large enough that six men are required for each. This is the first government-sponsored plant introduction expedition in recorded history. From the temple of Deir El Bahari, about 1500 B.C. (from Naville, 1898; with permission of the publishers).

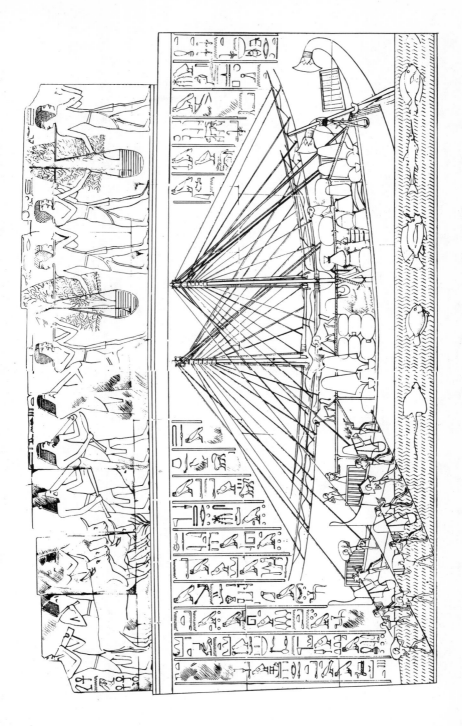

Chapter 10

THE CHINESE
CENTER

Learning without thinking is useless.
Thinking without learning is dangerous.

Confucius, sixth century B.C.
(Translated by Ezra Pound)

ARCHAEOLOGICAL PRELUDE

While the prehistoric record of man in China is not as long as that for Africa, it does reach back to *Homo erectus*. The Chinese race of that species (Peking man), which had already separated from those that ranged across the western half of Asia, Europe, and Africa, differed in his tool preparation traditions. He did not manufacture the classic pear-shaped Acheulean or Abbevillean "hand ax," but invented a characteristic "chopper" of his own. Even at that time the inhabitants of China seemed to be developing a unique and endemic tradition.

Geological evidence shows that from the middle of the Pleistocene, and perhaps earlier, the hinterland of China and Central Asia had a semiarid steppe environment and occasionally may have been desiccated even further to form an arid region over vast reaches of the interior. One result has been a fantastic accumulation of loess, some alluvial, but much of it windblown. There are sizeable sections of Shensi and Kansu with loess deposits over 250 m thick and still larger areas with 150 m or more. Downslope, huge tracts of Hopei, Honan, Shantung, and Anhwei are covered with redeposited loess. It is on the upland loess terraces that indigenous Chinese agriculture emerged (Figure 1).

Our view of the Chinese center has been heavily influenced by a smattering of archaeological information and later historical developments. Andersson (1934) started to develop the archaeological picture before World War II. He worked the site of Yang-shao and described the painted-pottery people. Since then we have found that the type site, Yang-shao, is late and not very typical of the culture which is now known from well over 1,000 sites in the Wei River basin north of the Chinling Mountains.

209

Yang-shao villages were situated on loess terraces well above the main streams. They were often large and well structured with separate parts of the village maintained for specialized functions. Burials were made in cemeteries outside of the living areas. Houses were often large and partly sunken into the loess soil. The pottery was finely made and rather elegant. The best known site is Pan-p'o-ts'un which covers an area over 50,000 m^2. It is located near Sian in Shensi Province, and four radiocarbon dates were published for it in 1972: 4115 ± 110 BC; 3955 ± 105 BC; 3890 ± 105 BC; 3635 ± 105 BC (Laboratory of the Institute of Archaeology, Peking, 1972a, 1972b). This clustering of dates is supported by two other Yang-shao sites, An-yang 3535 ± 105 BC and Shan-hsien 3280 ± 100 BC, both in Honan. The culture, then, would appear to have flourished through the fourth millennium B.C. and must have had antecedents. We can hardly believe that these people were at the very beginnings of agricultural development. Still, the Yang-shao are the oldest known agricultural people of China, and the only Mesolithic cultures known for China are also found in the same nuclear area (Chêng, 1966).

The main crop was *Setaria* millet. Remains of chestnuts, hazelnuts, and pine seeds were also found as well as bones of domesticated dog and pig. A few bones of sheep, cattle, and horse were represented together with remains of deer, gazelle, rabbits, and other wild animals, indicating some hunting was practiced. Despite the large size of the villages, the fine pottery, and the farming economy, the Yang-shao people maintained many cultural traits of their Paleolithic past, such as pebble-flake, bone and shell tools (Chêng, 1966).

The region was semiarid. In later historical times we know that a crop-fallow rotation was practiced. The fallow was primarily for storing moisture rather than a fertility-restoring device as in shifting cultivation. Other historical evidence suggests that the mulberry and therefore the silkworm and silk were important to the Yang-shao people. Chinese agriculture is basically a garden agriculture and was probably so from the beginning.

The Yang-shao were rather restricted geographically and give all the appearance of a nuclear area. As the system spread eastward to the swampy lowlands, two very important additional crops were taken into the fold: soybeans in the north and rice in the south.

A second tradition emerged in the nuclear area and spread outward primarily to the east. At first it was a Lung-shanoid tradition and then a fully developed Lung-shan or black pottery culture. In the Lung-shan we have wheel-turned pottery, domesticated cattle, sheep, and buffalo, and rice in abundance; *Panicum* millet, peach,

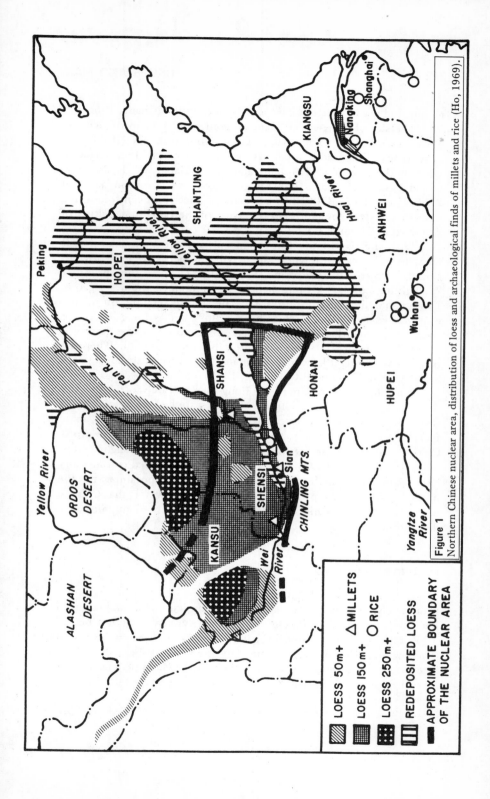

Figure 1
Northern Chinese nuclear area, distribution of loess and archaeological finds of millets and rice (Ho, 1969).

melon, and water chestnut have also been reported (Chang, 1968).

The site of Sung-tse in Shanghai contained remains of rice and is carbon dated at 3395 ± 105 B.C. or about 4000 B.C. if a bristle cone pine correction is used. It is classed as early Lung-shanoid, whereas the site of Ch'ien-shan-yang in Chekiang, which also contained rice, is classed as late Lung-shanoid and is carbon dated at 2750 ± 100 B.C. (3300 B.C. corrected). Rice has been found in a number of later sites and is characteristic of the Lung-shan culture of late third millennium B.C.

With the rise of the Lung-shan culture, the Yang-shao people were forced westward where some villages persisted until the beginning of recorded history and they continued to use their primitive "Paleolithic" tools. A Lung-shanoid group jumped the water gap to Taiwan sometime about 2500 B.C. The site of Feng-pi-t'ou on Taiwan was excavated by K. C. Chang (1969) and is Lung-shanoid in character rather than full Lung-shan. It is quite possible, however, that they were not the first agriculturalists on the island. There are traces of what might have been slash and burn agriculture dating back to the fifth millennium B.C. (Chang, 1970).

An interesting feature of the Lung-shan culture was the practice of scapulimancy. The shoulder blades (scapulae) of animals were thrown into a fire to divine where game was, to read omens, or to forecast the future. Later, these scapulae were engraved with proto-Chinese logomorphs and writing was developed in the Shang era. The writing was completely Chinese in character, but evolved considerably later than the cuneiform that emerged in Mesopotamia and the hieroglyphs of the Egyptians. It is to be noted, however, that Chinese writing is still in use while cuneiform and Egyptian hieroglyphics were discontinued long ago.

RECORDED HISTORY

Chinese civilization, as distinct from previous cultures, can be said to have begun with the founding of the Shang dynasty sometime before 1500 B.C. At about 1300 B.C., the Shang capital was established at An-yang and this city was captured by the Chou[1] tribe in 1027 B.C. The dates for An-yang became important in Chinese history for several reasons. Essentially all of the Shang literature falls between

[1]The legendary ancestor of the Chou tribe was Hou chi, the god of millets

1300 and 1027 B.C. and consists of oracle bone inscriptions and writing on cast bronze objects. Art had reached a high state of development and Shang bronzes are world-famous for their style and technique of casting.

It is from An-yang that we detect the first real evidence of contact with the West. Foreign importations of the time included wheat and barley, the horse chariot, probably the domesticated goat, and some art motifs borrowed from the Seima culture on the Volga. There is external evidence that the nomads of the Eurasian steppe were particularly active during the 13th century B.C., with much warfare, raiding, and sacking of towns and cities.

Among the earliest compilations of Chinese literature is the Book of Odes (Shih-ching) assembled from bits and fragments from the 11th century to the middle of the 6th century B.C. Botanically, it is the most informative of early literatures and mentions about 150 plants as compared to 55 in Egyptian literature, 83 in the Bible, and 63 in Homer (Ho, 1969). In the Odes, *Panicum* millet is mentioned 27 times, the mulberry 20 times, and *Artemisia* is mentioned 19 times with some 10 varieties.

The soybean is first mentioned in 664 B.C. in connection with tribute paid to the Chou by the Shan-Jung (Mountain Jung) tribe. Hemp (*Cannabis*) was not mentioned in Shang oracle literature, but occurs seven times in the Odes. Iron implements for agriculture became significant about 400 B.C. Manuring, crop rotation, double cropping, and intensive agriculture as well as the first large-scale irrigation projects all date to the third century B.C. (Ho, 1974).

After Alexander the Great (d. 323 B.C.) and the establishment of Greek states from Afghanistan to the Mediterranean, regular contact was maintained between China and Persia by way of the silk routes. Laufer, in his scholarly study *Sino-Iranica* (1919), traces the arrival in China of a number of Near Eastern cultigens: alfalfa and grape were introduced in 126 B.C.; walnut, cucumber, pea, spinach, broadbean, chive, coriander, fig, safflower, sesame, and pomegranate arrived from Iran at various times from the second to the seventh centuries A.D.

The Chinese crops were very slow to spread out from their homeland. The millets constitute a special case that will be discussed later, but cultigens of certain Chinese origin were unknown to the West until very late. The peach is said to have reached India by about the second century A.D. Many authors credit the Chinese with domestication of the apricot, but since the wild races range from Turkey to China it seems likely that other peoples were also involved.

The West did not know rice until after the era of Alexander the Great. Theophrastus (as translated by Arthur Hort, 1961) gave a good description of it and called it the emmer of the Indians. On the whole, Far Eastern agriculture may be characterized as introverted with very little dispersal until well into modern historical times, and many crops did not move out until the arrival of European shipping in the late 15th and early 16th centuries A.D. There was, in fact, a notable lack of long-range diffusion, as illustrated by the fact that the Chinese were casting iron for 2,000 years and using the crossbow for 1,000 years before the Europeans began to use them.

NORTH CHINA AS A CENTER

Northern China has all the attributes of a nuclear area and a hearth from which innovations were dispersed to the rest of China and to wherever the Chinese emigrated. The archaeological sequences from early Yang-shao to Lung-shanoid, Lung-shan, and Shang are consistent with the concept of a hearth in which agriculture flourished and from which it was dispersed. In addition, bronze casting, iron casting, writing, mathematics, certain agricultural techniques, and a series of other cultural elements developed within the center and spread outward from it. The area continues to be a center of political power and cultural influence.

Northern China is not so clearly a center of crop domestication. Many of the crops listed for the Chinese center (Chapter 3, Table 1) probably originated in southern China. Few domesticates can be assigned with certainty to the northern nuclear area. Even the soybean, which is from northern China, was probably domesticated east of the primary center. The Yang-shao culture thrived on millets and some locally domesticated fruits and vegetables, but Chinese agriculture as a system seems to have fed on addition crops from the outside. The appearance of a center may be due to the fact that Chinese culture was expansive rather than to an independent origin of an agricultural system that later spread over much of the Far East.

Li (1970) analyzed the crops of the Far East and indicated the different regions of origin for many. It is difficult to detect a convincing centric pattern either in North China or Southeast Asia from this analysis. Rather, it seems as if people domesticated useful elements of the local flora everywhere in eastern Asia and the South Pacific. This extremely diffuse pattern may also be an artifact be-

Figure 2
Known distribution of wild rice in Asia. The gaps in Burma and Vietnam are probably due to inadequate collection.

cause we are looking at the result of a long evolution of agricultural
economies. If we are to understand origins of agriculture in East Asia
we must have much more archaeological evidence than we now have.
The earliest stages have simply not yet been studied.

The greatest contribution of the Far East to human nutrition is
rice. It appeared in North China in early Lung-shanoid times and became very abundant in Lung-shan sites. Wild rices from which domesticated forms could be derived occur today from India to the
lower Yangtze (Figure 2). Where, when, and how many times in this
vast region rice was domesticated we do not know, but as fas as North
China is concerned, rice would appear to be an addition crop, coming
from the south.

One gets the impression, then, that Chinese agriculture was
dynamic and expansive because it accepted and exploited crops domesticated elsewhere. Without more evidence, however, we can only
speculate on the kind of feedback and cross stimulation that went on
between the different regions of East Asia (Chang, 1970).

Chapter 11

SOUTHEAST ASIA
AND OCEANIA

*According to one story the rice plant
existed from the beginning, but its ears
were not filled. This was the time when
men lived by hunting and gathering. The
goddess Kŭan Yin saw that men lived in
hardship and near starvation. She was
moved to pity and resolved to help
them. She went secretly into the rice
fields and squeezed her breasts so that
the milk flowed into the ears of the rice
plants. Almost all of them were filled,
but to complete her task she had to press
so hard that a mixture of milk and blood
flowed into the plants. That is why
there are two kinds of rice, the white
from the milk, the red from the mixture
of milk and blood.*

ARCHAEOLOGY

Christie, 1968

Man in Southeast Asia and Indonesia has left a record of respectable antiquity as indicated by *Homo erectus* remains in Java (*Pithecanthropus* or Java apeman), but much later sites are of more interest with respect to agricultural origins. Several sites that have yielded assemblages called Hoabinhian have been excavated. They are found in Burma, Thailand, and Vietnam and cover the time span from roughly 11,000 to 5500 B.C. The culture seemed to have some cohesion in the artifacts and was described by Gorman (1969) as having a broad-spectrum hunting-gathering economy.

The Spirit Cave site in Thailand has yielded evidence of plant utilization in occupation layers dated 8000 to 7000 B.C. The reported identification of some of the plants (cool-season Mediterranean plants, for example) must be viewed with extreme caution, but the remainder are tropical and might well be expected to occur (for example, *Lagenaria, Trapa, Areca, Terminalia, Piper, Madhuca, Canarium, Aleurites,* and *Cucumis*). The list is impressive and one is encouraged to hope that more excavations will yield primary evidence for plant domestication in Southeast Asia. At present there is no indication of cultivation in that time range.

Polished quadrangular adzes and bifacial slate knives sometimes make their appearance in Hoabinhian sites around 6000 B.C. A later culture with similar adzes and knives is revealed in the sites of Non Nok Tha and Ban Chiang. This culture had cord-marked pottery,

219

grew rice, and tended domestic cattle and perhaps tame pigs. Published dates have differed, but some of the newest evidence suggests that rice agriculture was established in northeastern Thailand before 4500 B.C. (Gorman, 1971, in press). There is also evidence for bronze metallurgy at Non Nok Tha layer 3, dated slightly earlier than 2000 B.C. (Bayard, 1972; Solheim, 1968).

These dates are slightly earlier than corresponding developments dated for China, but there has been so little work done in China and Southeast Asia that it is too early to draw firm conclusions. The next field season may change the picture drastically. It is most encouraging that work is finally underway in Southeast Asia and plant remains are being found. It had been thought that plants could not be preserved in the wet tropics and there would be no point in looking. It now appears that with a systematic effort we will be able to obtain the evidence we need. At present we have little more direct evidence than that just given.

Archaeologically, rice is known in India from about 2000 B.C. or some centuries earlier (Vishnu-Mittre, 1968, in press), but it was so widespread in the second millennium B.C. that it is reasonable to presume a considerably greater antiquity. Sites with rice remains dated to the second millennium B.C. occur in Gujarat, Rajasthan, Uttar Pradesh, Madhya Pradesh, Bihar, West Bengal, Orissa, and Mysore (Vishnu-Mittre, in press). The earliest Vedic literature does not mention rice despite frequent references to wheat and barley. The implication is that rice was imported into western India about 2000 B.C., but originated somewhere to the east. If northern China received rice from the south and western India received it from the east, we can at least bracket the vast region from eastern India to southern China as the area of domestication of Asian rice. At the moment, Thailand has the earliest rice reported from archaeological research.

The Hoabinhian appeared in that region at approximately the end of the European-North American glaciation. Presumably the sea levels had been substantially lowered during the height of the glaciation and were rising until the end of the Pleistocene. The Hoabinhian people may well have adapted to streamside habitats in areas now submerged. The rising waters might have precipitated a crisis in food procurement analogous to the desiccation of the Sahara in Africa. It has been estimated that the Southeast Asian-Southwest Pacific land mass was reduced by half in the post-Pleistocene submergence. Such a reduction could hardly help but affect population densities and a change in the food procurement system might have resulted (Gorman, in press).

PLANT EVIDENCE

With our present knowledge, it is only fair to say that the time range of the evolution of agriculture in Southeast Asia has not yet been determined. Archaeological work so far conducted is entirely inadequate to establish a sequence in any detail. Whatever picture we can develop must depend on piecing together what little we know about the plants themselves and from ethnology, ethnobotany, and historical sources. Unfortunately, even the plants have not been studied very systematically and the picture in Southeast Asia is probably the most obscure of any region in the world where agriculture is likely to have originated.

The earliest form of agriculture that developed in Southeast Asia appears to have evolved from intensive gathering techniques. Roots and tubers were dug with digging sticks. Fruits, nuts, and seeds were harvested from natural forest productions. Gradually, more and more of the useful plants were encouraged, tended, and finally deliberately cultivated in a shifting forest-type agricultural system. Slash and burn techniques were developed; mixed orchards and gardens were established. Sparse populations moved rather freely over the forest zones. Fishing, hunting, and gathering of wild plant productions from the forest continued to be important activities in supplying food until well into the period of recorded history.

The crops of this early agricultural complex were strictly indigenous and varied from place to place depending on the original natural distributions of the wild races. Roots and tubers were primarily taro, other aroids, yams, and *Pueraria lobata*. Fruits included bananas and plantains, mango, durian, and rambutan.

These are primarily plants of the forest margins or at least adapted to more light and less shading than is found in the rain-forest climax. The tubers in particular are adapted to zones with prolonged dry seasons. Wild taro and yams are abundant today in eastern Assam, upper Bruma, and southwest China. Wild citrus are common from southern China to northern Indochina, and wild bananas and mangos are found in Burma and China and down the Malay peninsula. Sugarcane is found in greatest diversity in New Guinea and Assam, but spontaneous canes are widespread throughout the region. Coconut is primarily coastal and perhaps largely an island plant until protected or planted by man along the mainland shores. The sago palm, breadfruit, fe'i banana, pandanus, and *Cyrtosperma* were South Sea island domesticates.

The whole region is enormously rich in useful plant species and an impressive number was domesticated (Chapter 3, Table 1). There is no clear evidence of a center, hearth, or nuclear area, however; plants were domesticated all over the region wherever they were found. Gorman (in press) has presented evidence that the piedmont was the arena of primary focus, preceding both the uplands and the swampy deltas, and suggests that rice and taro together might have formed the first successful agriculture of Southeast Asia.

There were two cereals in the ancient agricultural system, rice and *Coix* (Job's tears). There is some evidence that *Coix* was the older of the two, at least in the rain-forest zones. It spread into regions of the Philippines, Borneo, and New Guinea where rice did not reach. The great swampy deltas of Southeast Asia probably supported vast stands of wild rice at one time, but the rice in such environments was mostly, if not exclusively, of the perennial floating kinds. Seed was no doubt harvested by gatherers by canoe or from the tangled mass after flood waters receded at the end of the rains, but the perennial races are shy seeders compared to the annuals, and the environment is extremely difficult to exploit for agriculture. It is most unlikely that rice was domesticated in the delta zones which must have been sparsely settled until social and political systems evolved permitting the construction of dykes, canals, and other water control measures. Rice in Africa was domesticated in the savanna; the situation in Asia may have been similar.

Within modern historical times the traditional digging stick and hoe shifting cultivation has been replaced in many places by wet rice cultivation. The lower swamp areas in particular were intensively cultivated only in the last century or two and much of the settlement was so late that some census figures are available. In the 1850's Burma planted about 607,500 ha (1.5 million acres) to rice. The figure has now increased to over 4.86 million ha (12 million acres), 80% of it in the lower Burma Irrawadi swampland delta area. Thailand in the 1880's reported about 1.01 million ha (2.5 million acres) of rice, and today about 6.48 million ha (16 million acres) have been planted. Much of the increase has been in the lower Chao Phraya valley (the Bangkok plain). In Vietnam dyking and draining of the Mekong delta began in the 19th century. The delta as a whole is still not fully occupied but the increase in rice acreage has been phenomenal. Today in Vietnam about 5.27 million ha of 6.48 million ha (13 million of 16 million acres) in cultivation are planted to rice. North Vietnam, in recent years, has added about 2.03 million ha (5 million acres) of rice, all in swampy lowland areas. The rice area of Indonesia is about 7.5 million ha (18.5 million acres), much of it in Java and in the mangrove swampland of northeastern Sumatra. In the Philippines there are about 1.01 million ha (2.5 million acres) in shifting cultivation but about 3.5 million ha (8.5 million acres) of wet riceland. In Laos much of the agriculture is still of the original indigenous kind. Most of the country is mountainous upland and the population is very sparse. Malaysia is also sparsely populated, especially in Borneo. This permits the development of plantation crops on a large scale. On the whole, wet rice dominant landscapes are new in Southeast Asia and have replaced shifting cultivation of root and tree crops only in recent centuries.

Although the origin and antiquity of wet rice cultural techniques are uncertain, there seems to be little question that wet-field taro production had been developed earlier. Well-engineered, but small-scale terraces were constructed and water was led by canals to flood them. Such practices persist among tribes in New Guinea who have not yet taken up rice growing. The suggestion has been made that rice was domesticated from wild or weed races that infested the flooded taro fields. The suggestion has merit for limited regions of the Southeast Asia mainland and the larger islands, but if this sequence took place it was probably in addition to rice domestication in the savanna zones with prolonged dry seasons as in India and southeastern China, Burma, and Thailand.

The evidence for early rice cultivation in Thailand suggests that the cleavage between cereal agriculture and vegeculture is exaggerated and may never have been real. The fact is that there are more tropical cereals than temperate ones and that cereals play at least some role in most tropical agricultural systems. Wild rice is a food resource that could not be overlooked by gathering people and, as we have seen, is still harvested. The archaeological evidence suggests it had been domesticated at least once by the early fifth millennium B.C. Rice had been available for a long time, but rice-based agriculture did not become really expansive until population densities and social and political structures were such that intensive agriculture was not only demanded but could be practiced. The historical evidence of Ho (1974) indicates intensive agriculture got underway in China in the third century B.C.; when it developed in Southeast Asia we do not know.

Meanwhile, the original root and tree crop agriculture had spread slowly across the Malay Archipelago. Taro and Asian yams spread through Malaysia, the Philippines, Borneo, and New Guinea to New Caledonia. The time range is entirely unknown at the present, but it might be reasonable to suppose that this took place when pottery making was distributed through the region, about 2000 B.C. Later, Polynesian sailors began to travel across the South Pacific islands, taking with them taro, other aroid tubers, bananas, fe'i bananas, breadfruit, pandanus, pigs, and chickens. This apparently began in the first millennium B.C., as Polynesians went first to the Solomon Islands, then to the Marquesas (ca. 200 B.C.), the Society Islands (ca. 100 A.D.), and Easter Island (ca. 400 A.D.). The first settlement of Hawaii was probably about 750 A.D. and agricultural colonies were established on New Zealand perhaps around 900 A.D. At least a second expedition to Hawaii is thought to have taken place about 1250 A.D. (Emory and Sinoto, 1964), and later settlements in New Zealand are part of Maori tradition. Long-distance sailing continued into the missionary period of the 19th century. Meanwhile, Indonesians had settled in Madagascar about the beginning of the first century A.D. and took with them taro, Asian yams, bananas, plantains, and probably Asian rice.

By the first century A.D. sea trade was flourishing between India and Africa and between India and Indonesia. By the third century China had joined in long-distance shipping of goods and regular shipping routes were established between China and India and still later between China and the Horn of Africa. For all this, Asian crops had a remarkably minor impact on Africa. Banana became extremely important to the Buganda and some other tribes of Uganda where, in effect, a banana culture emerged, but this may well have been a rather late development. Early accounts by Europeans suggest that bananas and possibly Asian tubers were grown in West Africa at the time of Portuguese contact in the late 15th century.

Rice, the most important of all the Asian crops, was not generally accepted in Africa except in the areas where native African rice was already in use. Considering the importance of African domesticates to Asia, the reciprocal contributions of Asian plants to Africa are negligible.

Southeast Asian agriculture can also be described as introverted, although less so than the Chinese. Dispersals were late and depended on seafaring peoples who set out to colonize islands far from their homelands.

Chapter 12

THE AMERICAS

Then the Maker and Creator asked them: "What do you think of your estate? Do you not see it? Are you not able to hear? Is your speech not good and your manner of walking about? Behold! Contemplate the world; see if the mountains and valleys appear! Try, then, and see!

Mayan creation myth: Popol Vuh
(Recinos, 1947; my translation)

ARCHAEOLOGY

Agricultural complexes also arose in the New World. An impressive array of native American plants was domesticated by American Indians and agricultural systems eventually evolved sufficient to support the civilizations of Chavín, Olmec, Maya, Aztec, Inca, and others. Some extreme diffusionists have maintained that these developments were not independent of the Old World, and that the idea of cultivating plants was transmitted across the Pacific or Atlantic Ocean at a very early time (Riley et al., 1971). Basic to the argument is the implication that the American Indians were incapable of innovation and had to be taught how to cultivate plants by people who had already invented or discovered the arts of agriculture. As we shall see, the American Indians were among the most skillful of all plant domesticators and it is difficult to understand why it should be thought that they were devoid of originality with respect to plant manipulation.

Asian and African plants are conspicuously missing from American crop complexes. Most damaging to the diffusionist argument, however, is the time required to develop an indigenous American agriculture. As we have already seen, the advantages of growing plants on purpose are not conspicuous at the beginning and the differences between intensive gathering and cultivation are minimal. It is difficult to imagine that a few sailors from Asia or Africa could easily induce people to take up practices that would not achieve a developed agriculture for several thousand years. It would appear much more likely that American Indians began the processes of domestication for about the same reasons as people of the ancient Near East, Africa, China or Southeast Asia.

227

The archaeological evidence for the evolution of agriculture in the Americas is extremely tenuous and sketchy. The only sequences that give us much detail at the present time are the Tamaulipas Caves in northeastern Mexico, the Tehuacán Valley excavations southeast of Mexico City (Byers, 1967), the finds on coastal Peru (Rowe and Menzel, 1967; Pickersgill, 1969), and recent excavations in the inter-montane zone at Ancash, Peru (Kaplan, Lynch, and Smith, 1973). This is more evidence than we have for Southeast Asia or Africa, but is hardly adequate to trace the origins and dispersals of American crops.

What information we do have is summarized in Table 1. From this it appears that the American Indians were manipulating plants by about 7000 B.C. and had domesticated some before 6000 B.C. It was a long time, however, before a fully developed agriculture emerged (MacNeish, 1964).

Surveys of archaeological sites in southern Mexico indicate a seasonally nomadic pattern of people dispersed into family-sized microbands during the fall and winter dry season and aggregating into larger macrobands for the spring and summer rainy season. The pattern was well established by the El Riego phase of the Tehuacán sequence that started about 7000 B.C. The diet was probably typical of hunter-gatherers and consisted largely of harvested wild plant materials supplemented by game that was hunted and trapped. Remains of chili peppers and avocado were found and it is likely that these people were at least manipulating several of the more useful plants of the region.

A little before 5000 B.C. the Coxcatlán phase had developed out of the El Riego. The living pattern had not changed much, but the wet-season macrobands were larger and the people were farming at the spring-summer camp sites. Early maize, squash, pumpkins, gourd, chili peppers, and avocados are represented in the plant inventory. By about 3400 B.C., Coxcatlán had merged into a phase called Abejas, which maintained essentially the same living habits but with the addition of *Cucurbita moschata,* common beans, and jack-beans (*Canavalia*) (MacNeish, 1964).

It was not until the Ajalpan phase, beginning roughly at 1500 B.C., that the people of the Tehuacán valley were full-time farmers living in villages. By this time amaranth, zapote, and cotton had been added to the crop list. The Tehuacán sequence may or may not be typical, but other surveys suggest similar developments in Tamaulipas and Oaxaca (Flannery, 1968). In Tehuacán it took over 5,000 years

Table 1
Early appearances of cultivated plants in American
archaeological sites.

Approx. time	Tamaulipas	Tehuacán	Peru
7000 B.C.	Lagenaria Phaseolus coccineus "wild" Cucurbita pepo "wild?"	Capsicum Persea	Phaseolus vulgaris and P. lunatus (intermontane) cultivated
6000 B.C.		Setaria	
5000 B.C.		Zea C. mixta C. pepo Lagenaria	
4000 B.C.	Setaria P. vulgaris	C. moschata Canavalia	
3000 B.C.		P. vulgaris	(1)* { Lagenaria / P. lunatus / Gossypium / C. moschata / C. ficifolia } (2)* { Capsicum / Canavalia / Cana / Psidium }
2000 B.C.	C. moschata		(3)* { Zea / Arachis, Capsicum chinense / Manihot }
		Amaranthus Annona Gossypium	Inga Lucuma Pachyrrhizus
1000 B.C.			
CE		(4)* { Solanum / Arachis / P. lunatus }	
	P. lunatus		

* (1) First domesticates on Coast of Peru; (2) Contact with southern Peru and Bolivia; (3) Contact with Central America, Mexico, and Argentina; (4) Contact with South America.

from the time plants were being manipulated and 3.5 millennia from the time that plants are known to have been domesticated to reach a stabilized system complete with village settlements.

By about 900 B.C. a phase called Santa Maria had emerged; farming villages were then grouped about religious centers. Ceremonial structures were located in the larger villages or towns and associated with a number of smaller villages nearby. Irrigation was beginning to come into practice. During the following Palo Blanco phase, 200 B.C. to 700 A.D., ceremonial centers expanded and elaborate pyramids were constructed. Irrigation systems were laid out and crops that can be identified as being of South American origin were added to the local ones (e.g. potato, peanut, and lima bean). Domestic turkeys were also raised.

Preliminary surveys in South America have so far failed to reveal evidence of very early agriculture in the Andean highlands, but the discovery of domesticated common beans and lima beans in Peruvian intermontane valleys, dated to 6000 B.C. or earlier, shows clearly that plant domestication was underway at the lower elevations at the same time that Mesoamerican Indians were evolving an indigenous agriculture. Unfortunately, most of our direct plant evidence for South America comes from coastal Peru. Here, the climate is essentially rainless, and plant materials are preserved in great abundance and superb condition. On the other hand, the region is too dry to have been a center of plant domestication and essentially all remains are from imported domesticates. Evidence from coastal Peru records when a particular crop reached the area but not when or where it was first domesticated.

In the Near East and Africa, we have some indication that climatic changes might have been involved in producing food procurement crises and thereby stimulating the shift from gathering to husbandry. A similar suggestion has been made for southeastern Asia where perhaps half of the land surface exposed during the Pleistocene was submerged as the sea level rose. What was the situation in the Americas? Unfortunately, our information is not only limited but sometimes conflicting. Nevertheless, the changes in climate associated with the terminal Pleistocene could hardly have failed to affect the higher elevations and latitudes, and the rise of sea level must have had some effect on peoples near the shallow waters of the Caribbean and the land to the east of the present mouth of the Amazon. Such effects are not likely to be represented in archaeological sites in coastal Peru or in Tehuacán Valley.

Logic (not evidence) would seem to indicate that one does not begin agriculture on the cold Altiplano where it is extremely difficult to practice it today even after local domesticates have been developed. Both logic and evidence agree that agriculture could not have begun on rainless coastal Peru. C. O. Sauer (1952) believes it began in northwestern South America because of the great diversity of climates and ecological habitats, the fresh water food resources, and perhaps because it would be most accessible to sailors from across the Pacific. Lathrap (in press) suggests an opposite version, at least for lowland agriculture. He advances the interesting idea that lowland agriculture, based primarily on manioc, began in regions now submerged eastward of and in the present mouth of the Amazon. The terminal Pleistocene rise in sea level may have forced a shift toward food production in that region. The agricultural system that developed moved upriver, largely confined to the small amount of fertile soils along the river banks. The cultures grew in complexity and sophistication as they expanded along the rivers of lowland Amazonia and eventually culminated in the Chavín which assumed many of the elements of civilization. The Chavín, in turn, stimulated the evolution of Olmec and other civilizations of Mesoamerica as well as the highland cultures of the Andes (Lathrap, 1971).

The archaeological evidence would indicate that while the Chavín system was developing, other agricultural systems were also evolving. The Tehuacán Valley is not much different from coastal Peru in that it is too dry for much in the way of innovation, but the region does record the arrival of innovations made elsewhere. At any rate, the Tehuacán sequence suggests the practice of agriculture well before the Chavín is identifiable in South America (about 1500 B.C.) (Rowe and Menzel, 1967).

DISPERSALS

The pattern that emerges in the Americas is somewhat similar to those that we have described for the Near East and Africa and for China and Southeast Asia. There appears to be something of a center in Mesoamerica, a region stretching from approximately Mexico City to Honduras. In this center, corn, beans, squash, agave, avocado, cotton, cacao, jícama, tomate (*Physalis*), sweet potato, papaya, and possibly the American yam became important food plants. The squashes included at least three species, and one species of capsicum pepper was also included in the complex. The corn-bean-squash component of the complex dispersed northward adding sunflower and became the basis for agriculture in the eastern woodlands of North America. The complex, in due time, spread to what is now Canada and a branch moved across the plains into the southwestern United States where the tepary bean was added. To the south, diffusion of the Mesoamerican crops can probably best be traced by maize, which is documented in South America by 1800 B.C. (Pickersgill, 1969). The Mexican beans are confounded somewhat by independent South American domestications of the wild races. Furthermore, South America also had its own species of squash. The Mesoamerican agricultural complex thus acts like a center in that a group of plants, adequate to support agricultural societies, was domesticated within a limited geographic region and at least some of them were dispersed out of the center to other areas.

The situation in South America is very complex, partly because of the extremes in habitat provided by the Andean mountain chain. The Andean highland complex of plants resembles a center, but while an impressive number of domesticates evolved in the highlands, they were self-contained and did not disperse out of that ecological zone. The complex is characterized by highland tubers such as potato, Oca, *Ullucus, Tropaeolum,* and *Lepidum,* as well as quinoa and at least one minor cereal (*Bromus mango*). Midelevation crops included peanut, *Solanum* spp., coca, amaranth, lupines, beans, arracachi, *Pachyrrhizus, Polymnia, Bunchosia,* etc. Lowland crops were diverse and included manioc, sea island cotton, *Canavalia, Inga, Canna, Xanthosoma* and a number of fruits and nuts such as *Annona* spp., pineapple, cashew, papaya, avocado, Brazil nut, other solanums, *Physalis,* and peppers.

The activities of plant domestication were wide-ranging in South America, which takes on the characteristics of a noncenter rather than a center. The key plants for measuring diffusion northward out of the noncenter are the peanut, South American peppers, large lima beans, pineapple, manioc, and tobacco. The arrival of some of these crops in Mexico has been documented (Table 1). At least two routes were involved: one up through the arc of Caribbean islands from Venezuela, the other up the mainland spine of Central America.

It must be pointed out that few, if any, of these plants were domesticated in coastal Peru. The arrival of fully domesticated forms is documented in coastal Peru, but these were domesticated elsewhere at a much earlier date. One region that seems to have been particularly active in plant domestication is Jujuy, the northwestern province of Argentina. There *Ullucus,* peanut, and beans occur in the wild. The South American squash (*Cucurbita maxima*) is found wild in the north Argentine plains. Other plants were probably domesticated over a broad range northward along the eastern slopes of the Andean ranges of Colombia and eastward in Venezuela and perhaps northeastern Brazil. Cultivated beans and lima beans have been found in intermontane valleys of Peru dated earlier than 6000 B.C. (Kaplan, Lynch, and Smith, 1973).

Whatever the times and places of domestication may have been, we must credit the American Indian with a magnificent performance. Of the 15 crops listed by Mangelsdorf (personal communication) as those that really feed the populations of the world, no less than 6 are of American origin. Staple crops are maize, potato, manioc, sweet potato, the common bean, and peanut. Furthermore, American upland cotton has become the cotton of world commerce. Sisal and henequen are other American fibers. Tobacco is not particularly nutritious, but is a popular narcotic and earns vast sums of money in commerce. The most important of the American drug plants was coca, a source of cocaine, and cinchona, a source of quinine. In addition, such crops as capsicum peppers, pineapple, papaya, avocado, guava, custard apple, cashew nut, squashes, and tomato are very popular throughout the world. American crops have been widely dispersed in post-Columbian times and many of them have been extremely competitive with domesticated plants of the Old World.

A number of American crops have increased enormously in importance after leaving the New World. Sunflower, for example, was probably a relatively minor crop to some North American Indian tribes, but has become a major source of edible oil in eastern Europe and the Soviet Union. Rubber of several kinds was extracted from wild trees by the American Indians but no rubber plants were domesticated by them. Hevea rubber has become an important plantation crop in Southeast Asia and Africa. *Cinchona,* the source of quinine, may not even have been used at all by the American Indians but did become a commercial crop in Southeast Asia. While the potato was important to the American highland Indians, it was used little elsewhere in the Americas; when taken to Europe, it created a dietary revolution.

The peanut has become an enormously important crop in China and an export crop for several African countries. The sweet potato is not only a very important food source in China but created something of a dietary revolution in New Guinea (Watson, 1965). After its introduction, probably in the 16th century, it was readily accepted by the New Guinea natives particularly those in the highlands. The sweet potato is adaptable to conditions at much higher elevations than the traditional yams and taros of New Guinea. The result was apparently increased population due to increased food supply. This may have been assisted by the fact that these elevations were above the range of malarial mosquitoes so that this population leveler was not effective (Brookfield and White, 1968). The sweet potato provides 90% of the caloric intake of some tribes in the highlands of New Guinea. Additional sweet potatoes are raised to feed pigs, which are also consumed. It seems that these people could hardly have existed where they now live without the sweet potato.

Maize was perhaps the most important of the American Indian domesticates, but even it had potential unrealized by the American Indians. The productivity of maize as a cereal was not realized until the development of Corn Belt types in the United States. These types have been transported to many other parts of the world where maize has become a major crop, replacing previous cereals.

Details of the place and time of maize domestication remain to be worked out, and there is still some debate as to the most likely progenitor. For many years P. C. Mangelsdorf has maintained that maize was domesticated from wild races that have since become extinct and that teosinte was a late derivative of wild maize X *Tripsacum* hybridization (Mangelsdorf and Reeves, 1939). Recent evidence has caused him to abandon the latter part of the theory, but he still insists that there was once a wild maize progenitor to the domesticated races. The earliest cobs found in Tehuacán Valley represent wild maize, according to his interpretation. Few maize specialists now agree with his views, and most are inclined to consider some race or races of teosinte as the most likely progenitors (Beadle, 1972; Galinat, 1971).

The only difficulty in accepting teosinte as the progenitor of maize has been the rather spectacular differences in the female inflorescences or ears. Otherwise, teosinte and maize are very much alike and no one has any problem in visualizing an evolution from one plant type to the other. The ear of teosinte differs from that of maize primarily in the following characteristics:

Teosinte	Maize
Ear fragile	Ear (cob) nonfragile
Pedicellate spikelets suppressed	Both spikelets of a pair ♀ fertile

Ear two-ranked	Ear four-ranked (or more)
Glumes very hard	Glumes soft
Glumes covering seed	Glumes short (usually)
Seed imbedded in rachis cupule	Seed exposed
Seed small	Seed large

There are some other rather minor differences, but these are the conspicuous ones. They are all under genetic control, and conversion from one state to the other does not generally appear to be especially complex. The fragile vs nonfragile inflorescence situation is found in all cereals and is in no way unusual. A single gene can suppress the fragility of a rachis. The recovery of fertility of a suppressed spikelet or floret is known in barley, wheat, and sorghum as well as in maize. Increase in rank number is associated with the development of a terminal spike in the tassel and appears to be relatively simple genetically. Reduction of glumes and increase of seed size is common in the evolution of cereals. Remnants of the rachis cupule are represented in an ear of maize (Galinat, 1971). Beadle (1972) has found that the complete morphologies of both maize and teosinte ears can be recovered in large F_2 populations of maize-teosinte hybrids. Either the differences between the two are few or they are tightly linked into a few blocks of genes. Frequency of recovery of near-parental types in the F_2 suggests the major genetic differences are on the order of five or six.

Until more convincing evidence to the contrary is presented, I would have to conclude that the teosinte origin is, by far, the most economical theory of the origin of maize and the most likely. I would add only one caution: teosinte was probably much more variable formerly than now and there may well have been races more maize-like than those that have survived.

The present known distribution of wild maize or teosinte is shown in Fig. 1. There is good evidence that the distribution was much wider at one time. Teosinte has been found archaeologically in Tamaulipas where it does not occur today (Mangelsdorf, MacNeish, and Galinat, 1967). Specimens have been collected, and are on file in herbaria, from sites where teosinte no longer occurs (Wilkes, 1967). A perennial tetraploid race has become extinct except for material maintained in various breeding nurseries. Obviously, the last word has yet to be said about the origin of maize, but I find no reason to suppose that the evolution of maize is radically different from that of any other cereal.

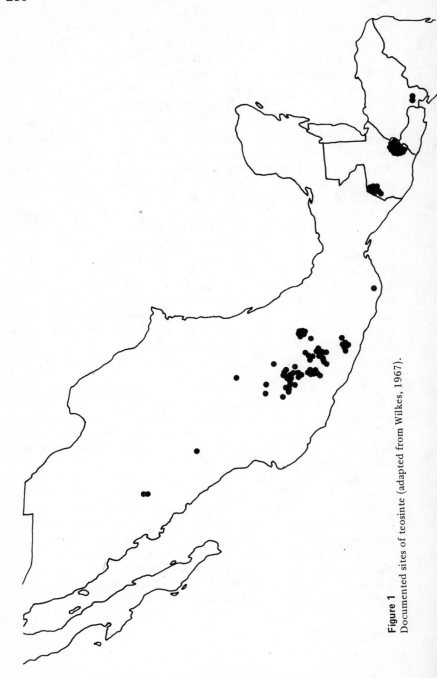

Figure 1
Documented sites of teosinte (adapted from Wilkes, 1967).

Chapter 13

SELECTED CROP DISPERSALS

EARLY DISTRIBUTIONS

The white flowered bottle gourd or calabash (*Lagenaria siceraria*) was widely dispersed early. It has been reported from Ocampo cave, Tamaulipas, ca. 7000 B.C. (Cutler and Whitaker, 1967), Coxcatlán cave, Tehuacán Valley, ca. 5000 B.C. (Cutler and Whitaker, 1967), sites near Ancón, Peru, ca. 2700 B.C. (Pickersgill, 1969), Njoro River cave, East Africa, ca. 1000 B.C. (Leakey and Leakey, 1950), a fifth dynasty Egyptian tomb, ca. 2500 B.C. (Schweinfurth, 1884), Spirit Cave, Thailand, ca. 7000 B.C. (Gorman, 1969), and from Lung-shan sites in China, perhaps 2000 B.C. (Chang, 1968). No other known crop had such a wide distribution from 7000 to 2000 B.C.; it is in a class by itself.

At the present time, the most likely explanation is simply that it was a pantropical species. It is the kind of plant that anyone would use. The dried fruits are too useful to be ignored even by people who never thought of cultivating the plant. They make excellent containers of all sizes and shapes, water bottles, plates, bowls, baskets, floats for fishnets, and sound boxes for musical instruments. Wherever the plant occurred it would have been used.

We know very little about it as a wild plant. What we find today are almost entirely cultivated races. Whitaker (1971) considers it to be endemic to Africa, but it is reported as wild in Australia (Irvine, 1957). Few people have ever studied the bottle gourd seriously and our understanding of the crop is clouded by ignorance.

A favorite speculative explanation of some plant geographers is that the gourds can float across oceans from one continent to another, carried by currents. Carter and Whitaker (1961) experimented with the possibility, and it seems that it could have happened, but there are other pantropical distributions that could hardly be explained that way and *Lagenaria* is not known as a strand plant. Some radical diffusionists insist that man was the dispersal agent even as early as 7000 B.C. It is more likely that the distribution was achieved long before *Homo sapiens* even evolved. Apart from its wide use, its presence in so many early sites may be partly attributed to the nature of the hard shell, which is more easily preserved than most plant materials.

The millets, *Setaria italica* and *Panicum miliaceum,* are thought to have been the staff of life for the Yang-shao people of China. Remains of the foxtail millet were found in enormous quantities in some Yang-shao sites, and the panic millet became basic to northern Chinese agriculture a little later. They are thought by some to have been domesticated in the Chinese center, yet both are found in a sprinkling of Neolithic village sites over Europe through the fourth millennium B.C. They were seldom important components of plant remains. They were reported only from Niederwil among the Swiss Lake dwellers, for example; but they occurred in enough sites that there can be little doubt of the presence of both millets in fourth millennium Europe. *Panicum* has also been reported from Jemdet Nasr, Mesopotamia, 3000 B.C., and possibly Argissa-Maghula, Greece, about 5500 B.C. (Renfrew, 1969).

The only European culture that grew *Panicum mileaceum* really extensively was the Tripolye of the Ukraine. The culture flourished from 3800 to 2900 B.C. and panic was one of the major crops. Neither millet has been studied intensively, and the archaeological studies of the vast Eurasian steppe between China and the Ukraine are not yet sufficiently advanced for us to choose between possible alternatives.

The possibilities are: 1) the millets were domesticated in China and dispersed to Europe before 4000 B.C., 2) they were domesticated in the West and were dispersed to China before Yang-shao times, and 3) there was more than one domestication. The presumptive progenitor of *Setaria italica* is *S. viridis*, a ubiquitous weed from Japan to England and now widespread to North America and elsewhere. It is frequently stated that the progenitor of *Panicum miliaceum* is not known, but in the *Flora of USSR* (Botanical Institute of the Soviet Academy of Sciences, 1968–1973) it is reported as weedy, naturalized or escaped, and common from European Russia to eastern Siberia. Without very careful analysis it is often difficult to separate wild from weedy races.

Both millets are adapted to the summer rainfall belt of temperate Eurasia. They were well known to the Greeks and Romans and to Indians of ancient times. It may be noted, however, that a number of Indian names for panic suggest that it came to India from China. In Sanskrit the name is *cinaka* (meaning Chinese); Hindi, *chena, cheen*; Bengali, *cheena*; and Gujarati, *chino*. The Persian word is essentially the same as the Chinese, *shu-shu* (Laufer, 1919).

No other known crops had such a distribution in that time range. Wide dispersals in the fifth millennium B.C. are certainly possible, but one might have expected more than the two millets if this was the explanation. The rather slow spread of agriculture across Europe at that time suggests that early European farmers were having enough trouble just getting across Europe without attempting the much longer trip to China. The Chinese crops, as we have seen, did not disperse much until very late.

In our present state of ignorance, independent domestications appear to be the most likely answer, but new information could easily lead to other conclusions.

TRANSPACIFIC DISPERSALS

The coconut is basically a South Pacific and Southeast Asian cultivated plant, but was reported on Cocos Island and the west coast of Panama by the Spanish natural historian Gonzalo Fernandez de Oviedo y Valdés (as reported in the edition of 1944). His first description was written in 1519, giving almost no time for a European introduction of the plant. The possibilities are: 1) Oviedo's account was garbled and the coconut was not there, 2) the coconut reached the west coast of Central America through natural means of dispersal not very long before Columbus, 3) the plant was brought to the area by human agency not very long before Columbus, and 4) the coconut is really American and was dispersed by some means throughout the South Seas.

The last option, supported by O. F. Cook (1910) and others, is the least likely of all. The major argument in its support is that the nearest relatives are American, but this is a slim argument in view of the great diversity and ancient usage of the coconut in the Orient and the relative lack of its usage by American Indians. Furthermore, in recent decades taxonomists have transfered a number of American species from *Cocos* to other genera and our understanding of palm taxonomy has improved considerably. The American origin of *C. nucifera* is highly suspect to say the least.

Oviedo's account was, indeed, garbled and early European observers give contradictory accounts. Oviedo's description of the coconut is accurate, detailed, and unmistakable, but he then supplies us with a line drawing of a palm which is *not* a coconut. He said it was particularly abundant in Cacique Chiman, yet Wafer (as reported in the edition of 1934), a very good and reliable observer, passed through Cacique Chiman in the 1680's and could not remember seeing a coconut on the mainland. Wafer did, however, report a very strange account of a "frolick" on Cocos Island, by several of the ship's company in which they cut down a number of "coconut" trees, harvested about 76 liters (20 gallons) of milk and drank until they were benumbed. Cook (1939) found a palm on Cocos Island that is "remarkably similar in size and general appearance" to the coconut, but is entirely unrelated. We cannot go into all the details here, but on balance, it seems most likely that the coconut had, in fact, established a foothold on American shores before the arrival of Europeans.

Was dispersal by natural or artificial means? Either is possible. If Polynesians could find Easter Island, they surely could find a continent. During the period of the great voyages, Polynesians were were very much at home on the high seas and long voyages were often made with relative ease and safety. If Cocos Island should prove to be an extreme outpost of Polynesia and if the coconut was established by colonizers, some archaeological traces should be available. A survey of the island did reveal traces of Costa Rican Indians, but to date there is no clear evidence of Polynesians. The question remains to be settled.

The sweet potato is a domesticate of American Indians, but was found in the 1770's on Easter Island, Tahiti, New Zealand, and Hawaii. The alternatives are: 1) Polynesians sailed to American shores and returned with the sweet potato, 2) American Indians sailed into Polynesia where it was accepted and distributed by Polynesians, and 3) the crop was introduced into Polynesia one or more times by Europeans during the two and a half centuries between Magellan and Captain Cook (Barrau, 1957).

Each alternative is possible, and, indeed, all three events might have taken place. At present there is no evidence that is really conclusive, but I am inclined to think that more than one of the three alternatives were probably operating. This much seems evident: whatever the role of Europeans or American Indians might have been, much of the dispersal was made by Polynesian ocean-going craft. However, the dispersal could well have been as late as the 16th or 17th centuries.

It is highly significant that these few examples constitute the only known cases of anomalous or unexplained dispersal problems in cultivated plants. Wild plants are dispersed by natural means but crops may be considered artifacts and are usually carried about by men. In general, they moved slowly until modern times. We had domestic maize in Mexico by 5000 B.C.; the earliest reported so far from coastal Peru was 3000 years later. Potato, peanut, and lima bean from South America are reported in Mexico about the start of the first century A.D. Rice did not reach the Mediterranean region until after Alexander the Great, and sorghum was introduced to Italy only in the first century A.D. Despite many claims to the contrary, American crops were not known on other continents before the time of Columbus. On the whole, the prehistory and history of crops blend together to form a consistent and rational pattern. We can show that a number of crops were domesticated several thousand years before written history began, yet their major dispersals out of their regions of origin were usually so late that historical records are of use in tracing them. A pattern of widespread early dispersals is simply not apparent from the evidence.

TRANSDOMESTICATION

The dispersal of a number of crops falls under the category called *transdomestication* by T. Hymowitz (1972). He used as his model guar (*Cyamopsis tetragonaloba*) which is a legume cultivated in certain parts of India. All of its relatives appear to be African, although the nearest relative may extend across Arabia. None of the wild *Cyamopsis* species is known from India. The suggestion was made that *C. senegalensis* was shipped to India as horse fodder and then became a domesticated plant.

The pattern may be more common than generally supposed. The tomato might even be a case of double transdomestication. The wild races appear to be native to the coasts of Peru and Ecuador. There is no indication that South American Indians ever used it, although they domesticated several *Solanum* spp. We do have evidence that the plant was developed as a minor cultigen in the lowland Maya area of Mexico. In Mexico, the Indian word "tomate" refers to *Physalis* whereas the tomato is usually called "jítomate," suggesting the tomato was domesticated later than the *Physalis*. Wild tomatoes have two locules in the fruit and the multiloculate forms are derived. There is a two-loculed domesticated race in southern Mexico and Guatemala and one would suppose the earliest cultivars would have been of this type.

The tomato was introduced to Europe during the 16th century and this became the arena of real domestication. Italy was probably involved more than other countries. The material imported from Mexico was multiloculate, small, heavily ridged, and compressed. From the 16th century woodcuts it looked like a miserable tomato. Four centuries of selection and development, first in Europe and later in the United States, produced a crop that is popular throughout the world. Modern Mexico is shifting rapidly toward the production and consumption of new, highly-derived tomato cultivars.

Modern examples of transdomestication are numerous. The Monterrey pine (*Pinus radiata*) contributes aesthetically to one of the most spectacularly picturesque coastlines of the world. On the coast of California it hardly looks like a wood-producing plant, but it is a highly productive forest tree in artificial stands in New Zealand and Australia. *Hevea* rubber is wild in the Amazon basin and domesticated in Malaysia and Indonesia. Arabica coffee is wild and, until recently, only half domesticated in Ethiopia, yet it is a major cash crop in Brazil and some other Latin American countries. Many, if not most, of our ornamental plants have been domesticated outside of their natural ranges.

Obviously, there are all degrees of the pattern. Crops may be wild in one area and cultivated elsewhere. More commonly, crops may be minor in the area of original domestication and major elsewhere. Manioc is now more important in Africa than in the Americas, the United States produces six times as many soybeans as China, the potato is a larger crop in Europe than South America, and Latin America produces more bananas than the region where the crop originated. Corn Belt maize has a different order of production capacity than the races of Indian corn from which it was derived, and the United States produces more maize than Latin America. All of these examples are recent developments and, except for manioc in Africa, made possible by plant breeding programs.

Late dispersals are understandable and usually fairly well documented. The significant point is that dispersals before 1500 A.D. are also consistent and, with very few exceptions, can be traced by historical or archaeological evidence. The few mysteries that remain might be cleared up by adequate study unless the needed evidence has been destroyed.

MODERN DISPERSALS

In recent decades, plant breeding has become a remarkably international operation. Wheats developed in Mexico have had a tremendous impact on wheat production in Asia and North Africa. Rice cultivars bred in the Philippines have made a real impact in many parts of Asia and West Africa. Maize germplasm from Ecuador has transformed production in Kenya, and Caribbean maize has had an impact in India. World-wide exchanges of germplasm of sorghum, barley, potatoes, grain legumes, and other major crops are contributing to substantial increases in production on all continents.

In the process of moving breeding material from region to region, genetic adjustment of adaptation is often necessary. Response to daylength is especially critical. As Columella remarked nearly 2,000 years ago, one "must not be ignorant of the variations in latitude" (Ash, 1941). Tropical materials, in particular, are likely to be extremely sensitive. In cereals, grain legumes, and other seed crops, it is essential that plants mature during the dry season at the end of the rains. To mature during the rains invites such an infestation of diseases and insects that total failure is likely. Close to the equator, the difference between the longest and shortest day of the year may be only a matter of minutes, but tropical cultivars and landraces often respond to such small differences.

To incorporate tropical materials into temperate cultivars it is usually necessary to convert them to conditions of temperate latitudes. A sizeable conversion program with sorghum has been underway for several years. Some races convert better than others, but in most cases, four backcrosses are sufficient to produce usable materials that resemble the tropical lines rather closely. This is, however, a rather lengthy program. The short-day response is dominant, and the procedure is to make the initial cross in the tropics and grow the F_1's there under short-day conditions. The F_2 is then grown at higher latitudes and those that both flower and set seed are selected. The F_2 is returned to the tropics for the first backcross to the tropical line. The BC_1 must be grown in the tropics and selections must be made in the next generation in temperate zones. The entire process is repeated four times. The product presumably contains most of the genes of the tropical line but will flower and make seed in temperate zones.

Some cultivars are called daylength insensitive; they will flower in approximately a given number of days regardless of daylength. This feature may be controlled by a single gene or at least is often rather simply inherited. Adjustment of daylength response to make a line early or late, however, may be quantitative and many genes may be involved.

Selection by local cultivators may have a profound effect on daylength response even in the tropics. Throughout the pearl millet belt of West Africa (Chapter 9, Figure 2), every region has two kinds of landrace populations, early and late. The early ones bloom and set seed in Illinois, the late ones do not. The African farmers had developed relatively insensitive types to fit a particular need.

A primary reason for the enormous success of the Mexican (CIMMYT) wheats and Philippine (IRRI) rices is that they have been bred to be daylength insensitive. They can be grown over a very wide range of latitudes and two or three crops can be raised per year wherever the climate and rainfall regimes are suitable.

To move temperate, long-day plants into the tropics requires adjustment in daylength response as well. This is usually relatively simple and wheat, barley, alfalfa, etc. can be grown at the equator after suitable cultivars are developed.

Even after modern plant breeding methods were developed, non-adapted materials were not used for a long time. Plant breeders in temperate zones ignored tropical germplasm for decades because it would not flower in their regions and it was too much trouble to make conversions except for very special purposes. Greenhouse facilities are too expensive and too limited for much work of this type to be conducted. With the internationalization of plant breeding efforts, however, conversion on a large scale becomes much more feasible and vast arrays of variation are made available for modern plant breeding programs.

Another problem of adaptation concerns the basic physiological differences between cool-season and warm-season crops. Whereas ranges of tolerance can be increased by breeding, we have found no way to make a warm-season crop out of a cool-season one or vice versa. The differences are too fundamental.

The Near Eastern and Mediterranean complex of crops evolved from plants adapted to a winter rainfall regime. They are cool-season plants, usually planted in the fall and harvested in late spring or early summer. They can be grown as summer crops at high latitudes where the summers are cool or at low latitudes at high elevations when proper adjustments of daylength response are made. They are grown in India during the cool *rabi* or winter dry season, but cannot be grown in *kharif*, the hot, summer rainy season. Cool-season crops are not adapted to hot, humid conditions, and so far, we have found little we can do to make them do so.

Warm-season crops demand a considerable amount of heat to grow well. If the soils are cold and/or the air temperature too low, they grow very slowly and often become diseased and die. Tropical crops can be grown at fairly high latitudes if there is sufficient heat and short-season cultivars are developed. Perhaps the most adaptable of tropical crops is maize. It had undergone a long period of selection for cold tolerance and short season while being cultivated by North American Indians. More recently, very strong selection pressures have been applied to develop cultivars whose seedlings are tolerant to cold soils so that they could be planted earlier in the spring. Similar attempts are being made to adapt other tropical crops to more northerly regions.

Within the warm-season, cool-season dichotomy are rather fundamental differences in adaptation to elevation. Races of maize or sorghum adapted to high elevations are very different from lowland races. Lowland races of sorghum may grow fairly well in the cool highlands but are likely to be sterile. Highland sorghums do poorly in the lowlands. The same is true for maize. Conversions can be made with modern breeding methods, but the adaptations are complex and the inheritance is not simple. Similar differences occur within cool-season crops. For example, barley and wheat from high elevations are not well suited to the lowlands.

There are other problems in moving plants out of their adapted homelands, of course. The moisture regime is one of the most important. To take a swamp or water-hole plant like rice or taro and grow it on uplands even under high rainfall requires some genetic adjustment, and there are limits to how much change in environment a crop can tolerate. In moving legumes, *Rhizobia* populations are often limiting. The local strains may be unsuited and innoculation is necessary. With many trees, the mycorrhiza population is equally important. Some plants are extremely sensitive to pH; others have a wide tolerance. Some crops are better suited to sandy soils and others prefer higher clay content. All of these factors are rather self-evident and are treated in detail in the general literature of crop science.

Chapter 14

EPILOGUE: THE COMPUTER AGE

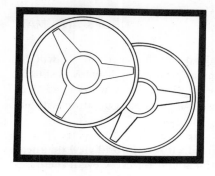

We dye even the rivers and the elemental substances of nature, and turn the very means of life into a bane.

Pliny, first century A. D.
(Translated by H. Rackham)

This is an age of much knowledge and little wisdom.

Albert Szent-Györgi
(personal communication)

GENETIC RESOURCE MANAGEMENT

Looking back from a perspective of several thousand years, it is apparent that agriculture had several origins in widely separated parts of the world. Sometimes there seemed to be sufficient continuity that we can say it originated in a center and sometimes it seems that it emerged from activities spread over vast areas that I call noncenters. Whatever the geographic pattern, it always took several millennia for a complete system to emerge in which people were full-time farmers and usually lived in villages. Agriculture evolved; it was not a revolution, and certainly not a "Eureka!" type of discovery.

The systems that did evolve provided a basic subsistence pattern which became widespread. Here and there, productivity was such that surpluses could accrue and towns and incipient cities came into being. If all went well, the trend continued and the first cities emerged complete with the characteristics of "civilization." Temples were erected; writing was invented; society was stratified, with professional classes, artisans, soldiers and standing armies, politicians, and a priestly class; metals were worked; and all the other criteria of civilization were developed. City-states, nations, and finally empires arose.

The ancient civilizations were generally limited in geographic area and often in duration. The more enduring ones were in Mesopotamia, Egypt, Greece, the Mediterranean basin, China, India,

251

Ethiopia, Mesoamerica, and highland South America. It will be noted that these are precisely the areas outlined by Vavilov (1926) as centers of origin. But agriculture was much more widespread than that and vast areas developed basic subsistence agriculture without the embellishment of high civilization.

It was in Greece at the city-state level, based on village agriculture, that rational philosophy emerged. It was a world view that held that the universe is whole and rational and for every event there is a preceding cause. It was a simple view but in most ages held only by a minority of people. The more commonly held view was that the universe is irrational and capricious, being governed by conflicting spirits and witches, by gods and goddesses at war with each other, or by an omnipotent god who deals out bounty and disaster in incomprehensible ways. In the view of rational philosophy, or science if you will, the universe is comprehensible if we study it well. Further, knowledge of the forces of nature can be put to use for the benefit of mankind, even if we do not understand what we know.

After suffering an eclipse through the Middle Ages, science revived in the Renaissance and the modern era of history began. A fundamental body of knowledge about the nature of the universe began to build up. Physics, chemistry, and mathematics began to be understandable. We found we could manipulate the forces of nature. Machines were invented that could transform energy from one form to another. Water power could turn mills or even spinning wheels. Steam power could do it even better and more consistently. The industrial revolution began to take shape. It was a revolution more fateful and total than the evolution from hunting-gathering to food production, but there was no turning back in either case.

Industrial productivity began to pull people away from the farm. Job markets opened up and even if wages were low and working conditions miserable, people flocked to the cities. Many machines took the place of farm labor. Production per man or per man-hour tended to rise, but production per hectare did not rise at all or rose only as better rotations which included legumes and ley farming were employed. The cities were mushrooming; the farms were producing very little more than before (Figure 1).

By the 20th century, industry, technology, and science began to work together. Studies in plant physiology described what the plant needed for greater production; soil studies showed how to supply the nutrients. Plant pathologists and entomologists were able to find methods of protecting crops, and plant breeders began to develop varieties that would respond to fertilizers. Japan led the world in crop production per hectare. Yields in that country began to climb even before the turn of the century, but for the United States, Western Europe, and most of the world, it was not until World War II that significant increases in per-hectare yields were achieved (Figures 1 and 2).

Much of the increase in production per hectare is due to fertilizers, and disease and insect control, but plant breeding has also been enormously important. Improvement by plant breeding depends on a continuous supply of genetic variability. Without variation, the plant breeder can do little or nothing. Traditionally, the sources of variability have come from the primitive landraces of "far off" lands called "underdeveloped countries" where centers of variability are located.

When plant breeding was done in only Western Europe, Canada, the United States, Japan, Australia, and New Zealand, there was little danger of losing the needed variation. If more materials were needed, one could always send a collector to Turkey, Iran, Afghanistan, Ethiopia, Mexico, or Peru and get vast amounts of variation. Genetic resources seemed inexhaustible.

But since World War II plant breeding programs have been established within the developing countries and within the hearts of centers of diversity. What is more they have often been successful, and new,

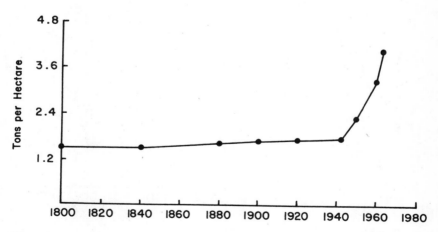

Figure 1
Corn yields in the United States (adapted from Brown, 1968).

improved, high-yielding varieties are replacing the old variable land-race populations. The sources of variation required for future improvement are drying up, disappearing before our eyes.

In the late 1960's and early 1970's, the most disturbing situation concerned wheat. The famous Mexican wheats of Nobel Laureate Borlaug have marched across Asia and much of Africa with amazing speed, wiping out old centers of diversity and replacing traditional, mixed populations with uniform related varieties. The same thing was happening with rice and the pattern was set, indicating that all other crops would follow. There is no way out, no turning back. The increase in yield is not only welcome relief from perennial shortages, but we have already come to depend on the higher productivity of these crops. We have passed the point of no return and cannot go back to the old landrace materials, even if we wanted to.

There are two enormous dangers in the situation: 1) the variable populations being replaced may be lost forever if not collected and conserved in time, and 2) the replacement of adapted, mixed, landrace populations with uniform genetic materials is an invitation to disaster from epidemics of diseases and pests.

The mixed genotypes of landraces had built-in safeguards against epidemics, in that no race of pathogen could attack all the genotypes, although no genotype was resistant to all races of pathogen. A reasonably stable equilibrium was established in subsistence agriculture,

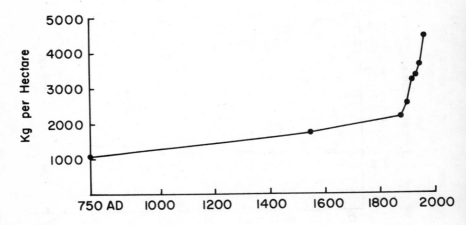

Figure 2
Rice yields in Japan. Historical estimates from Japanese
Ministry of Agriculture (adapted from Brown, 1968).

but this is almost impossible to maintain in modern systems with enormous areas planted to uniform genetic materials.

Both dangers are real and the potential hazards are frightening to contemplate. Erosion of genetic resources has become a concern of the Food and Agriculture Organization of the United Nations, the Rockefeller Foundation, the Ford Foundation, the Consultative Group, Eucarpia, the USDA, the Vavilov Institute of the Soviet Union, CSIRO of Australia, the Kihara Institute of Japan, and several nations, notably the United Kingdom, West Germany, Italy, Bulgaria, Poland, and Turkey. An international concern was expressed at the United Nations Conference on the Human Environment Stockholm meeting in 1972, but concern does not necessarily translate into adequate action, and invaluable materials continue to slip away. Once gone, they are lost forever.

Collections have been made over several decades. Some of the largest that have accumulated are maintained by the USDA and the Vavilov Institute. Other sizeable collections are maintained in the United Kingdom, West Germany, Japan, Italy, Canada, Australia, Bulgaria, Turkey, Poland, and France. Most of these collections are in the Western countries and very few are in the developing nations. Adequate facilities for long-term storage which require conditions of low temperature and low humidity are rare. There is a facility for the United States at Fort Collins, the National Seed Storage Laboratory, which has a very large capacity and which can store enormous quantities of material. Other long-term storage facilities are found at Bari, Italy; Braunschwieg, West Germany; Izmir, Turkey; and in Japan. New facilities are being established in Bulgaria, Poland, the United Kingdom, and Australia.

There have been recent proposals for an international network of genetic resources centers which would attempt to conserve the major genetic resources of the world. This program has not yet been put into effect, and it would be a very expensive system. At the present time, it is virtually impossible to decide which crops should be conserved and which should not.

With respect to the genetic hazards of uniformity, there are various solutions possible. First, it is necessary to discard the idea of uniform varieties; mixed populations are much safer. It is theoretically possible to devise deliberately prepared populations, all of high-yielding, disease-resistant genotypes which vary in genetic constitution with respect to disease resistance. It is also becoming apparent that total breeding programs, in which all germplasm within genetic reach is exploited, will become necessary. These would include the wild and weedy races as well as the species included in secondary gene pools and possibly even those in tertiary gene pools. We can no longer afford to let potentially usable materials disappear. Everything that is genetically accessible must be utilized eventually by plant breeders of the future.

A serious charge is handed to the crop evolutionist. He has a function to fulfill and a service to perform. He has an obligation to explore the gene pools of at least our most important crops so thoroughly that pathways can be worked out for transferring desirable traits from related species into the crop. Only the crop evolutionist can work out these biosystematic relationships adequately. The plant breeder does not have time for this kind of study. He has more than enough to do in improving genetic materials with respect to yield, quality, adaptation, disease and insect resistance, and so on. Improvement by means of wide crosses is difficult, exacting, intricate, frustrating, and so time-consuming that practical plant breeders should not be burdened with that kind of genetic manipulation. It is the role of the crop evolutionist to search out the pathways, do the chromosome engineering, repattern the genomes, produce the substitution lines and addition lines or do whatever needs to be done in order to exploit the total range of germplasm within genetic reach.

Indeed, it is the obligation of the crop evolutionist to *define* the limits of usable germplasm and to insist that adequate collections be made of all races and species of potential use for the improvement of our major crops. At the present time we do not even know what we can use, for want of adequate biosystematic and cytogenetic studies. Our world collections are shockingly deficient in wild and weedy races of cultivated plants and usually completely lacking in species from the secondary and tertiary gene pools. A great deal of basic work is needed to support plant breeding programs and this kind of effort has been dangerously neglected.

The whole field of germplasm assembly, storage, maintenance, study, classification, and utilization can be put under the heading of genetic resource management. The field increases in importance as the genetic bases of our food supply erode. The fate of mankind hangs on a forever narrowing genetic base. Man gathered more species than he domesticated, and domesticated many more than he now grows. The number of crops in production is declining, and those that remain are becoming genetically more uniform.

From the National Academy of Sciences 1972 report, *Genetic Vulnerability of Major Crops,* we find that current U.S. production rests upon a very restricted base. Five publicly developed and released inbred lines of corn represented half of the parentage in 70% of the 1970 seed corn requirements. Approximately 40% of the hard red winter wheat hectarage is planted to two varieties and their related derivatives. Most of the widely grown soybean varieties for the northern area involve 'Richland' and 'Mukden' in their parentage. Of the soybeans grown in the Mississippi Delta area 58% have both 'AK' and 'Clemson' as ancestors. All of the current sorghum hybrids have a common cytoplasmic sterility component. The shocking statistics are shown in Table 1. These findings suggest that all of our cultivated crops have such a narrow genetic base as to be highly vulnerable to some new race of a current pathogen or some new biotype of insect pest.

Table 1

Hectarage and farm value of major U.S. crops and extent to which small numbers of varieties dominate crop hectarage; 1969 figures (adapted from National Academy of Sciences report, 1972).

Crop	Hectarage, millions	Value, millions of dollars	Total varieties	Major varieties	Hectarage, %
Bean, dry	567.0	143	25	2	60
Bean, snap	121.5	99	70	3	76
Cotton	4,536.0	1,200	50	3	53
Corn*	26,851.5	5,200	197†	6	71
Millet	810.0	?		3	100
Peanut	567.0	312	15	9	95
Peas	162.0	80	50	2	96
Potato	567.0	616	82	4	72
Rice	729.0	449	14	4	65
Sorghum	6,804.0	795	?	?	?
Soybean	17,091.0	2,500	62	6	56
Sugar beet	567.0	367	16	2	42
Sweet potato	62.65	63	48	1	69
Wheat	17,941.5	1,800	269	9	50

* Corn includes seeds, forage, and silage.   † Released public inbreds only.

From Table 3, Chapter 8, National Academy of Sciences, 1972.

UNCONVENTIONAL FOOD SOURCES

There are some who argue that agriculture is obsolete for scientific-industrial societies. It belongs to a past revolution, and what is needed is the invention of entirely new sources of food. Can we not devise more efficient methods of converting solar energy into chemicals that would nourish our bodies? Could we bypass photosynthesis altogether? If we must depend on living organisms, are there not other plants more efficient than field crops? What about yeasts and algae or bacteria that convert petroleum into protein? What about the seas that cover most of the earth and that yield such a small proportion of the world's food supply? What are the possibilities for a new revolution appropriate for the industrial age?

A candid assessment of the world food situation shows that there is not enough high-quality food to go around, and that the distribution of what is available is extremely biased. The primary deficiency is protein, and more than half of the people in the world do not consume enough good-quality protein for a nutritionally balanced diet. Most people are malnourished, while some (North Americans, for example) consume far more than is necessary for an adequate diet. Supplies are only part of the problem. The price of protein tends to put it beyond the reach of the poor. The situation is not likely to get better at least for some time. Populations are increasing most rapidly in the countries with the lowest per capita income. Protein deficiency is most serious for the young, and children raised on too little protein of poor quality may survive but suffer permanent brain damage. What is now a serious protein shortage threatens to become a real nutritional disaster in the near future.

We can sharpen the focus on the world food situation by concentrating on the protein problem. A world-wide concern is expressed by the establishment of a Protein Advisory Group (PAG) sponsored jointly by the FAO, WHO, and UNICEF organizations of the United Nations and the International Bank for Reconstruction and Development. (For those interested in keeping up with current developments on the international protein scene, a PAG bulletin is published by the United Nations, New York, New York 10017.) I shall attempt to sketch some of the possibilities to solve the protein crisis in a sequence from the more conventional to the most radical.

In the first place, the human body does not require protein at all; what is required is a supply of certain essential amino acids which the body cannot synthesize. We can do something about improving the protein situation by increasing the biological value of the proteins that are produced. The most common deficiencies in protein quality of cereals are in lysine, methionine, and tryptophan. Rice also tends to be deficient in threonine. In some cases, the shortages are border-line. Good-quality, high-protein wheat, for example, is a good source of dietary protein. Lysine is the primary limiting amino acid, but there is enough available to sustain life and health. In maize, how-ever, lysine is so low that serious symptoms of malnutrition may de-velop, especially in children. The dietary disease called *kwashiorkor* is caused by lysine deficiency in a background of low protein intake.

The amino acid profile of cereals is, to some extent, under genetic control. Two genes are known that affect lysine content of maize protein, and strains of maize have been produced that contain enough lysine to be nearly complete. The lysine in high lysine maize is still a little below optimum but it is high enough to cure children of kwashiorkor. Protein modification programs are under way for other cereals and enormously important improvements in human nutrition appear to be possible by genetic manipulation. A single gene in 'Hyproly' barley confers both high lysine and high protein content. The nutritional value of some cultivars of oats is excellent, and much better strains of sorghum and rice are on the way.

When soybeans were first grown in the United States, the crop was thought of as a hay or fodder plant or the beans were processed for oil. The older varieties were relatively high in oil and low in pro-tein. Gradually the emphasis has shifted to protein, and varieties of the future will probably be considerably higher in protein and lower in oil. The soybean is emerging as a major source of protein for the world, largely because of U.S. production.

High hopes were once placed on the possibilities of fish protein concentrates (FPC). High-quality protein can be extracted from fish that are not ordinarily considered edible. A considerable tonnage of fish meal, much of it from the Peruvian anchovy catch, has been pro-cessed for poultry and swine feeds. Fish protein concentrates have been incorporated into human dietary supplements with excellent results. The outlook at present is not so optimistic, primarily because of erratic supply. Less than 5% of the world's protein comes from fish, and yield of some of the best fishing grounds is declining. It turns out that the oceans of the earth are mostly salt-water deserts with little marine life. The rich areas are few and some of these have been overfished. The great Peruvian fishing waters suffer disastrous declines from time to time. It seems obvious that if FPC is going to be a major factor on the world scene we will have to use different approaches than the present ones.

Effective use of animal and vegetable proteins

Obviously, much more protein would be available if we stopped feeding protein-rich crops to animals. The United States produces 70% of the world's soybeans, but only about 2% of it is consumed directly by humans. Almost all of it is processed for feeding poultry, swine, and cattle. The animals are then consumed and while animal protein is of better quality than vegetable proteins, the conversion is wasteful in terms of total protein for human food. The time will probably come when North Americans will eat less meat, and that time has long been at hand for most of the people of the world (Table 2). In Asia and Africa about 80% of the protein of human diets is supplied by plants and about 20% is from animal sources. In North America about 70% of the protein is from animal sources and only 30% from plants. Population pressures may force changes in these ratios.

Most people in the United States have converted from butter to margarine, although there were some strange legal battles along the way. Animal fats no longer compete with plant sources of edible oils. Protein is moving in the same direction. It might be more difficult for meat eaters to give up meat than butter eaters to substitute margarine, but the economic lever is a powerful one. If meat were to sell at $8 or $10 per kilogram and the equivalent in food value of plant protein was $0.80, meat consumption would probably decline. Such meat prices already occur in some countries.

Research is under way to develop acceptable meat substitutes and some products are already available in limited quantities. In the United States, textured vegetable protein (TVP) is usually based on defatted soybean flakes, but other sources such as peanut, sesame, and other oil seed meals are being explored elsewhere. Texturing is considered important in giving the product some of the physical characteristics of meat, and various flavors can be added. At present, TVP is used as a meat extender, but the cost is not low enough at this time to give it much advantage. Nutritional studies indicate most

Table 2

Percentage contribution of various commodities to percentage supplies; protein supplies 1963 to 1965 (from Autret, 1970; with permission).

	Cereals	Starchy roots and tubers	Pulses nuts and seeds	Vegetables and fruits	Vegetable proteins	Meat	Eggs	Fish	Milk	Animal proteins
FAR EAST (incl. China Mainland)	59.3	3.3	18.0	3.3	84.3	6.6	0.7	4.6	3.8	15.7
South Asia	64.5	1.0	19.6	1.0	87.1	1.4	0.2	1.4	9.9	12.9
Southern Asia Mainland	58.8	2.0	8.3	4.0	73.5	7.1	1.4	15.4	2.6	26.5
Eastern Asia	48.2	2.1	14.0	8.4	72.7	6.1	2.9	15.6	2.7	27.3
South Eastern Asia Major Islands	64.4	6.4	7.4	3.9	82.6	7.1	1.0	8.6	0.7	17.4
China Mainland	57.8	4.6	20.3	3.2	86.1	10.0	0.5	2.7	0.5	13.9
NEAR AND MIDDLE EAST	67.8	1.0	6.7	4.9	80.1	8.0	0.7	1.4	9.5	19.6
AFRICA	54.7	9.1	15.7	1.9	81.4	9.2	0.5	4.1	4.8	18.6
North Africa	69.9	1.1	5.1	4.2	80.3	7.8	0.8	1.6	9.5	19.7
West and Central Africa	51.2	14.8	18.1	1.6	85.7	6.8	0.4	5.1	2.0	14.3
East and Southern Africa	55.1	4.5	15.6	1.7	76.9	12.5	0.6	3.4	6.6	23.1
LATIN AMERICA	39.8	4.0	16.9	3.4	64.3	18.3	1.9	2.7	12.7	35.7
Brazil	37.9	3.6	26.6	3.7	71.8	13.5	2.2	2.3	10.2	28.2
Mexico and Central America	44.3	2.1	18.2	3.0	67.9	12.7	1.8	2.4	14.9	32.1
Northern and Western countries of South America	41.0	7.5	8.5	4.3	61.8	18.8	1.2	4.8	13.2	38.2
River Plate Countries	32.7	4.2	2.5	2.9	42.3	41.0	2.1	1.4	13.0	57.7
DEVELOPING REGIONS	57.2	3.8	16.8	3.3	81.4	8.3	0.9	4.0	5.4	18.6
EUROPE (incl. U.S.S.R.)	36.8	5.5	3.8	5.4	51.5	21.5	3.8	4.2	18.8	48.5
Eastern Europe	50.0	6.4	3.0	4.2	63.6	16.4	2.5	1.5	15.1	36.4
Western Europe	33.5	5.4	3.9	5.6	48.4	22.8	4.1	4.9	19.8	51.6
NORTH AMERICA	17.6	2.6	4.6	5.2	30.1	36.3	5.8	2.9	24.9	69.9
OCEANIA	24.9	2.4	2.2	3.6	33.1	36.8	4.2	3.1	22.5	66.9
DEVELOPED REGIONS	31.9	4.7	3.9	5.3	45.8	25.4	4.3	3.9	20.4	54.2
WORLD	47.9	4.1	12.1	3.9	68.2	14.7	2.1	3.9	10.9	31.8

TVP preparations are good but somewhat inferior to high-quality animal proteins (Figure 3) (Lawrie, 1970).

While searches for meat substitutes are essential for many undernourished populations, there is no intention of doing away with domestic animals altogether. They can utilize plant productions that man cannot utilize. Only a relatively small part of the land surface is suitable for agriculture. Most of it is better suited for range and forests. Rangelands can best be exploited by livestock, and forests can often be used for range and recreation as well as for timber production. When livestock feeds and fodders are produced on productive farmland, thus competing with the production of human food, priority decisions must be made. In countries like India or China where population pressures are very high, the choice would seem to favor human food production and discourage livestock feeding. Even in those countries, however, there are wastes and inedible residues that can be converted to useful and nutritious foods by livestock.

Some plants produce much more protein per hectare than soybeans or peanuts. Alfalfa is one example, and the possibilities of using its leaf proteins have aroused considerable interest. To date, there have been problems in extraction that have not made the leaf proteins especially cheap and they are not likely to be popular without improved processing methods. Bickoff and Kohler (1973) reported on possibilities of commercial production and described a process of extracting a nutritious concentrate from alfalfa leaves. An article in a PAG bulletin [3(1):19-20. 1973] suggests that enough protein to supply the entire human population could be produced from alfalfa on an area the size of the state of Texas. If space is the main problem, however, there are systems far more efficient than growing alfalfa.

Leaf protein may have the most application in the tropics. Production can be high and dietary protein deficiencies are most prevalent in the wet tropics. Manioc leaves are especially high in protein They are eaten to some extent, but the potential use would be much greater if appropriate techniques of processing were developed. Several other tropical plants, including several species of trees, have a considerable potential for production of leaf protein. However, their potential is not going to be realized without adequate research and development.

Figure 3 →
Essential amino acid composition of unconventional proteins (adapted from Kosaric, 1973).

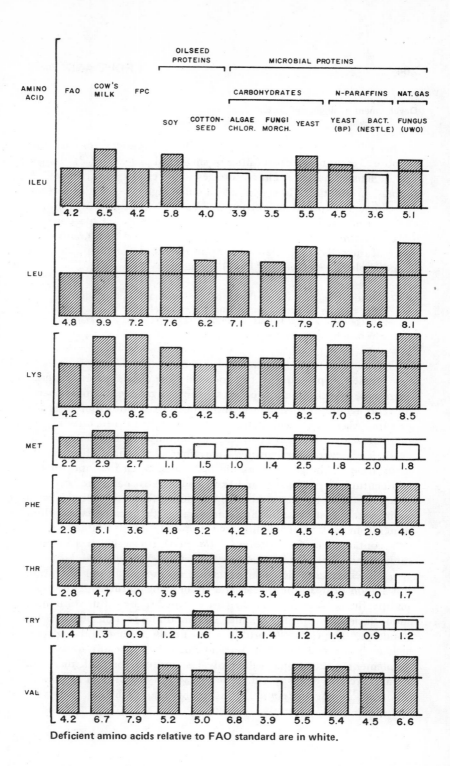

Deficient amino acids relative to FAO standard are in white.

Development of single cell protein

Rather extensive research projects have been underway for a decade or more to explore the possibilities of single cell protein (SCP). Single cell organisms have certain advantages with respect to efficiency of biomass production. In single cells, a much higher percent of surface to volume is exposed to nutrient media, and the entire organism is metabolically active. In higher plants, many cells are set apart as support structures, conductive tissues, protection,. and so on, and only some of the cells are specialized for photosynthesis or the production of metabolites. As Gordon (1970) comments:

> Traditional agricultural methods for plant and animal production require the use of vast areas of land for relatively low yields. Unicellular algae can be cultivated in compact units such as fermenters which, although complex, occupy only a relatively small area.

The relative efficiency is shown in Table 3.

Single cell protein can be produced from algae, yeasts, bacteria, fungi, and, conceivably, protozoa. Of these, algae are the most nearly conventional in that they use the processes of photosynthesis for growth. Algae have been consumed since ancient times, but only on a minor scale. Certain seaweeds are popular foods, especially in Japan, and several are cultured somewhat like a field crop. Blue-green algae of the genus *Spirulina* have been eaten for food for untold centuries by people near Lake Chad in Africa and similar forms were consumed by the Aztecs of Mexico. These species thrive in warm waters rich in carbonates and some of the metabolized carbon comes from the carbonate and some from CO_2. Dried *Spirulina* products contain over 60% protein. *Chlorella* is the green alga most studied and yields a product containing about 50% protein.

Protein quality depends somewhat on the conditions of culture and a good deal on the species and strain being cultured. The amino acid profile of *Spirulina* is excellent except for the sulfur-containing amino acids, but both cystine and methionine fall below FAO standards. The *Chlorella* profile is not nearly as good, although it is high in lysine and *Chlorella* protein might be especially useful as a supplement. Nutritional values of algal protein for both man and animals are still being tested. The digestibility of protein from both *Chlorella* and *Scenedesmus* seems to be poor, whereas that from

Table 3
Theoretical protein productivity for algae as compared to
other sources (adapted from Gordon, 1970).

Source	Protein dry wt, kg/ha per year
Spirulina platensis	24,304
Chlorella pyrenoidosa	15,680
Fish	627.2
Peanuts	470.4
Peas	395.36
Wheat	301.28
Milk	100.8
Eggs	60.48

Spirulina appears to be good. The whole field of utilization of algal
protein remains to be explored, and the productive potential is considerable. Gordon (1970) estimated that if "half the human daily requirement of 70 grams of protein was to be obtained from algae, an
area no greater in size than the county of Essex [3,886 km² (1,500
mi²)] would be required to fill the requirements of the present world
population." Essex is smaller than Texas but that would still be a
large culture tank.

Oswald and Golueke (1968) reported:

> In studies with our large-scale pilot plant at Richmond, California we
> demonstrated that with proper cultivation, at least 20 tons (dry wt)
> [18 metric tons] of algae having a protein concentration of 50%
> will be produced per acre [0.405 ha] of pond per year. In terms of
> yield of digestible protein on an areal basis, this yield is 10 to 15
> times greater than that of an acre of land planted with soybeans and
> 25 to 50 times that planted with corn.

At present algal protein is too expensive to be competitive, but
there are possibilities of developing production as a byproduct of
waste disposal management. Algae may be grown partly to provide
oxygen for aerobic bacteria breaking down waste materials, for example.

Yeasts and fungi can be cultured on a variety of waste materials.
Since they do not carry on photosynthesis, the carbon is obtained
from the substrate and not from CO_2. Some of the substrates used
are: molasses, sulfite wastes from the paper pulp industry, sugars obtained by hydrolyzing wood, beet pulp, bagasse from sugarcane,
dairy wastes, brewery wastes, and cannery wastes. Such raw materials
can be very cheap and it would be more sensible to convert them into

usable protein than to dump them into rivers. The nitrogen can be supplied by inorganic salts.

Of particular interest in recent years is the use of refined petroleum fractions as substrates for culturing yeasts and bacteria, and natural gas or methane for bacteria and fungi. The petroleum fraction is the straight-chain paraffin hydrocarbons, perhaps about 10% of a typical crude oil. Small production plants have already been constructed in the United Kingdom, France, Czechoslovakia, the Soviet Union, India, Taiwan, China, and Japan. Larger plants are being planned or constructed. The potential is too great not to be pursued vigorously. To date, the leading organization in pilot plant development, testing, and evaluation is British Petroleum Proteins Ltd., but research in several other countries is very active.

On the whole, protein produced by these methods is of good quality (Figure 3). Methionine is the amino acid most likely to be deficient and often is not critically short. Yields are good and the substrates are abundant and low in cost. These approaches appear to be economically and nutritionally feasible. Most of the trials so far have been with animals. In diets using soybean meal and fish meal as the protein source, it was found that yeast protein could replace all the fish meal and part of the soybean meal (Shacklady, 1970). A considerable volume of feeding trials with very encouraging results has accrued. Petroleum hydrocarbons and natural gas appear to be useful, low-cost substrates for SCP production.

Of the several classes of organisms tried, bacteria would have some advantage because of extremely rapid biomass production. Kosaric (1973) estimated that a 2.59 km^2 (1 mi^2) fermenting surface could supply the protein requirements for the entire human population. There is some concern, however, about the high nucleic acid content that might cause toxic levels of urea and uric acid in the blood. Still, these problems can probably be solved with adequate research.

Some of the advantages of single cell protein are rather obvious. The process does not require good soil or climate; it can be carried out almost anywhere. If the substrates are easily portable, as in petroleum, natural gas, or methane, the protein can be produced near population centers. If the substrate is expensive to transport as in industrial and plant wastes, the protein could be produced at the source and help dispose of the wastes at the same time. The production potential is much higher than in conventional agriculture. With efficient production plants the products should be sufficiently low in price that poor people could enjoy a better diet than they now have.

There are, however, problems of utilization and acceptability, and in developing countries, problems of production. The plants are complex and sophisticated and require highly skilled operators. Compared to conventional agriculture the labor requirements are very low. This is an advantage in industrial societies but is no help to countries with an underemployment problem. SCP may or may not become a significant feature of the world food supply. There are too many unsolved questions to predict at this time.

Conclusions

The most radical solution of all to the protein question would be to synthesize the essential amino acids in a chemical plant. All of them have been synthesized in the laboratory on a small scale, but only two are in commercial production: lysine and methionine. These two are the most critical for people on cereal diets and routine enrichment of cereal products could prove very beneficial for those not receiving adequate dietary protein.

Research on unconventional foods will continue and many of the problems in production and utilization will be solved, but all of this striving may turn out to be fruitless. As long as the population of the world continues to rise indefinitely, no rational solution is possible. There is no procedure, process, or technique that will prevent eventual mass starvation unless the world population is stabilized. I am optimistic enough to believe that one country after another will find a forever rising population a burden and that zero growth or even negative growth will eventually be achieved. The trend toward population control will be very uneven, however, and some nations may not be able to avert serious nutritional catastrophes. In recent decades the more prosperous nations have stepped in to help out; now even they don't have enough for everyone. Famine has never been a stranger to agricultural peoples.

An industrial solution to food problems inevitably brings with it characteristic problems of industrial societies. Man sinks ever deeper into his artificial, technological jungle. There seems to be no way out. He can, perhaps, recall a dim vision in which man and nature lived in harmony, when he could marvel at the beauty and perfection of creation, where meadows were bespangled with flowers and tall trees reached toward the heavens, where lakes were blue and streams ran clear and a man could lie on his back at night and be awed and amazed at the brilliance of the stars shining through clear, unpolluted air. Yes, man has traveled a long road, but his restless spirit has yet to find peace.

REFERENCES

CHAPTER 1

BANCROFT, J. 1884. Food of the Aborigines of central Australia. Roy. Soc. Queensland, Proc. 1:104–106.

BAUMHOFF, MARTIN A. 1963. Ecological determinants of aboriginal California populations. Univ. of Calif. Publ. in Amer. Archaeol. and Ethnol. 49:155–236.

BURKILL, I. H. 1935. A dictionary of the economic products of the Malay Peninsula. Oxford Univ. Press, London. 2 vols.

CHEVALIER, A. 1932. Resources végétales du Sahara et de ses confins nord et sud. Musée d'Histoire Naturelle. Paris.

COON, CARLETON S. 1971. The hunting peoples. Little, Brown and Co., Boston.

COURSEY, D. G. 1972. The civilizations of the yam: interrelationships of man and yams in Africa and the Indo-Pacific region. Archaeol. Phys. Anthrop. Oceania 7:215–233.

DOWNS, J. 1964. Significance of environmental manipulation in Great Basin cultural development. p. 39–56. In W. L. D'Azevedo, W. A. Davis, D. D. Fowler, and W. Suttles (ed.) The current status of anthropological research in the Great Basin. Desert Res. Inst. Tech. Rep. Ser. SH, Social Sci. and Human. Publ. No. 1.

ELTON, CHARLES A. (trans.) 1815. Hesiodus, 2nd ed. Baldwin, Cradock and Joy, London.

FLANNERY, KENT V. 1968. Archaeological systems theory and early Mesoamerica. p. 67–87. In Betty J. Meggers (ed.) Anthropological archaeology in the Americas. Anthrop. Soc. of Washington, Washington, D. C.

GENTRY, HOWARD SCOTT. 1942. Rio Mayo plants; a study of the flora and vegetation of the valley of Rio Mayo, Sonora. Carnegie Inst. Publ. 527.

GIFFORD, E. W. 1967. Ethnographic notes on the southwestern Pomo. Univ. of Calif. Anthrop. Rec. 25:1–48.

GREGORY, A. C. 1886. Memoranda on the Aborigines of Australia. J. Anthrop. Inst. 16:131–133.

GREY, SIR GEORGE. 1841. Journals of two expeditions of discovery in northwest and western Australia during the years 1837, 38 and 39. T & W Boone, London. 2 vols.

HARLAN, J. R. 1967. A wild wheat harvest in Turkey. Archaeology 20:197–201.

HO, PING-TI. 1969. The loess and the origin of Chinese agriculture. Amer. Hist. Rev. 75:1–36.

IRVINE, F. R. 1957. Wild and emergency foods of Australian and Tasmanian Aborigines. Oceania 28:113–142.

JARDIN, CLAUDE. 1967. List of foods used in Africa. FAO, Rome.

JOHNSTON, T., and J. BURTON CLELAND. 1933. The history of the aboriginal narcotic, pituri. Oceania 4:201–223, 268–289.

KÖRNICKE, FRIEDR. 1885. Die Arten und Varietäten des Getreides. Handbuch des Getreidebaues, Vol. I. Paul Parey, Berlin.

LATHRAP, D. W. 1968. The "hunting" economies of the tropical forest zone of South America: An attempt at historical perspective. p. 23–29. In R. B. Lee and I. DeVore (ed.) Man the hunter. Aldine, Chicago.

LEE, R. B. 1968. What hunters do for a living, or how to make out on scarce resources. p. 30–48. In R. B. Lee and I. DeVore (ed.) Man the hunter. Aldine, Chicago.

LEE, R. B., and I. DE VORE (ed.). 1968a. Man the hunter. Aldine, Chicago.

LEE, R. B., and I. DE VORE. 1968b. Problems in the study of hunters and
   gatherers. p. 3–12. In R. B. Lee and I. DeVore (ed.) Man the hunter.
   Aldine, Chicago.
LÉVI-STRAUSS, CLAUDE. 1950. The use of wild plants in tropical South
   America. p. 465–486. In Handbook of South American Indians. Smith-
   sonian Inst. Bur. Amer. Ethnol. Bull. 143, Vol. 6.
LOEB, E. M. 1934. The eastern Kuksu cult. Univ. of Calif. Publ. in Amer.
   Archaeol. and Ethnol. 33:139–231.
MAIDEN, J. H. 1889. Useful native plants of Australia. Trubner and Co.,
   London.
MARSHALL, LORNA. 1960. !Kung Bushman bands. Africa 30:325–355.
MURDOCK, GEORGE PETER. 1967. The ethnographic atlas: a summary.
   Ethnology 6:109–236.
NICOLAISEN, JOHANNES. 1963. Ecology and culture of the pastoral Tuareg.
   Copenhagen Nat. Mus., Copenhagen.
OKA, HIKO-ICHI, and WEN-TSAI CHANG. 1964. Observations of wild and
   cultivated rice species in Africa. Rep. of trip from Sierra Leone to Tchad,
   1963. Unpublished.
PALMER, E. 1883. On the plants used by the natives of North Queensland,
   Flinders and Mitchell Rivers for food and medicine, etc. Roy. Soc. New
   South Wales, Trans. 17:93–113.
RAY, VERNE F. 1963. Primitive pragmatists: the Modoc Indians of northern
   California. Amer. Ethnol. Soc. Seattle, Univ. of Wash. Press, Seattle.
ROY, S. C. 1921. A preliminary classification of wild rices of the Central
   Provinces and Berar. Agr. J. India. 16:365–380.
SAHLINS, MARSHALL. 1968. Notes on the original affluent society. p. 85–
   89. In R. B. Lee and I. DeVore (ed.) Man the hunter. Aldine, Chicago.
SCHAPERA, I. 1951. The Khoisan peoples of South Africa. Routledge & Kegan
   Paul Ltd., London.
SKOLNICK, M. H., and C. CANNINGS. 1972. Natural regulation of numbers
   in primitive human populations. Nature 239(5370):287–288.
SPENCER, SIR BALDWIN. 1967/1928. Wanderings in wild Australia. Johnson
   Reprint Co., London. 2 vols.
STEWARD, J. H. 1934. Ethnography of the Owens Valley Paiute. Univ. of
   Calif. Publ. of Amer. Archaeol. and Ethnol. 33:233–340.
STEWARD, J. H. 1941. Culture element distributions: XIII Nevada Shoshoni.
   Univ. of Calif. Anthrop. Rec. 4. 4(2):209–359.
STICKNEY, GARDNER P. 1896. Indian uses of wild rice. Amer. Anthrop. 9:
   115–21.
STORY, D. 1958. Some plants used by the Bushmen in obtaining food and
   water. Dept. of Agr. Bot, Pretoria, South Africa.
SUTTLES, WAYNE. 1968. Coping with abundance: Subsistence on the North-
   west Coast. p. 56–68. In R. B. Lee and I. DeVore (ed.) Man the hunter.
   Aldine, Chicago.
SZAFER, WLADYSLAW (ed.). 1966. The vegetation of Poland. Pergamon
   Press, New York.
THOMAS, E. MARSHALL. 1959. The harmless people. A Knopf, New York.
WARNER, W. LLOYD. 1958. A black civilization, revised ed. Harper and Bros.,
   New York.
WASHBURN, S. L., and C. S. LANCASTER. 1968. The evolution of hunting.
   p. 293–303. In R. B. Lee and I. DeVore (ed.) Man the hunter. Aldine,
   Chicago.
YANOVSKY, ELIAS. 1936. Food plants of the North American Indians.
   USDA Misc. Publ. No. 237.

CHAPTER 2

ANDERSON, EDGAR. 1954. Plants, man and life. A. Melrose, London.

BERNDT, RONALD M., and CATHERINE H. BERNDT. 1970. Man, land and myth in North Australia. Mich. State Univ. Press, East Lansing.

BINFORD, LEWIS R. 1968. Post-Pleistocene adaptations. p. 313–341. *In* S. R. Binford and L. R. Binford (ed.) New perspectives in archaeology. Aldine, Chicago.

BLACK, J. N. 1971. Energy relations in crop production—a preliminary survey. Ann. Appl. Biol. 67:272–278.

BOOTH, G. 1814. The historical library of Diodorus the Sicilian. W. McDowall, London.

BRAIDWOOD, R. J. 1972. Prehistoric investigations in southwestern Asia. Amer. Phil. Soc., Proc. 116:310–320.

BRÜCHER, H. 1969. Gibt es Gen-Zentren? Naturwissenschaften 56:77–84.

CANDOLLE, ALPHONSE DE. 1959. Origin of cultivated plants, 2nd ed. Hafner, New York. Translated from the 1886 edition.

CARTER, G. F. 1971. Pre-Columbian chickens in America. p. 178–218. *In* C. L. Riley et al. (ed.) Man across the sea. Univ. of Texas Press, Austin.

CHANG, KWANG-CHIH. 1970. The beginnings of agriculture in the Far East. Antiquity 44:175–185.

CHAVANNES, EDOUARD. 1895–1905. Les mémoires historiques de Se-ma-Ts'ien traduits et annotés par Édouard Chavannes. E. Leroux, Paris. 5 vols.

CHILDE, V. GORDON. 1925. The dawn of European civilization. Alfred A. Knopf, New York.

CHILDE, V. GORDON. 1952. New light on the most ancient East. Routledge & Paul, London.

CHRISTIE, ANTHONY. 1968. Chinese mythology. Hamlyn Publ. Group, Fetham (Middlesex), England.

CUMMINS, J. S. (ed.) 1962. The travels and controversies of Friar Domingo Navarrete 1618–1686. Hakluyt Soc., Univ. Press, Cambridge, England.

DARWIN, CHARLES. 1896. The variation of animals and plants under domestication, 2nd ed. D. Appleton & Co., New York. 2 vols.

DARWIN, CHARLES. 1909. The descent of man and selection in relation to sex, 2nd ed. D. Appleton & Co., New York.

FITZGERALD, C. P. 1938. China, a short cultural history. D. Appleton—Century Co., New York.

FLANNERY, KENT V. 1966. The postglacial 'Readaptation' as viewed from Mesoamerica. Amer. Antiq. 31:800–805.

FLANNERY, KENT V. 1968. Archaeological systems theory and early Meso-america. p. 67–87. *In* Betty J. Meggers (ed.) Anthropological archaeology in the Americas. Anthrop. Soc. of Washington, Washington, D. C.

FOX, WILLIAM SHERWOOD. 1916. Greek and Roman, Vol. 1. *In* Louis Herbert Gray (ed.) Mythology of all races. Marshall Jones Co., Boston. 13 vols.

GÖKGÖL, M. 1941. Über die Genzentrentheorie und den Ursprung des Weizens. Zeitschrift fur Pflanzenzüchtung 23:562–578.

GORMAN, C. 1969. Hoabinhian: a pebble-tool complex with early plant associations in Southeast Asia. Science 163:671–673.

HAHN, EDUARD. 1896. Die Haustiere und ihre Beziehungen zur Wirtschaft des Menschen. Duncker und Humbolt, Leipzig.

HAHN, EDUARD. 1909. Die Entstehung der Pflugkultur. C. Winter, Heidelberg.

HARLAN, J. R. 1951. Anatomy of gene centers. Amer. Nat. 85:97–103.

HARLAN, J. R. 1969. Evolutionary dynamics of plant domestication. Jap. J. Genet. 44(Suppl.):337–343.

HARLAN, J. R. 1970. The evolution of cultivated plants. p. 19–32. In O. H. Frankel and E. Bennett (ed.) Genetic resources in plants—their exploration and conservation. Blackwell Scientific Publ., Oxford.

HARLAN, J. R. 1971. Agricultural origins: centers and noncenters. Science 174:468–474.

HARLAN, J. R., and D. ZOHARY. 1966. Distribution of wild wheats and barley. Science 153:1074–1080.

HAWKRIDGE, EMMA. 1945. The wisdom tree. Books for Libraries Press, Freeport, New York.

ISAAC, ERICH. 1970. Geography of domestication. Prentice-Hall Inc., Englewood Cliffs, New Jersey.

KUCKUCK, HERMAN. 1962. Vavilov's Genzentren theorie in Heutiger Sicht. Eucarpia:177–196.

LANGDON, S. H. 1931. Semitic. Vol. 5. In J. A. Macculloch (ed.) The mythology of all races. Marshall Jones Co., Boston. 13 vols.

LATOURETTE, KENNETH SCOTT. 1941. The Chinese, their history and culture. Macmillan, New York. 2 vols.

LEE, R. B., and I. DE VORE. 1968. Man the hunter. Aldine, Chicago.

PRESCOTT, WILHAM H. 1936. History of the conquest of Mexico and history of the conquest of Peru. Modern Library, New York.

RECINOS, A. 1947. Popol Vuh, Las antiguas historias del Quiché. Fondo de Cultura Económica, Mexico D. F.

SAUER, C. O. 1952. Agricultural origins and dispersals. M.I.T. Press, Cambridge, Mass.

SCHIEMANN, ELISABETH. 1939. Gedanken zur Genzentrentheorie Vavilovs. Naturwissenschaften 27:377–383.

SMITH, C. EARLE, JR. 1969. From Vavilov to the present—A review. Econ. Bot. 23(1):2–19.

SOLHEIM, W. G., II. 1971. New light on a forgotten past. Nat. Geogr. 139:330–339.

STORR-BEST, LLOYD. 1912. Varro on farming. G. Bell & Sons, London.

VAVILOV, N. I. 1926. Studies on the origin of cultivated plants. Inst. Appl. Bot. Plant Breed., Leningrad.

VEGA, GARCILASO DE LA. 1961. The royal commentaries of the Inca Garcilaso de la Vega. Orion, New York.

ZOHARY, D. 1970. Centers of diversity and centers of origin. p. 33–42. In O. H. Frankel and E. Bennett (ed.) Genetic resources in plants—their exploration and conservation. Blackwell Sci. Publ., Oxford.

CHAPTER 3

BARRAU, JACQUES. 1965. L'humide et le sec, an essay on ethnobotanical adaptation to contrastive environments in the Indo-Pacific area. J. Polynesian Soc. 74:329–346.

CALLEN, E. O. 1967. The first New World cereal. Amer. Antiq. 32:535–538.

DANCETTE, C., and J. F. POULAIN. 1968. Influence de l'*Acacia albida* sur les facteurs pédoclimatiques et les rendements des cultures. Sols Africains 13:197–239.

JOHNSON, SAMUEL. 1827. Dictionary of the English language. Longman, Rees, Orme, Browne and Green, London. 3 vols.

LÉVI-STRAUSS, CLAUDE. 1950. The use of wild plants in tropical South America. p. 465–486. *In* Handbook of South American Indians. Smithsonian Inst. Bur. Amer. Ethnol. Bull. 143, Vol. 6.

LI, HUI-LIN. 1969. The vegetables of ancient China. Econ. Bot. 23:253–260.

CHAPTER 4

AFFLECK, THOMAS. 1884. Letter to the editor. Amer. Agr. 3:335–336.

AKIHAMA, T., and T. WATABE. 1970. Geographical distribution and ecotypic differentiation of wild rice in Thailand. Tonan Ajia Kenkyu 8:337–346.

ANDERSON, EDGAR. 1954. Plants, man and life. A. Melrose, London.

ANTONOVICS, JANIS. 1971. The effects of heterogeneous environment on the genetics of natural populations. Amer. Sci. 59:593–599.

BARRAU, JACQUES. 1963. Plants and the migrations of Pacific peoples: A symposium. Bishop Museum Press, Honolulu.

BHALERAO, S. G. 1928. The wild rice (*Oryza sativa*) of the Bombay Presidency. Poona Agr. Coll. Mag. 20:45–49.

BLATCHLEY, W. S. 1912. The Indiana weed book. Nature Publ. Co., Indianapolis.

BUNTING, A. H. 1960. Some reflections on the ecology of weeds. p. 11–26. *In* J. L. Harper (ed.) The biology of weeds. Blackwell Scientific Publ., Oxford.

CHANG, KWANG-CHIH. 1970. The beginnings of agriculture in the Far East. Antiquity 44:175–185.

COCANNOUER, JOSEPH A. 1950. Weeds, guardians of the soil. Devin-Adair, New York.

DAYTON, W. A. 1950. Glossary of botanical terms commonly used in range research, revised. USDA Misc. Publ. 110.

DIMBLEBY, G. W. 1967. Plants and archaeology. Humanities Press Inc., New York.

FOGG, JOHN M. 1945. Weeds of lawn and garden. Univ. of Penn. Press, Philadelphia.

FOWLER, MELVIN L. 1971. The origin of plant cultivation in the Central Mississippi Valley: A hypothesis. p. 122–128. *In* Stuart Struever (ed.) Prehistoric agriculture. Natural History Press, Garden City, New York.

GEORGIA, ADA E. 1914. A manual of weeds. Macmillan Co., New York.

GHOSE, R. L. M., M. B. GHATGE, and V. SUBRAHMANYAN. 1956. Rice in India. Indian Council Agr. Res. New Delhi.

GILMORE, MELVIN R. 1930. Dispersal by Indians, a factor in the extension of discontinuous distribution of certain species of native plants. Papers of Mich. Acad. of Sci., Arts and Letters 13:89–94.

HAMILTON, A. C. 1972. The interpretation of pollen diagrams from highland Uganda. p. 45–149. *In* E. M. Van Zinderen Bakker (ed.) Palaeoecology of Africa, Vol. 7. A. A. Balkema, Cape Town.

HARLAN, H. V. 1929. The weedishness of wild oats. J. Hered. 20:515–518.

HARLAN, J. R. 1970. *Cynodon* species for grazing and hay. Herb. Abstr. 40: 233–238.

HARLAN, J. R., and J. M. J. DE WET. 1965. Some thoughts about weeds. Econ. Bot. 19:16–24.

HARLAN, J. R., and J. M. J. DE WET. 1969. Sources of variation in *Cynodon dactylon* (L.) Pers. Crop Sci. 9:774–8.

HARLAN, J. R., J. M. J. DE WET, and K. M. RAWAL. 1970. Origin and distribution of the selencidus race of *Cynodon dactylon* (L.) Pers. var. *dactylon* (Gramineae). Euphytica 19:465–469.

HARLAN, J. R., and D. ZOHARY. 1966. Distribution of wild wheats and barley. Science 153:1074–1080.

HARPER, JOHN L. (ed.) 1960. The biology of weeds. Blackwell Scientific Publ., Oxford. p. xi.

ISELY, DUANE. 1960. Weed identification and control. Iowa State Univ. Press, Ames.

JOHNSON, SAMUEL. 1827. Dictionary of the English language. Longman, Rees, Orme, Browne, and Green, London. 3 vols.

KING, F. C. 1951. The weed problem, a new approach. Faber & Faber Ltd., London.

KLINGMAN, GLENN C. 1961. Weed control: as a science. John Wiley and Sons, New York.

KÖRNICKE, FRIEDR. 1885. Die Arten und Varietaten des Getreides. Handbuch des Getreidebaues, Vol. 1. Paul Parey, Berlin.

LUNDELL, C. L. 1938. Plants probably utilized by the Old Empire Maya of Peten and adjacent lowlands. Papers of Mich. Acad. of Sci., Arts and Letters 24:37–56.

MERRILL, E. D. 1922-26. An enumeration of Philippine flowering plants. Bur. of Printing, Manila. 4 vols.

MITRA, S. K., and P. M. GANGULI. 1932. Some observations on the characters of wild rice hybrids. Indian J. Agr. Sci. 2:271–279.

MOORE, JOHN HEBRON. 1958. Agriculture in ante-bellum Mississippi. Bookman Associates, New York.

MOSELEY, E. L. 1930. Some plants that were probably brought to Northern Ohio from the West by Indians. Papers of Mich. Acad. of Sci., Arts and Letters 13:169–172.

MUENSCHER, W. C. 1946. Weeds. Macmillan, New York.

MURRAY, J. A. H., H. BRADLEY, W. A. CRAGIE, and C. T. ONIONS (ed.) 1961. Oxford English Dictionary. The Clarendon Press, Oxford. 12 vols + supplements.

PORTÈRES, R. 1957. Paysages floristiques des parcours cultureaux en Afrique tropicale. C. R. Soc. Biogeogr. 294:16–20.

PRITCHARD, TOM. 1960. Race formation in weedy species with special reference to *Euphorbia cyparissias* L. and *Hypericum perforatum* L. p. 61–66. *In* J. L. Harper (ed.) The biology of weeds. Blackwell Scientific Publ., Oxford.

RADEMACHER, B. 1948. Gedanken über Begriff und Wesen des "Unkrautes". Pflanzenkrankheiten v. Pflanzenschutz 55:3–10.

RAMIAH, K., and R. L. M. GHOSE. 1951. Origin and distribution of cultivated plants of South-Asia rice. Indian J. Genet. Plant Breed. 11:7–11.

ROBBINS, W. W., A. S. CRAFTS, and R. N. RAYNOR. 1942. Weed control. McGraw Hill, New York.

SALISBURY, EDWARD. 1961. Weeds and aliens. Collins, London.

SPALDING, THOMAS. 1844. Letter to the editor. Amer. Agr. 3:335.

WILKES, H. G. 1967. Teosinte: the closest relative of maize. Bussey Inst., Harvard Univ., Cambridge, Mass.

WODEHOUSE, R. P. 1960. Weed. Encyclopaedia Britanica 23:477–479.

YABUNO, T. 1961. *Oryza sativa* and *Echinochloa crus-galli* var. *oryzicola* Ohwi. Seiken Ziho 12:29–34.

YARNELL, R. A. 1965. Implications of distinctive flora on Pueblo ruins. Amer. Anthrop. 67:662–674.

ZOHARY, D. 1971. Origin of south-west Asiatic cereals: Wheats, barley, oats, and rye. p. 235–263. *In* P. H. Davis et al. (ed.) Plant life of southwest Asia. Bot. Soc. of Edinburgh, Edinburgh.

CHAPTER 5

BOWDEN, W. M. 1959. The taxonomy and nomenclature of the wheats, barleys and ryes and their wild relatives. Can. J. Bot. 37:657–684.

BUKASOV, S. M. 1933. The potatoes of South America and their breeding possibilities. Suppl. 58, Bull. Bot. Genet. Plant Breed., Leningrad.

CANDOLLE, ALPHONSE DE. 1867. Lois de la nomenclature botanique. V. Masson + Fils, Paris.

CANDOLLE, ALPHONSE DE. 1883. Nouvelles remarques sur la nomenclature botanique. H. Georg, Genève.

CHU, YAW-EN, and HIKO-ICHI OKA. 1970. Introgression across isolating barriers in wild and cultivated *Oryza* species. Evolution 24:344–355.

DARWIN, C. R. 1859. On the origin of species by means of natural selection. J. Murray, London.

DARWIN, C. R. 1897. The variation of animals and plants under domestication. J. Murray, London. 2 vols.

DE WET, J. M. J., and J. P. HUCKABAY. 1967. The origin of *Sorghum bicolor*. II. Distribution and domestication. Evolution 21:787–802.

DE WET, J. M. J., R. J. LAMBERT, J. R. HARLAN, and S. M. NAIK. 1970. Stable triploid hybrids among *Zea-Tripsacum-Zea* backcross populations. Caryologia 23:183–187.

HARLAN, J. R. 1966. Plant introduction and biosystematics. p. 55–83. *In* K. J. Frey (ed.) Plant breeding. Iowa State Univ. Press, Ames.

HARLAN, J. R. 1969. Evolutionary dynamics of plant domestication. Jap. J. Genet. 44(Suppl. 1):337–343.

HARLAN, J. R. 1970. The evolution of cultivated plants. p. 19–32. *In* O. H. Frankel and E. Bennett (ed.) Genetic resources in plants—their exploration and conservation. Blackwell Scientific Publ., Oxford.

HARLAN, J. R., and J. M. J. DE WET. 1963. The compilospecies concept. Evolution 17:497–501.

HARLAN, J. R., and J. M. J. DE WET. 1971. Toward a rational classification of cultivated plants. Taxon 20:509–517.

HARLAN, J. R., and J. M. J. DE WET. 1972. A simplified classification of cultivated sorghum. Crop Sci. 12:172–176.

HAWKES, J. G. 1963. A revision of the tuber-bearing Solanums, 2nd ed. Scottish Plant Breed. Sta. Rec. p. 76–181.

IVANOVSKAYA, E. V. 1946. Hybrid embryos of cereals grown on artificial nutrient medium. Comptes Rend. (Doklady) Acad. Sci. USSR 54:445–448.

JAKUBZINER, M. M., and S. F. DOROFEEV. 1968. World wheat resources in serivce of Soviet breeding. Bull. Appl. Bot. Genet. Plant Breed. 39:65–79.

JAKUSHEVSKY, E. S. 1969. Varietal composition of sorghum and its use for breeding. Bull. Appl. Genet. Plant Breed. 41:148–178.

PERCIVAL, J. 1921. The wheat plant, a monograph. Duckworth and Co., London.

PISSAREV, V. E., and N. M. VINOGRADOVA. 1945. Trigeneric hybrids Elymus × wheat × rye. Comptes Rend. (Doklady) Acad. Sci. USSR 49:218–219.

PRICE, S. 1957. Cytological studies in Saccharum and allied genera. III. Chromosome numbers in interspecific hybrids. Bot. Gaz. 118:146–159.

SCHOOLER, A. B. 1967. A form of male sterility observed in Hordeum L. hybrids. Agron. Abstr. p. 17.

SCHOOLER, A. B. 1968. Cytoplasmic sterility and the production of hybrid barley seed. N. Dak. Farm Res. 25:10–11.

SNOWDEN, J. D. 1935. A classification of the cultivated sorghums. Roy. Bot. Garden, Kew No. 5. p. 221–255.

SOULIER, E. J. 1945. A composite perennial Elymus-Wheat-Agropyrum hybrid. Comptes Rend. (Doklady) Acad. Sci. USSR 47:578–579.

TSITSIN, N. V. 1962. The significance of wide hybridization in the evolution and production of new species and forms of plants. p. 2–30. In N. V. Tsitsin (ed.) Wide hybridization of plants. Israel Prog. for Sci., Trans. (Jerusalem, 1958). Vol. 1.

CHAPTER 6

ALLARD, R. W., S. K. JAIN, and P. L. WORKMAN. 1968. The genetics of inbreeding populations. Advan. Genet. 14:55–131.

ANDERSON, E., and W. L. BROWN. 1953. The popcorns of Turkey. Ann. Mo. Bot. Garden 40:33–49.

CANDOLLE, ALPHONSE DE. 1959. Origin of cultivated plants, 2nd ed. Hafner, New York. Translated from the 1886 edition.

CHEVALIER, A. 1936. Contribution a l'étude de quelques espèces africaines du genre Dioscorea. Bull. Mus. Nat. Hist. Paris, 2e Ser. 8:520–551.

COLLINS, G. N. 1919. Structure of the maize ear as indicated in Zea-Euchlaena hybrids. J. Agr. Res. 17:127–135.

COURSEY, D. G. 1972. The civilizations of the yam: interrelationships of man and yams in Africa and the Indo-Pacific region. Archaeol. Physiol. Anthrop. Oceania 7:215–233.

DARWIN, C. R. 1859. On the origin of species by means of natural selection. J. Murray, London.

DOGGETT, H., and B. N. MAJISU. 1968. Disruptive selection in crop development. Heredity 23:1–23.

DOWNING, CHARLES (ed.). 1869. The fruits and fruit-trees of America. John Wiley & Son, N. Y.

FISHER, R. A. 1930. The genetical theory of natural selection. Oxford Univ. Press, Oxford.

FRANKEL, O. H., B. SHINEBERG, and A. MUNDAY. 1969. The genetic basis of an invariant character in wheat. Heredity 24:571–591.

GALINAT, W. C. 1971. The origin of maize. Ann. Rev. Genet. 5:447–478.

GRANT, V. 1967. Linkage between morphology and viability in plant species. Amer. Natur. 101:125–139.

HARLAN, J. R. 1966. Plant introduction and biosystematics. p. 55–83. *In* K. J. Frey (ed.) Plant breeding. Iowa State Univ. Press, Ames.

HARLAN, J. R. 1968. On the origin of barley. *In* Barley: origin, botany, culture, winterhardiness, genetics, utilization. USDA Handbook 338, Washington, D. C.

HARLAN, J. R., J. M. J. DE WET, and E. GLEN PRICE. 1973. Comparative evolution of cereals. Evolution 27:311–325.

HARLAN, J. R. and ANN STEMLER. In press. The races of sorghum in Africa. *In* J. R. Harlan, J. M. J. de Wet, and Ann Stemler (ed.) The origins of African plant domestication. Mouton, The Hague.

HUTCHINSON, JOSEPH. 1959. The application of genetics to cotton improvement. Cambridge Univ. Press, Cambridge.

JAIN, S. K., and R. W. ALLARD. 1960. Population studies in predominately self-pollinated species. I. Evidence for heterozygote advantage in a closed population of barley. Nat. Acad. Sci., Proc. 46:1371–1377.

JAIN, S. K., and R. W. ALLARD. 1966. The effects of linkage, epistasis and inbreeding in population changes under selection. Genetics 53:633–659.

KAPLAN, L., T. F. LYNCH, and C. E. SMITH, JR. 1973. Early cultivated beans (*Phaseolus vulgaris*) from an intermontane Peruvian valley. Science 179:76–77.

KNEEBONE, W. R., and C. L. CREMER. 1955. The relationship of seed size to seedling vigor in some native grass species. Agron. J. 47:472–477.

LANGHAM, D. G. 1940. The inheritance of intergeneric differences in *Zea-Euchlaena* hybrids. Genetics 25:88–107.

LEWONTIN, R. C. 1964a. The interaction of selection and linkage. I. General consideration; heterosis models. Genetics 49:49–67.

LEWONTIN, R. C. 1964b. The interaction of selection and linkage. II. Optimum models. Genetics 50:757–782.

LEWONTIN, R. C., and P. HULL. 1967. The interaction of selection and linkage. III. Synergistic effect of blocks of genes. Der Züchter 37:93–98.

MATHER, K. 1955. Polymorphism as an outcome of disruptive selection. Evolution 9:52–61.

PATRICK, G. T. W. 1889. The fragments of Heraclitus of Ephesus. N. Murray, Baltimore.

ROGERS, J. S. 1950. The inheritance of inflorescence in maize-teosinte hybrids. Genetics 35:541–558.

SEARS, E. R. 1969. Wheat cytogenetics. Ann. Rev. Genet. 3:451–468.

WELLHAUSEN, E. J., L. M. ROBERTS, and E. HERNANDEZ X in collaboration with P. C. Mangelsdorf. 1952. Races of maize in Mexico. Bussey Inst., Harvard Univ., Cambridge, Mass.

WILKE, P. J., R. BETTINGER, T. F. KING, and J. F. O'CONNELL. 1972. Harvest selection and domestication in seed plants. Antiquity 46:203–208.

WRIGHT, G. M. 1958. Grain in the glume of wheat. Nature 181:1812–1813.

ZOHARY, D. 1959. Is *Hordeum agriocrithon* the ancestor of six-rowed cultivated barley? Evolution 13:279–280.

ZOHARY, D. 1963. Spontaneous brittle six-rowed barleys, their nature and
     origin. Barley Genet. 1:27–31.
ZOHARY, D. 1971. Origin of south-west Asiatic cereals: Wheats, barley, oats,
     and rye. p. 235–263. *In* P. H. Davis et al. (ed.) Plant life of south-west
     Asia. Bot. Soc. of Edinburgh, Edinburgh.

CHAPTER 7

ANDERSON, EDGAR. 1954. Plants, man and life. A. Melrose, London.
BAKHTEYEV, F. KH. (ed.) 1969. The world resources of the useful plants
     [in Russian]. Leningrad.
BRÜCHER, H. 1968. Die Evolution der Gartenbohne *Phaseolus vulgaris* L. aus
     der sudamerikanischen Wildbohne *Ph. aborigineus* Buck. Angewandte
     Botanik 42:119–128.
BURGESS, SAM (ed.) 1971. The national program for conservation of crop
     germ plasm. Univ. of Georgia Printing Dept., Athens, Ga.
CALLEN, E. O. 1967. The first New World cereal. Amer. Antiq. 32:535–538.
DARLINGTON, C. D., and E. K. JANAKI AMMAL. 1945. Chromosome atlas
     of cultivated plants. G. Allen and Unwin, London.
FRANKEL, O. H. (ed.) 1973. Survey of crop genetic resources in their centres
     of diversity: first report. IBP/FAO, Rome.
FRANKEL, O. H., and E. BENNETT (ed.) 1970. Genetic resources in plants—
     their exploration and conservation. F. A. Davis Co., Philadelphia.
GADE, DANIEL W. 1972. Setting the stage for domestication: *Brassica* weeds
     in Andean peasant ecology. Ass. Amer. Geogr., Proc. 4:38–40.
GENTRY, H. S. 1969. Origin of the common bean *Phaseolus vulgaris*. Econ.
     Bot. 23:55–69.
HARLAN, J.R. 1951. Anatomy of gene centers. Amer. Nat. 85:97–103.
HARLAN, J. R. 1963a. Two kinds of gene centers in Bothriochloininae. Amer.
     Nat. 97:91–98.
HARLAN, J. R. 1963b. Natural introgression between *Bothriochloa ischaemum*
     and *B. intermedia* in West Pakistan. Bot. Gaz. 124:294–300.
HARLAN, J. R., and J. M. J. DE WET. 1972. A simplified classification of cul-
     tivated sorghum. Crop Sci. 12:172–176.
HARLAN, J. R., and ANN STEMLER. In press. The races of sorghum in
     Africa. *In* J. R.Harlan, J. M. J. de Wet, and Ann Stemler (ed.) The origins
     of African plant domestication. Mouton, The Hague.
LÉON, JORGE. 1964. Plantas alimenticias andinas. Inst. Interamericano de
     Ciencias, Boletin Tecnico No. 6, Lima, Peru.
NATIONAL ACADEMY OF SCIENCES. 1972. Genetic vulnerability of major
     crops. Washington, D. C.
PORTÈRES, R. 1956. Taxonomie agrobotanique des riz cultivés *O. sativa* Linné
     et *O. glaberrima* Steudel. J. Agr. Trop. Bot. Appl. 3(7–8):341–856.
SINSKAYA, E. N. 1928. The oleiferous plants and root crops of the family
     Cruciferae. Bull. Appl. Bot. Genet. Plant Breed. 19(3):1–648.
SNOWDEN, J. D. 1936. The cultivated races of sorghum. Adlard and Son,
     London.
VAVILOV, N. I. 1926. Studies on the origin of cultivated plants. Inst. Appl.
     Bot. Plant Breed., Leningrad.
VAVILOV, N. I. 1949/1950. The phytogeographic basis of plant breeding. *In*
     The origin, variation, immunity and breeding of cultivated plants. Trans-
     lated by K. Starr Chester. Chronica Botanica, Waltham.

WELLHAUSEN, E. J., L. M. ROBERTS, and E. HERNANDEZ X. in collaboration with P. C. Mangelsdorf. 1952. Races of maize in Mexico. Bussey Inst., Harvard Univ., Cambridge, Mass.

ZHUKOVSKY, P. M. 1968. New centres of the origin and new gene centres of cultivated plants including specifically endemic micro-centres of species closely allied to cultivated species. Botanicheskii Zhurnal 53:430–460.

CHAPTER 8

ADAMS, ROBERT M. 1958. Salinity and irrigation agriculture in antiquity. Diyala Basin Archeological Project. Prog. Rep., June 1, 1957 to June 1, 1958, U. of Chicago Mimeo.

BELL, BARBARA. 1971. The dark ages in ancient history. I. The first dark age in Egypt. Amer. J. Archaeol. 75:1–26.

BRAIDWOOD, R. J., and B. HOWE. 1960. Prehistoric investigations in Iraqi Kurdistan. Chicago Univ. Press, Chicago.

CLARK, J. G. D. 1965. Radiocarbon dating and the spread of farming economy. Antiquity 39:45–48.

CONTENSON, HENRI DE. 1971. Tell Ramad, a village of Syria of the 7th and 6th millennia B.C. Archaeology 24:278–285.

ERMAN, A. 1927. The literature of the ancient Egyptians. E. P. Dutton, New York.

HARLAN, J. R. 1967. A wild wheat harvest in Turkey. Archaeology 20:197–201.

HARLAN, J. R. 1969. Ethiopia: a center of diversity. Econ. Bot. 23:309–314.

HARLAN, J. R. 1971. Agricultural origins: centers and noncenters. Science 174:468–474.

HARLAN, J. R., and D. ZOHARY. 1966. Distribution of wild wheats and barley. Science 153:1074–1080.

HELBAEK, HANS. 1964. First impressions of the Catal Hüyük plant husbandry. Anatolian Studies 14:121–23.

HELBAEK, HANS. 1966. Commentary on the phylogenesis of Triticum and Hordeum. Econ. Bot. 20:350–60.

HO, PING-TI. 1969. The loess and the origin of Chinese agriculture. Amer. Hist. Rev. 75:1–36.

HOLE, F., K. FLANNERY, and J. NEELY. 1965. Early agriculture and animal husbandry in Deh Luran, Iran. Current Anthrop. 6:105–06.

HOPF, MARIA. 1969. Plant remains and early farming in Jericho. p. 355–359. In P. J. Ucko and G. W. Dimbleby (ed.) The domestication and exploitation of plants and animals. Aldine Publ. Co., Chicago.

JACOBSEN, T., and R. M. ADAMS. 1958. Salt and silt in ancient Mesopotamian agriculture. Science 128:1251–1258.

LANGDON, S. H. 1931. Semitic. Vol. 5. In J. A. Macculloch (ed.) The mythology of all races. Marshall Jones Co., Boston. 13 vols.

MURRAY, JACQUELINE. 1970. The first European agriculture. Edinburgh Univ. Press, Edinburgh.

PERKINS, DEXTER. 1964. Prehistoric fauna from Shanidar, Iraq. Science 144:1565–1566.

PERROT, JEAN. 1966. Le gisement Natoufien de Mallaha (Eynan), Israel. L'Anthropologie 70:437–84.

RENFREW, J. M. 1969. The archaeological evidence for the domestication of plants: methods and problems. p. 149–172. In P. J. Ucko and G. W. Dimbleby (ed.) The domestication and exploitation of plants and animals. Aldine, Chicago.

TRINGHAM, RUTH. 1971. Hunters, fishers and farmers of Eastern Europe 6000–3000 B.C. Hutchinson Univ. Library, London.

UCKO, P. J., and G. W. DIMBLEBY. 1969. The domestication and exploitation of plants and animals. Aldine Publ. Co., Chicago.

VAN ZEIST, W. 1969. Reflections on prehistoric environments in the Near East. p. 35–46. *In* P. J. Ucko and G. W. Dimbleby (ed.) The domestication and exploitation of plants and animals. Aldine Publ. Co., Chicago.

VAN ZEIST, W. 1972. Palaeobotanical results of the 1970 season at Cayönü, Turkey. Helinium 12:1–19.

VAN ZEIST, W., and W. A. CASPARIE. 1968. Wild einkorn, wheat and barley from Tell Mureybit in Northern Syria. Acta Bot. Neerl. 17:44–53.

WRIGHT, G. A., and A. A. GORDUS. 1969. Distribution and utilization of obsidian from Lake Van sources between 7500 and 3500 B.C. Amer. J. Archaeol. 73:75–77.

WRIGHT, H. E., JR. 1968. Natural environment of early food production north of Mesopotamia. Science 161:334–39.

CHAPTER 9

CLARK, J. D. 1967. Atlas of African prehistory. Univ. of Chicago Press, Chicago.

CLARK, J. D. 1970. The prehistory of Africa. Thames & Hudson, London.

CLARK, J. D. In press. Prehistoric populations and pressures favouring plant domestication in Africa. *In* J. R. Harlan, J. M. J. de Wet, and Ann Stemler (ed.) The origins of African plant domestication. Mouton, The Hague.

COURSEY, D. G. 1972. The civilizations of the yam: interrelationships of man and yams in Africa and the Indo-Pacific region. Archaeol. Phys. Anthrop. Oceania 7:215–233.

DORESSE, JEAN. 1957. L'empire du Pretre-Jean. Librairie Plan, Paris. 2 vols.

FLIGHT, COLIN. In press. The Kintampo culture and its place in the economic prehistory of West Africa. *In* J. R. Harlan, J. M. J. de Wet, and Ann Stemler (ed.) The origins of African plant domestication. Mouton, The Hague.

HAMILTON, A. C. 1972. The interpretation of pollen diagrams from highland Uganda. p. 45–149. *In* E. M. Van Zinderen Bakker (ed.) Palaeoecology of Africa, Vol. 7. A. A. Balkema, Cape Town.

HARLAN, J. R., and JEAN PASQUEREAU. 1969. Décrue agriculture in Mali. Econ. Bot. 23:70–74.

HERODOTUS. 1928. The history of Herodotus. Translated by George Rawlinson, Manuel Komroff, editor. Tudor Publ. Co., New York.

MUNSON, P. J. 1968. Recent archaeological research in the Dhar Tichitt region of south central Mauritania. W. Afr. Newsl. 10:6–13.

MUNSON, P. J. 1971. The Tichitt tradition: a late prehistoric occupation of the southwestern Sahara. Unpublished Ph.D. thesis. Anthropology Department, University of Illinois, Urbana-Champaign, Illinois.

MUNSON, P. J. In press. Archaeological data on the origins of cultivation in the southwestern Sahara and its implications for West Africa. *In* J. R. Harlan, J. M. J. de Wet, and Ann Stemler (ed.) The origin of African plant domestication. Mouton, The Hague.

NAVILLE, EDOUARD. 1898. The temple of Deir El Bahari. Egypt Exploration Society, London. 6 vols.

SHAW, THURSTAN. In press. Early crops in Africa: a review of evidence. *In* J. R. Harlan, J. M. J. de Wet, and Ann Stemler (ed.) The origin of African plant domestication. Mouton, The Hague.

VISHNU-MITTRE. 1968. Protohistoric records of agriculture in India. Bose
Res. Inst. Calcutta, Trans. 31:87–106.
VISHNU-MITTRE. In press. Changing economy in ancient India. *In* C. A.
Reed (ed.) The origins of agriculture. Mouton, The Hague.
WENDORF, F., R. SAID, and R. SCHILD. 1970. Egyptian prehistory:
some new concepts. Science 169:1161–71.

CHAPTER 10

ANDERSSON, J. G. 1934. Children of the yellow earth, studies in prehistoric
China. Macmillan, New York.
CHANG, KWANG-CHIH. 1968. The archaeology of ancient China. Yale
Univ. Press, New Haven, Conn.
CHANG, KWANG-CHIH. 1969. Fengpitou, Tapenkeng and the prehistory of
Taiwan. Yale Univ. Publ. in Anthrop., New Haven, Conn.
CHANG, KWANG-CHIH. 1970. The beginnings of agriculture in the Far East.
Antiquity 44:175–185.
CHÊNG, TE-K'UN. 1966. Archaeology in China. Vol. 1. Prehistoric China
Supplement, New light on prehistoric China. W. Heffer, Cambridge,
England.
CONFUCIUS. Confucian analects. Translated by Ezra Pound. P. Owen, London.
1956.
HO, PING-TI. 1969. The loess and the origin of Chinese agriculture. Amer.
Hist. Rev. 75:1–36.
HO, PING-TI. 1974. The cradle of the East: an inquiry into the indigenous
origins of techniques and ideas of Neolithic and early historic China,
5000–1000 B.C. Univ. of Chicago Press and the Chinese Univ. of
Hong Kong, Chicago, Hong Kong.
LABORATORY OF THE INSTITUTE OF ARCHAEOLOGY, PEKING. 1972a.
Report on radiocarbon determined dates. I. K'ao-ku 1:52–56.
LABORATORY OF THE INSTITUTE OF ARCHAEOLOGY, PEKING. 1972b.
Report on radiocarbon determined dates. II. K'ao-ku 5:56–58
LAUFER, B. 1919. Sino-Iranica. Field Museum Publ. 201, Anthrop. Ser. Vol.
15, Chicago
LI, HUI-LIN. 1970. The origin of cultivated plants in Southeast Asia. Econ.
Bot. 24:3–19.
THEOPHRASTUS. Enquiry into plants. Translated by Arthur Hort. Harvard
Univ. Press, Cambridge, Mass. 2 vols. 1961.

CHAPTER 11

BAYARD, D. T. 1972. Early Thai bronze: analysis and new dates. Science
176:1411–12.
CHRISTIE, ANTHONY. 1968. Chinese mythology. Hamlyn Publ. Group,
Middlesex, England.
EMORY, KENNETH P. and YOSHINIKO H. SINOTO. 1964. Prehistoire de la
polynésie. J. Soc. Océanistes 20:39–41.
GORMAN, C. 1969. Hoabinhian: a pebble-tool complex with early plant
associations in Southeast Asia. Science 163:671–673.

GORMAN, C. 1971. The Hoabinhian and after: subsistence patterns in South-
    east Asia during the late Pleistocene and early Recent periods. World
    Archaeol. 2:300–20.

GORMAN, C. In press. A priori models and Thai prehistory: A reconsideration
    of the beginnings of agriculture in southeastern Asia. *In* C. A. Reed (ed.)
    Origins of agriculture. Mouton, The Hague.

HO, PING-TI. 1974. The cradle of the East: an inquiry into the indigenous
    origins of techniques and ideas of Neolithic and early historic China,
    5000–1000 B.C. Univ. of Chicago Press and Chinese Univ. of Hong Kong,
    Chicago, Hong Kong

SOLHEIM, W. G., II. 1968. Early bronze in northeastern Thailand. Curr.
    Anthrop. 9:59–62.

VISHNU-MITTRE. 1968. Protohistoric records of agriculture in India. Bose
    Res. Inst. Calcutta, Trans. 31:87–106.

VISHNU-MITTRE. In press. Changing economy in ancient India. *In* C. A.
    Reed (ed.) The origins of agriculture. Mouton, The Hague.

CHAPTER 12

BEADLE, G. W. 1972. The mystery of maize. Field Mus. Nat. Hist. Bull. 43:
    2–11.

BROOKFIELD, H. C., and J. PETER WHITE. 1968. Revolution or evolution
    in the prehistory of the New Guinea Highlands: a seminar report.
    Ethnology 7:43–52.

BYERS, DOUGLAS S. 1967. The prehistory of the Tehuacán Valley. Univ.
    of Texas Press, Austin. 2 vols.

FLANNERY, KENT V. 1968. Archaeological systems theory and early Meso-
    america. p. 67–87. *In* Betty J. Meggers (ed.) Anthropological archaeology
    in the Americas. Anthrop. Soc. of Washington, Washington, D. C.

GALINAT, W. C. 1971. The origin of maize. Ann. Rev. Genet. 5:447–478.

KAPLAN, L., T. F. LYNCH, and C. E. SMITH, JR. 1973. Early cultivated
    beans (*Phaseolus vulgaris*) from an intermontane Peruvian valley. Science
    179:76–77.

LATHRAP, D. W. 1971. The tropical forest and the cultural context of Chavin.
    p. 73–100. *In* E. Benson (ed.) Dumbarton Oaks conference on Chavin.
    Dumbarton Oaks Res. Libr., Washington, D. C.

LATHRAP, D. W. In press. Our father the cayman, our mother the gourd.
    Spender revisited, or a unitary model for the emergence of agriculture in
    the New World. *In* C. A. Reed (ed.) The origin of agriculture. Mouton,
    The Hague.

MAC NEISH, R. S. 1964. Ancient Mesoamerican civilization. Science 143:
    531–537.

MANGELSDORF, P. C., R. S. MAC NEISH, and W. C. GALINAT. 1967. Pre-
    historic maize, teosinte, and Tripsacum from Tamaulipas, Mexico. Bot.
    Mus. Leaflets, Harvard Univ. 22(2):33–63.

MANGELSDORF, P. C., and R. G. REEVES. 1939. The origin of Indian corn
    and its relatives. Texas Agr. Exp. Sta. Bull. 574. p. 1–315.

PICKERSGILL, BARBARA. 1969. The archaeological record of chili peppers
    (*Capsicum* spp.) and the sequence of plant domestication in Peru. Amer.
    Antiq. 34:54–61.

RECINOS, A. 1947. Popol Vuh, Las antiguas historias del Quiché. Fondo de
    Cultura Económica, Mexico, D. F.

RILEY, C. L., J. C. KELLEY, C. W. PENNINGTON, and R. L. RANDS (ed.). 1971. Man across the sea. Univ. of Texas Press, Austin.

ROWE, J. H., and DORTHY MENZEL. 1967. Peruvian archaeology. Peck Publ., Palo Alto, Calif.

SAUER, C. O. 1952. Agricultural origins and dispersals. M. I. T. Press, Cambridge, Mass.

WATSON, JAMES B. 1965. From hunting to horticulture in the New Guinea Highlands. Ethnology 4:295–309.

WILKES, H. G. 1967. Teosinte: the closest relative of maize. Bussey Inst., Harvard Univ., Cambridge, Mass.

CHAPTER 13

ASH, HARRISON BOYD (trans.). 1941. Lucius Junius Moderatus Columella on agriculture. Harvard Univ. Press, Cambridge, Mass.

BARRAU, JACQUES. 1957. L'enigme de la patate douce en Océanie. Etudes d'Outre-mer 1:83–87.

BOTANICAL INSTITUTE OF THE SOVIET ACADEMY OF SCIENCES. 1968–1973. Flora of USSR. Translated by Israel Program for Scientific Translations, Jerusalem. Publ. Nat. Sci. Found. and Smithsonian Inst., Washington, D.C.

CARTER, G. F., and T. W. WHITAKER. 1961. Note on the longevity of seed of *Lagenaria siceraria* after floating in water. Torrey Bot. Gard. Bull. 88(2):104–106.

CHANG, KWANG-CHIH. 1968. The archaeology of ancient China. Yale Univ. Press, New Haven, Conn.

COOK, O. F. 1910. History of the coconut palm in America. Contr. U. S. Nat. Herb. 14:271–342.

COOK, O. F. 1939. A new palm from Cocos Island, collected on the Presidential Cruise of 1938. Smithsonian Misc. Publ. 98, Washginton, D. C.

CUTLER, HUGH C., and THOMAS W. WHITAKER. 1967. Cucurbits from the Tehuacan caves. p. 212–219. In D. S. Byers (ed.) The prehistory of the Tehuacan valley. Univ. of Texas Press, Austin.

GORMAN, C. 1969. Hoabinhian: a pebble-tool complex with early plant associations in Southeast Asia. Science 163:671–673.

HYMOWITZ, T. 1972. The trans-domestication concept as applied to guar. Econ. Bot. 26:49–60.

IRVINE, F. R. 1957. Wild and emergency foods of Australian and Tasmanian Aborigines. Oceania 28:113–142.

LAUFER, B. 1919. Sino-Iranica. Field Museum Publ. 201, Anthrop. Ser. Vol. 15, Chicago.

LEAKEY, M. D., and L. S. B. LEAKEY. 1950. Excavations at the Njoro River cave. The Clarendon Press, Oxford, England.

OVIEDO Y VALDÉS. 1944. Historia general y natural de las Indias. Guaranía, Asunción, Paraguay.

PICKERSGILL, BARBARA. 1969. The archaeological record of chili peppers (*Capsicum* spp.) and the sequence of plant domestication in Peru. Amer. Antiq. 34:54–61.

RENFREW, J. M. 1969. The archaeological evidence for the domestication of plants: methods and problems. p. 149–172. In P. J. Ucko and G. W. Dimbleby (ed.) The domestication and exploitation of plants and animals. Aldine, Chicago.

SCHWEINFURTH, G. 1884. Neue Funde auf dem Gebiete der Flora des alten
    Agyptens. Bot. Jahrb. f Pflanzengeschichte 5:189-202.
WAFER, LIONEL. 1934. A new voyage and description of the Isthmus of
    America. Hakluyt Soc. Ser. 2. Vol. 73. Oxford, England.
WHITAKER, T. W. 1971. Endemism and pre-Columbian migration of the bottle
    gourd, *Lagenaria siceraria* (Mol.) Standl. *In* C. L. Riley, J. C. Kelley, C. W.
    Pennington, and R. L. Runds (ed.) Man across the sea. Univ. of Texas
    Press, Austin.

CHAPTER 14

AUTRET, M. 1970. World protein supplies and needs. *In* R. A. Lawrie (ed.)
    Proteins as human food. AVI Publ. Co., Westport, Conn.
BICKOFF, E. M., and G. O. KOHLER. 1973. Commercial production of leaf
    protein for animal and human use. PAG Bull. 3:19-20.
BROWN, LESTER R. 1968. World food problems. p. 11-26. *In* R. I. Mateles
    and S. R. Tannenbaum (ed.) Single cell protein. MIT Press, Cambridge,
    Mass.
GORDON, J. F. 1970. Algal proteins and the human diet. p. 328-345. *In*
    R. A. Lawrie (ed.) Proteins as human food. AVI Publ. Co., Westport,
    Conn.
KOSARIC, NAIM. 1973. Nutrition: develop new technologies. Ceres 6:32-37.
LAWRIE, R. A. (ed.). 1970. Proteins as human food. AVI Publ. Co., Westport,
    Conn.
MATELES, R. I., and S. R. TANNENBAUM (ed). 1968. Single cell protein.
    MIT Press, Cambridge, Mass.
NATIONAL ACADEMY OF SCIENCES. 1972. Genetic vulnerability of major
    crops. Washington, D. C.
OSWALD, W. J., and C. G. GOLUEKE. 1968. Large-scale production of algae.
    p. 271-305. *In* R. I. Mateles and S. R. Tannenbaum (ed.) Single cell pro-
    tein. MIT Press, Cambridge, Mass.
PLINY. Natural history. Translated by H. Rackham. Harvard Univ. Press,
    Cambridge, Mass. 1938-1963.
SHACKLADY, C. A. 1970. Hydrocarbon-grown yeasts in nutrition. p. 317-
    327. *In* R. A. Lawrie (ed.) Proteins as human food. AVI Publ. Co.,
    Westport, Conn.
VAVILOV, N. I. 1926. Studies on the origin of cultivated plants. Inst. Appl.
    Bot. Plant Breed., Leningrad.

INDEX